CATALOGUE OF MANUSCRIPTS
in the Libraries of the
UNIVERSITY OF PENNSYLVANIA
to 1800

Compiled by NORMAN P. ZACOUR *and* RUDOLF HIRSCH
Assisted by JOHN F. BENTON *and* WILLIAM E. MILLER

Philadelphia
UNIVERSITY OF PENNSYLVANIA PRESS

© 1965 *by the* TRUSTEES OF THE UNIVERSITY OF PENNSYLVANIA

Published in Great Britain, India, and Pakistan
by the Oxford University Press
London, Bombay, and Karachi

Library of Congress Catalogue Card Number: 64-24501

7469
Printed in the United States of America

Contents

INTRODUCTION	v
DESCRIPTION OF MANUSCRIPTS	1
RARE BOOK COLLECTION MANUSCRIPTS	1
Greek (1–3)	1
Latin (1–198)	1
Dutch (1–4)	47
Flemish (1–3)	48
English (1–29)	49
French (1–103)	54
German (1–60)	78
Italian (1–210)	92
Portuguese (1)	135
Rhaeto-Roman (1–2)	135
Spanish (1–50)	136
HENRY C. LEA LIBRARY MANUSCRIPTS (1–402)	146
EDGAR F. SMITH COLLECTION MANUSCRIPTS (1–42)	231
VETERINARY LIBRARY MANUSCRIPT (1)	244
ADDENDA ET CORRIGENDA	245
INDEX	247

NOTE: Numbers not described in this catalogue pertain to post-1800 manuscripts.

Introduction

THE *Catalogue of Manuscripts* describes 1,150 European manuscripts dating from the year 1000 A.D. (*Lea 27*) to the year 1800, from the reign of Emperor Otto III of Germany to the beginning of the year VIII of the French Revolution. Approximately half of these items were written during the Middle Ages and the Renaissance period.

The 1,150 manuscripts came to the University over an extended period. Some were donated by benefactors, among them the autograph manuscript of Lope de Vega's *Carlos V* (*Span. 3*), presented by the late Mrs. John B. Stetson, Jr. Several years later another autograph play by Lope de Vega, his *Benavides* (*Span. 50*), was acquired with the help of a small group of generous friends among the Trustees. A considerable number of manuscripts came to the library as part of larger, more general collections: the F. C. Macauley collection of Italian literature, bequeathed in 1896, contained ten manuscripts, the H. A. Rennert collection of Spanish literature, purchased in 1928, seven. The library of the great medievalist Henry Charles Lea, presented by his family in 1923–24, added almost one hundred manuscripts to the University's collections; some of these are not listed because they belong to the 19th century. The majority of manuscripts was added by purchase, especially during the past fifteen years, when book funds of the University were more adequate, though they were rarely, if ever, lavish. In a few instances the President and Provost granted special appropriations for the purchase of important items. To them and to the many gracious benefactors we extend our sincere thanks.

Our collection does not measure up to those of the more illustrious European libraries, nor can it compare with a number of American institutions. It does not contain any large number of famous manuscripts, and very few are illuminated. The library's main emphasis has been placed on text manuscripts, hoping that they would serve faculty members and doctoral candidates, and that they would be useful in the training of students. Bibliographical citations throughout this volume prove that quite a few manuscripts have already served this purpose (e.g. *Greek 1, Lat. 95, Eng. 3, Fr. 32, Span. 3, Lea 71*). To illustrate the variety and the usefulness of the collection we mention more or less at random a few individual items and a few groups of manuscripts:

Lat. 7 contains a text originally described as Pseudo-Petrarch. It has now been authoritatively assigned to Petrarch.

Lat. 167 are laws, edicts and proclamations of Emperor Charles V, specifically brought together for a notary in Lombardy in the 1530's. Among the edicts are prohibitions against the smuggling of arms to the Turks, and promulgations against the followers of Martin Luther.

Fr. 15 is a chansonnier of some importance, written about the year 1400 and containing a large number of unpublished poems.

Fr. 90 is a collection of letters by Jean Baptiste Colbert, minister and financier under King Louis XIV.

Ger. 4 includes a hitherto unpublished dramatized version of the story of Aristotle and Phyllis, written during the early part of the 15th century.

Ital. 44, 95, 100, 146, 184, 187, Lea 83 and 85 are Venetian ambassadorial reports. Other diplomatic papers are to be found throughout the *Catalogue*.

Lea 28 briefly describes thirty-five letters by and to members of the famous Florentine family Acciaioli, dating from 1342 to 1395.

Lea 212–355 record a sizable collection of Gondi-Medici account books and other business records. This collection has since been supplemented by a second larger collection which will be described at a later date.

Lat. 12–15, 17–19, 22–25, 27–31, 43, 49–50, 65–68 and many others are Aristotle texts and commentaries.

When Seymour de Ricci's *Census of Medieval and Renaissance Manuscripts* appeared (1935–40), it credited the University of Pennsylvania with a mere nine manuscripts, all in the Lea Library (and with ten documents in the Biddle Law Library). The poor showing was not de Ricci's fault, but the library's, which was then unable to provide a more complete listing.

Manuscripts were shelved in many different places. Descriptions, if available at all, fell short even of the comparatively simple standards set by the compiler of the *Census*. Soon thereafter the late Arthur C. Howland prepared a more complete index of Lea manuscripts, upon his retirement from the Lea professorship of medieval history. Late in the 1940's most manuscripts in the general collections were taken from the cages and put together under the care of the newly established Rare Book Collection. At this time a few more manuscripts were reported to the editor of the *Supplement to the Census*, then in its first stage of preparation. Real progress began in 1955 when Kenneth M. Setton, Lea Professor of Medieval History and Director of Libraries, appointed his one-time student and colleague Norman P. Zacour to a newly created position of custodian of manuscripts. Well prepared for the task, Mr. Zacour set to work with zest and energy. When the *Supplement* finally appeared in 1962 it listed one hundred and forty-three items in the University's collections, including revised descriptions of the few titles which had already appeared in the original *Census*. Many more items had by then been collated and described.

We have attempted to identify as many former owners as possible and to enter their names in the index. There are too many to list here, but a few should perhaps be named in this introduction. Twenty-four manuscripts had once been the property of Sir Thomas Phillipps, who was undoubtedly one of the most gregarious and successful collectors. Six manuscripts come from the collection of Frederick North, the Earl of Guilford, and eight from that of the Rev. Walter Sneyd, who had in 1835 purchased the manuscripts of Matteo Luigi Canonice (S.J.). Eight manuscripts once belonged to the well-known professor of Romance philology in Halle, Hermann Suchier. Ten of the manuscripts had for centuries rested undisturbed in the library of the Carthusian monastery of Buxheim. At the time of sequestration manuscripts, books and prints were given as compensation to the Counts Waldbott-Bassenheim (1810). They were auctioned off seventy-three years later in Munich. Then the once glorious library was dispersed among collectors and dealers, and a few manuscripts came ultimately to the United States.

The descriptions in the *Catalogue* have been prepared over an extended period, with the perhaps inevitable, yet unfortunate, result that style and attention to detail are not always consistent. In general, and especially for the earlier manuscripts, the policy has been to transcribe the titles as they are found in the text, and to provide *incipits* and occasionally *explicits* when they seemed useful. The compilers hope that the *Catalogue* will serve inquiring scholars and students well, in spite of its shortcomings. For errors we apologize.

The major part of the *Catalogue* appeared originally in *The Library Chronicle* (volumes XXVI 2–XXIX 1). John F. Benton published in a subsequent issue revisions, additions and corrections, which are incorporated in the present publication. Revised descriptions have been identified by adding an asterisk (*); volumes here described for the first time are marked with a circle (°).

Manuscripts are listed in the order in which they are placed on the shelves, a common but not a logical arrangement. Manuscripts with language designation only (e.g. *Lat. 1*) are to be found in the Rare Book Collection; the location of all others is obvious from the designation preceding the number (e.g. *Lea 1*). Numbers omitted are assigned to manuscripts dated post-1800. To assist in the use of this *Catalogue*, an extensive index lists (1) title entries, (2) names of authors, scribes, and owners, (3) persons referred to in the text as far as they have been extracted in the descriptions, (4) names of places and countries, as well as (5) a few other entries, e.g. Jesuits, Turks, etc. It is not a subject index.

The *Catalogue* includes manuscripts catalogued before the end of the year 1963. Others which have not yet been properly recorded, and future accessions, will be published in later issues of *The Library Chronicle*.

It is our pleasant duty to acknowledge the assistance and help of many. Credit for the publication of the "Catalogue" in article form goes to the Friends of the Library, who financed its publication. Specific mention should be made of John F. Benton, who, in turn, speaks of the individuals who furnished him information for his compilation of revisions, additions and corrections.

Stephan Kuttner, then at The Catholic University of America, and Gino Corti, visiting professor at the University of Pennsylvania during the winter-spring semester, 1964, provided corrections. During the process of cataloguing we have had the advice of several faculty colleagues and a few graduate students. In many cases we have used the descriptions of earlier owners, and of dealers from whom manuscripts have been purchased. To these often unnamed or even unknown persons also go our thanks. Throughout the final stages William E. Miller assisted by checking new descriptions and the index, and he accepted a major share in seeing the *Catalogue* through the press. We gladly express appreciation to those who have shared in the exacting and laborious task of typing the descriptions and the index, Mrs. Ilse Gottesmann, Mrs. Thomas Helmstadter, Mrs. Richard O'Gorman and Mrs. Natalie Terrell.

RUDOLF HIRSCH

A Catalogue of Manuscripts in the Libraries of the University of Pennsylvania to 1800

Rare Book Collection Manuscripts

Greek 1*

IOANNES DOKEIANOS (Joannes Docianus). Addresses and letters, ff.2r–36v.—*With* NICEPHORUS GREGORAS. Orations and letters, ff.37r–45v.—GREGORIOS OF CONSTANTINOPLE (Georgios of Cyprus). Encomia, ff.49r–85r. *N.p., 16th cent.*

Paper. 10 prel. blank, 87 (ff.1, 46–8, 77–80 and 86–7 blank), 8 blank ff. 20.5 x 15 cm. Contemp. (?) boards. Identical with ms. 51 of Notre Dame de Pilar, Salamanca, and the same ms. which belonged to Andreas Darmarios Epidaurios Lakon, used by Martin Crusius in 1584.—For greater details on the contents and the ms. see article by Peter Topping in *The Library Chronicle*, XXIX (1963), 1–15.

Greek 2

PARTHENIOS, patriarch of Jerusalem. Funeral oration on the hospodar Nicholar Mavrocordatos (d.1730). *N.p., 18th cent.*

Paper. 8 ff. 20 x 16 cm. 19th-cent. gilt calf.

Greek 3°

GREEK ORTHODOX CHURCH. Manual of Greek Orthodox canon law. *Venice?, ca. 1800.*

Paper. 13 ff. (instead of 14, f.1 missing), 373 pp., 3 ff. 21 x 16 cm. Contemp. vellum.

Lat. 1

WILLIAM OF OCKHAM. Summa totius logicae. *Italy, last half of 14th cent.* Written in several hands, the final portion by Matthew of Faventia (f.102).

Vellum. 103 ff. 24 x 18 cm. First leaf illum., with portrait (Ockham?) inside initial, and unidentified coat of arms, illum. capitals. H/morocco.—Cf. T. Bruce Birch, *The "De sacramento altaris" of William of Ockham* (Burlington, Iowa, 1930), p. xxxvii.

Lat. 2

[PETRUS LOMBARDUS]. Commentary on the Sentences of Petrus Lombardus. *Germany(?), early 15th cent.*

Vellum. 150 ff. (one leaf at beginning and several leaves between ff. 149 and 150 known to be wanting). 34 x 26 cm. Illum. initials. Contemp. calf over wooden boards.—Not identified in F. Stegmüller, *Repertorium commentariorum in sententias P.L.* (Würzburg, 1947).

Lat. 3

GEBER (JĀBIR IBN AFLAH). Liber de astronomia (seven books rather than the usual nine). *Spain(?), ca. 1300*, in several hands.

Vellum. 69 ff. 26 x 21 cm. Astronomical figures, copious marginal notes. 17th-cent.(?) vellum. Bookplate of Don A. Canovas del Castillo.—Cf. L. Thorndike, *Catalogue of Incipits* (Cambridge, 1937), col. 649.

Lat. 4

HEINRICH VON LANGENSTEIN. De improbatione concentricorum et epicyclorum, ff.1–14, *inc.*: Cum inferiorum cognitio . . . (cf. L. Thorndike, *op. cit.*, col. 143, with references).—*With* ALBERTUS MAGNUS (or ROGER BACON). Speculum philosophiae seu astrologiae, ff.15–20, *inc.*: Occasione quorundam librorum . . . (cf. L. Thorndike, *ibid.*, col. 456: Albertus Magnus; Mandonnet in *Rev. néoscholastique de phil.*, XVII <1910>, 313–35: Roger Bacon). *England, after 1362.*

Vellum. 20 ff. 27 x 20 cm. Capitals in gold, red and blue, astronomical figures. Boards.

Lat. 5

RAYMONDUS LULLUS. Liber de homine. *Italy, 15th cent.*

Paper. 80 ff. 21 x 15 cm. H/vellum over original wooden boards. Prov.: Monastery of St. Antonius, Venice, (Ms.41); later owned by Julius de Cardelinis.

Lat. 6

HORAE. *Italy, 16th cent.*

Vellum. 145 ff. 11 x 8 cm. Initials in gold, red and blue. Contemp. calf, rebacked. Prov.: John C. Jackson (autograph) 1849; Rev. William Ely of Philadelphia (purchased in Rome 1875); Jacob Riegel 1934; Edwin H. Fetterolf.

Lat. 7

RENAISSANCE MISCELLANY: 1. LEONARDO BRUNI ARETINO. Laudatio clarissimi viri Nannis Stroze equitis Florentini, ff.1–10.—2. LUCIAN. Contentio de presidentia P. Scipionis, Hanibalis et Alexandri, tr. from the Greek by Johannes Aurispa, ff.11–14.—3. PSEUDO-PETRARCH. Collatio facta inter Scipionem Romanum, Alexandrum Macedonem, Annibalem Penum et Pyrhum Epirotharum regem, quis eorum prestantior fuerit, ff.14–19.—4. PSEUDO-LUCIAN [LEON BATTISTA ALBERTI]. Libellus de virtute conquerente, tr. from the Greek by Carolus Aretinus, ff.19–20.—5. POGGIO BRACCIOLINI. Comparatio P. Scipionis et C. Julii Cesaris, ff.20–26.

Ad. Lat. 4: For further bibliogr. see Thorndike, *Incipits*, 2nd ed. (1963), cols. 309 and 975.

—6. GUARINUS OF VERONA. Guarinus Veronensis impatiens quod Pogius scripserit Scipionem prestare Cesari, preceded by a letter to Leonello d'Este, ff.26–45.—7. POGGIO BRACCIOLINI. Disceptatio habita inter doctissimos viros Nicolaum Niccolum et Carolum Aretinum: an seni sit uxor ducenda, preceded by dedicatory letter to Cosimo de' Medici, ff.45–52.—8. LEONARDO GIUSTINIANI. Oratio habita in funere clarissimi viri Caroli Zeno, ff.52–57.—9. POGGIO BRACCIOLINI. Defensio contra Guarini oppugnationes de prestantia Cesaris et Scipionis, preceded by letters to Leonello d'Este, marquis of Ferrara, and to the Venetian patrician Francesco Barbaro, ff.58–78.—10. ANTONIO BECCADELLI of Palermo. Correspondence with Filippo Maria, Duke of Milan, and Luigi Crotto, ff.78–83.— 11. CICERO. De laudibus Gn. Pompei oratio, preceded by summary of the humanist commentator Antonio Loschi extracted from his "Inquisitiones super XI orationes Ciceronis," ff.83–95.—12. Four anonymous distichs, f.96v.—13. ROME. Legislative acts from republican period compiled from literary sources, ff.97–100.—14. LIVY. Extract: the repeal of the Lex Oppia against luxurious dress of women, ff.101–105.—ANTONIO CERMISONI, Recipes for pills f.105v. *Italy, ca. 1475.*

Paper. 105 ff. 23 x 17 cm. 18th-cent. vellum. Prov.: Lancinus Curtius, "artium scolaris," Milan, 1484 (f.105r); Dean Lockhart, Haverford, Pa.

Lat. 8

NICHOLAS TRIVET. Exposicio super regulam Beati Augustini, ff.1–47r.—*With* Notice of different texts of Augustinian rule with incipits, f.47v.—List of orders living under Augustinian rule, f.48. *Lower Rhine or Lowlands, 15th cent.*

Vellum. 48 ff. 29 x 20 cm. Vellum binding.

Lat. 9

RITUALE PRAEDICATORUM. *Rhineland, ca. 1450,* several hands.

Vellum. 204 ff. (few leaves missing). 9 x 8 cm. Illum. figurated initial D, Madonna with child (f.1), musical notation. 18th-cent. calf.

Lat. 10*

CONRADUS DE SOLTAU. Lectura super cap. "Firmiter credimus." (According to article in *Dict. d'hist. et de géogr. eccl.*, XIII, 503, this unpublished work was written in 1388). Author's autograph? *Bologna, 19 April 1388.*

Paper. 2 blank, 4 prel., 103, 1 blank ff. 29 x 20 cm. 19th-cent. calf over old wooden boards.—Prov.: Dominican Convent of St. Augustine at Padua.

Ad. Lat. 7, no. 3: Recently ascribed to Petrarch by Guido Martellotti in *The Library Chronicle*, XXVIII (1962), 109–14.

Lat. 11

AUGUSTINIANS. Rule. With tr. in French. *N. E. France, 15th cent.*

Vellum. 28 ff. 16 x 12 cm. Illum. initial. 18th-cent. calf. Prov.: M. Swartzwelder, Jan. 1, 1859, Pittsburgh (fly leaf).

Lat. 12

ARISTOTLE. Organon, tr. by Joannes Argyropoulos. *Italy, last half of 15th cent.*

Paper. 96 ff. 24 x 17 cm. Illum. initial; diagrs. Contemp. wooden boards.—Cf. L. W. Riley, "Aristotle Texts and Commentaries to 1700 . . . ," *Library Chronicle*, XXII, 86–95; XXIII, 16–31, 63–81; XXIV, 37–53, 83–103, no.M7. Acc. to Dr. Ernst Schulz ms.lat.12 represents a version which precedes GW2341, ff.142v–150r (B-form of text) and Oxf. Bodl.Canon lat.class. 277, ff.3r–18v (C-form).

Lat. 13

COSMOGRAPHIES. Four ancient Greek cosmographies in Latin tr.: 1. PLATO. Timaeus, tr. with commentary by Chalcidius, ff.2–218.—2. PSEUDO-ARISTOTLE. De mundo, tr. by Joannes Argyropoulos, ff.219–234.—3. PHILO JUDAEUS. De incorruptione mundi (tr. unknown) ff.237–274.—4. CLEOMEDES. De contemplatione orbium coelestium, tr. by Carolus Valgulius and dedicated to Cesare Borgia, ff.277–338. *Italy, ca. 1500.*

Paper. 340 ff. 20 x 14 cm. Diagr., marginal annotations. Contemp. tooled calf.—Cf. L. W. Riley, *op. cit.*, M2.—2. G. F. Muscarella, *A Latin Transl. of the . . . De mundo* (Philadelphia, 1958), unpubl. PhD. diss.

Lat. 14

[ARISTOTLE]. Anonymous Latin commentary on the Physica. *Germany, 1579.*

Paper. 304 ff. 21 x 16 cm. Contemp. blind-stamped pigskin. Prov.: Carthusian monastery, Buxheim.—Cf. L. W. Riley, *op. cit.*, M11.

Lat. 15

ARISTOTLE. Ethica Nicomachea, tr. by Leonardo Bruni Aretino. *Italy, 15th cent.*

Vellum. 120 ff. 26 x 19 cm. Illum. capitals. Contemp. tooled morocco. Sir Thomas Phillipps Ms. 16239; Geo. Dunn; Lawrence W. Hodson.—Cf. L. W. Riley, *op. cit.*, M3.

Lat. 16

PAULUS PERGULENSIS. Dubia, ff.6–56.—*With* RALPH STRODE. Consequentia, ff.57–70.—PAULUS PERGULENSIS. De sensu diviso et composito, ff.71–73. *Bologna, 1454,* written by Brother Chiracus de Fulginio of the Servite Order.

Vellum and paper. 5 blank, 69 (instead of 70), 6 blank ff. (first f. of text missing). 21 x 14 cm. Contemp. blind-stamped calf over wooden boards. Prov.: John Edgar Ker.

Lat. 17

CHRISTOPHER BRANDIS. Compendium totius commentarij in octo libros physicorum [Aristotelis] . . . enucleatum per Joannem Huoberum. *Dillingen, 1609–1610.*

Paper. 1 f., 263 pp. 16 x 10 cm. Contemp. vellum. Carthusian monastery, Brixen.—Cf. L. W. Riley, *op. cit.*, no. M24.—A. A. de Backer and C. Sommervogel, *Bibl. de la Compagnie de Jésus* (Brussels, 1891–1900), II, 86 B.

Lat. 18

PETER GOTTRAW, 1577–1640. 1. In libros Aristotelis De generatione et corruptione, 112 ff.—2. IDEM. In tres priores libros meterologicos Aristotelis, 38 ff.—3. IDEM. In tres libros Aristotelis De anima quaestio proaemialis, 206 ff.—4. IDEM. Tractatus metaphysicus De ente, et eius passionibus, 45 ff. Lecture notes, written by Hieronymus Mesmer. *Dillingen, 1610.*

Paper. 405 ff. 21 x 16 cm. Contemp. blind-stamped pigskin over wooden boards. Writer's signature on fly-leaf. Bound at end: *Theses miscellaneae ex philosophia . . . depromptae* (Dillingen, [1610]) containing on pp. 13–14 an abstract of the thesis of H. Mesmer.—Cf. Backer-Sommervogel, *op. cit.*, III, 1626–8, esp. 1628, A.—Not in L. W. Riley.

Lat. 19

ANTONIO MARSIGLI. In Aristotelis physicam tractatus. Lecture notes written by LVD^{co} MOR$^{[?]}$ BER^{si}. *Rome, 1606.*

Paper. 515 ff. and 1 fold. sheet (Conclusiones physicae. De subiecto physice). 19 x 13 cm. Contemp. vellum. Jacobus Laidi, 1836 (ff. 164 and 516v.)—Cf. L. W. Riley, *op. cit.*, no. M29.—Backer-Sommervogel, *op. cit.*, V, 611, B (same ms.?).

Lat. 20

BIBLE. *England or Northern France, first half 14th cent.*

Vellum. 330 ff. 38 x 26 cm. Miniatures, illum. H/pigskin over wooden boards. Presented by Catherine and Thomas Coleman (1548–1649) to Ellia Fitzpatrick (f.252r); William Farrell (252r).—Cf. *A Catalogue of the T. Edward Ross Collection of Bibles Presented to The University of Pennsylvania Library* (Phila., 1947), pp. 19–20.

Lat. 21

BIBLE. *France, ca. 1300.*

Vellum. 465 ff. 22 x 15 cm. 18th-cent. brown morocco. Miniatures, illum. Prov.: James Augustus St. John and S. Vandenyer, cf. letter tipped in, 1837(?). —Cf. *A Catalogue of the T. Edward Ross Collection . . .*, p. 19.

Lat. 22

[ARISTOTLE]. Disputatio in Organum Aristotelis, *inc.:* Cum praecognitionis nominis logicae et huius obiecti coniungas originem, divisionem, finem, utilitatem supponentes. *Milan(?), 1617.*

Paper. 356 (falso 358) numb. ff., f. 259 (2 poems), and 1 f. with schematic drawing and inscription V. V. Braÿdense Collegium mediolanense e Soc. Jesu. 21 x 16 cm. Vellum. Decorated titles and initials.—Cf. L. W. Riley, *op. cit.*, no. M17.

Lat. 23

CORNELIUS, S. J., professor of philosophy. Commentarius cum quaestionibus in universam Aristotelis Physicam, lecture notes of Franciscus Krembser, O.M. *Germany, 1594.*

Paper. 303 ff. 16 x 11 cm. Contemp. vellum.—Cf. L. W. Riley, *op. cit.*, no. M26.—Backer-Sommervogel, *op. cit.*, II, 1472, A (same ms.?).

Lat. 24

[ARISTOTLE]. Commentaries on the De generatione et corruptione and Analytica, *inc.:* Solent in initio suorum operum . . . *Italy, ca. 1550.*

Paper. 6, 407 ff. 13 x 9 cm. Cloth.—Cf. L. W. Riley, *op. cit.*, no. M10.

Lat. 25

FERDINANDUS ACATIUS. Philosophiae Aristotelis traditae et propugnatae per R. P. Ferdinandum Acatium e Societate Iesu et exceptae a F. Constantino Gayer ordinis S. Benedicti in monasterio Admontensi professo, pars I[–III]. Part I is preceded by "Summulae seu institutiones logicae" (84 pp.). Part I is on the Organon, Part II on the Physica and De coelo, Part III on the Metaphysica. *Austria, 1660–1663.*

Paper. 3 vols. (84, 677, 1442, 38 pages). Contemp. stamped pigskin over wooden boards. With marginalia and corrections.—Cf. L. W. Riley, *op. cit.*, no. M20.

Alanus de Insulis. De planctu naturae. Lat. 26.

Lat. 26

ALANUS DE INSULIS. De planctu naturae. *Bohemia, 22 April 1365,* written by Johannes de Polna (f.54v).

Paper. 54 ff. 30 x 23 cm. Contemp. vellum. Copious marginal and interlinear notes.

Lat. 27

CHRISTOPHORUS STEBORIUS. Commentarius in universam Aristotelis Logicam . . . , exceptus a Ioanne Hirningero Riedlingensi. *Ingolstadt, 1608.*

Paper. 298 ff. 18.5 x 15 cm. Contemp. stamped pigskin. Carthusian monastery, Buxheim.—Cf. L. W. Riley, *op. cit.*, no. M34.—Backer-Sommervogel, *op. cit.*, VII, 1521. Bound in front is the printed dissertation of Paul Mayer, *Disp. phil. de universali logica* (Ingolstadt, 1608).

Lat. 28

[ARISTOTLE]. Lecture notes on the Physica by an unnamed Jesuit scholar. *Ingolstadt, ca. 1600.*

Paper. 256 ff. 18 x 15 cm. Contemp. vellum. Prov.: M. Joannis Hirningeri (autograph). Carthusian monastery, Buxheim.—Not listed by L. W. Riley, *op. cit.* (but cf. his appendix no. M16B).

Lat. 29

[ARISTOTLE]. Commentarius in octo libros Aristotelis De auditu phisico a Ioanne Zorn exceptus, *inc.* (Proemium): Altera pars philosophiae facilior et amaenior quam logica vocabulo a graecie sumpto dicite phisica seu phisologia. *Germany, early 17th cent.*

Paper. 1 f., 203 numb. ff. 20 x 16 cm. Contemp. stamped pigskin over wooden boards. Cf. L. W. Riley, *op. cit.*, no. M16.

Lat. 30

[ARISTOTLE]. Commentarius in IV libros De coelo Aristotelis a Joanne Zorn exceptus [treats also of the Meteorologica and De generatione et corruptione], *inc.* (Proemium): Corpore naturali in communi eiusque proprietatibus exsplicatis ad species pergit Aristoteles. *Germany, early 17th cent.*

Paper. 1 f., 203 (i.e. 206) numb. ff. illus. 20 x 16 cm. Contemp. pigskin over wooden boards.—Cf. L. W. Riley, *op. cit.*, no. M13.

Lat. 31

JOHANN BERNARD THANHAUSEN. Tractatus in universam Aristotelis Logicam . . . exceptus a . . . Friderico Schumio ordinis S. Benedicti professo Admontensi. *Graz, 1634–1635.*

Paper. Painted t.–p., 259 ff. 19 x 14.5 cm. Contemp. vellum.—Cf. L. W. Riley, *op. cit.*, no. M36.—Backer-Sommervogel, *op. cit.*, VII, 1958.

Lat. 32

GUILLELMUS ROTHWELLUS, O. P. Commentary on the Sentences of Petrus Lombardus, *inc.:* Quaeritur utrum theologia sit scientia (F. Stegmüller, *Repertorium*, I, 138, no. 301). *France, 6 Feb. 1362.*

Vellum. 137 ff. 16 x 12 cm. Red dyed pigskin. Explicit in 15th-cent. hand assigns the text to Petrus de Tarantasia (Pope Innocent V). Prov.: Jacobus P. R. Lyell.

Lat. 33

WILLIAM PAGULA (Page, Pagham, Paghaner, Paghanerus). Oculi sacerdotis.—*With* Middle English poem, "erthe oute of erth" (f.91v). *England, early 15th cent.*

Vellum. 91 ff. 31 x 20 cm. Decorated initials. Blue morocco. Prov.: "Liber magistri Antonii molineux [?] ex dono magistri W. G. . . ."

Lat. 34

RENAISSANCE MISCELLANY. 1. PIETRO PAULO VERGERIO, the Elder. De ingenuis moribus, ff.1–33.—2. ST. BASIL OF CAESAREA. De legendis antiquorum libris, tr. by Leonardo Bruni Aretino, ff.33v–48.—3. LEONARDO BRUNI ARETINO. De studiis et litteris, ff.48–61.—4. IDEM. Isagocicon moralis disciplinae, ff.62–77. *Italy, late 15th cent.*, in two hands.

Paper. 77 ff. 16 x 23 cm. Illum. initials. 16th-cent. green vellum.

Lat. 35

JOHN FELTON. Sermones dominicales, ff.1–180; subject index, ff.181–187.—*With* Sermon [De cruce], ff.181r–181v, *expl.*: Gregorius libro primo et quarto de pharetra, and Alphabetical index, ff.182r–182v. Poem of 16 lines, beginning "I ham as I ham and so will I be" added by early 16th-cent. owner on f.3r (of 4 prel.ff.; cf. J. Morford in *Library Chronicle* XXV <1959>, 80–3). *England (Oxford?), ca. 1450.*

Vellum. 186 ff. 22 x 16 cm. Modern leather. Bookplate of J. P. Lyell.

Lat. 36

FIFTEENTH CENTURY MISCELLANY. 1. ST. BENEDICT OF NURSIA. Regula, ff.1–58.—2. Musical notes, ff.58v–60.—3. JOHANNES DE TAMBACO. De consolatione theologie, ff.63–186.—4. ST. AUGUSTINE. Sermo de vanitate, ff.187–191.—5. HENRICUS SUSO. Excerpta ex Orologio sapiencie, ff.192–196.—6. HENRICUS DE HASSIA. De proprietate monachorum, ff.197–206.—7. Anonymous tract on rondeaux, ballades, virelais, etc., f.207, *inc.:* Differentia est inter rondellis, balladis, vireletis et motetis et fugas [sic].—8. Anonymous. De musica, ff.207v–216, *inc.:* Musica est motus vocum racionabilium.—9. NICOLAUS DE DINKELSBÜHL. Confessionale, ff.217–233.—10. JOHANNES GERSON. De diversis temptationibus, ff.235–261. *Germany, 1437* (f.58) and following years, in a variety of hands.

Paper. 263 ff (last 2 blank). 15 x 11 cm. Musical notations and diagrs. Contemp. pigskin over wooden boards.

Lat. 37

JUAN DE TORQUEMADA, cardinal. Meditationes, *expl.:* "Ffinite sunt contemplaciones supradicte et continuate Rome per Vlricum Han [Ulrich Han, printer in Rome] Anno domini Millesimo Quadringentesimo Sexagesimo nono die vltima Mensis Octobris. *Rome, 1469.*

Paper. 27 ff. 27 x 20 cm. Some colored initials and floral ornaments, space for illus. left blank. H/vellum.—Cf. L. Donati, "A Manuscript of '*Meditationes*' Johannis de Turrecremata (1469)," *Library Chronicle*, XXI (1955), 51–60.

Lat. 38

GIROLAMO ANGERIANO. Erotopaignion, with dedication to Joannes Jacobus de Castillione, abp. of Bari. *Naples (?), ca. 1510.*

Paper. 35 ff. 19 x 14 cm. Original cardboard wrappers. With a few corrections in text. Autograph?

Lat. 39

GUILLELMUS BRITO. Expositiones difficiliorum vocabulorum de bibliotheca per ordinem alphabeti. Monastery of St. Mary, *Royaumont, ca. 1350.*

Vellum. 264 ff., double columns. 30 x 21 cm. Initial letter in gold and colors; red and blue capitals; marginal notes. French 18th-cent. green morocco. Gives equivalents in Old French in various instances.—Extensive postscript, incl.: "Hic liber est scriptus, qui scripsit sit benedictus. . . Qui titulum delevit ut ab eadem ecclesia furtive alienavit hunc librum sit a deo anathema maranata."

Lat. 40

DUO DIALOGI DE PHILOSOPHIA MORALI. Proemium, ff.1–3r, *inc.:* Veritatis vim sepenumero cogitanti.—Dialogus primus, ff.3r–32v, *inc.:* Ultimis estatis fervoribus . . .—Dialogus secundus, ff.32v–63v, *inc.:* Cum ad edes Andree arisii omnes . . . *Northern Italy (?), ca. 1450.*

Paper. 64 ff. 20 x 14 cm. Decorated initials. 16th-cent. green vellum. "Questo libro sia dato ad nostro patre domino facino de sanctopetro in portanova ne la perochia de sancto victore. . ." (f.64v).

Ad. Lat. 40: By Umbertus Decembrius, cf. P. O. Kristeller, *Iter Italicum* (Leyden, 1963), pp. 312 and 328.

Lat. 41

ST. AUGUSTINE. De vita christiana. *Germany, 1467.*

Paper. 12 ff. 21 x 15 cm. H/vellum. Contemp. inscription on upper margins of f.1v and 2r: Frater Rudolfus Rasser Donatus (name of scribe?). 17th-cent. ownership: Carthusian monastery in Brixen.

Lat. 42*

CANON LAW MISCELLANY. 1. GRATIAN. Extracts from the Decretum, beginning with c. 7 D. I, ff.1–137r.—2. LIBER SEXTUS. De regulis iuris, ff.141–5r.—3. CODEX JUSTINIANI. Extracts relating to ecclesiastical affairs, beginning with 1.1, ff.147–57v. *Italy, late 15th cent.*

Vellum. 158 ff. 13.5 x 10 cm. 16th-cent. vellum.—Written for Cesare Luigi Strada? (Inscr. on fly leaf): Caesar Strada Apostolicarum literarum scriptor. . . . Eius gloria est.—Acc. to inscription of f.158r, signed B[onifacius] Car[dina]lis Maior, Strada was received, he confessed, and was granted absolution, in Compostella in 1534. Library of the Cappuccini of Ferrara (17th-cent. inscription).

Lat. 43

ALPHABETUM MALARUM MULIERUM, ff.2–6, *inc.:* Ut ergo videatis chun [sic] Salamone, quam hamara sit mulier, formabo de eis unum alfabetum.—*With* ARISTOTLE. De bona fortuna, interprete Bartholomeo of Messana, ff.7–10.—PETRARCH. Psalmi septem poenitentiales, ff.11–14. *Italy, 15th cent.*

Vellum. 14 ff. 18 x 13 cm. Red and blue capitals, and marginal decoration. Paper boards. Prov.: [Dr. Ernst Schulz, Munich].

Lat. 44

HISTORIA GESTORUM ALEXANDRI PUERI MAGNI. Late medieval version of the Historia de preliis, *inc.:* Sapientissimi namque Egyptii sub omni natione que sub celo est scientes . . . *Germany, first half of 15th cent.*

Paper. 40 ff. 18 x 14 cm. Modern paper boards. Prov.: [Dr. Ernst Schulz, Munich].

Lat. 45

ALEXANDER DE VILLA DEI. Doctrinale. *France(?), late 13th cent.*

Vellum. 27 ff. (incomplete at beginning). 18th-cent. leather Copious later annotations. Phillipps ms. 190.

Lat. 46

PETRUS PANDONI. Porcelii poetae clarissimi et oratoris Ortographia. *Italy, Feb. 1, 1460* (f.4v).

Paper. 86 ff. 17 x 12 cm. 2 illum. initials. Contemp. vellum. Prov.: D. Andreas Parisinus (ff.3r, 83v, 85v).

Lat. 47

GUIDO DE COLONNA. Historia Troiana. *Northern Italy, ca. 1370.*

Paper. 141 ff. 27 x 21 cm. H/morocco. F.139v: "Hunc librum non comodabis. Si comodabis non de [h]abebis. Si dehabebis non tacito. Si tacito perdes amicum," followed on ff.141v and 142 by transcript of documents given at Pieve di Sacco by Jacobus, "comes palatinus," in 1370, removing the stain of illegitimacy from 3 inhabitants, and creating a notary. Library of William Harrison Woodward.

Lat. 48

MICHAEL DE MASSA. In quatuor Evangelistas (Glosa super Matheum, etc.).—IDEM. Tractatus de vitiis, ff.102v–123v, *inc.:* Quia ut ait augustinus.—Tabula, ff.124–136v.—DE VITIIS, ff.137–138, *inc.:* Superbia est radix omnium malorum. *Germany, 15th cent.*

Paper. 138 ff. 29 x 22 cm. Contemp. blind-stamped calf over wooden boards, rebacked. Prov.: J. P. R. Lyell.

Lat. 49

ARISTOTLE. Metaphysica, in the translation of Guilelmus de Moerbeke, with anonymous commentary. *Germany, 15th cent.*

Paper. 185 ff. 29.5 x 21 cm. Stamped h/calf over wooden boards. Same commentary as ms.lat.59.—Cf. L. W. Riley, *op. cit.*, no. M6.

Lat. 50

[ARISTOTLE]. Commentary on the Ethica Nicomachea, *inc.:* Sicut dicit philosophus natura humana multipliciter est ancilla. *Italy, ca. 1400.*

Paper, outer conjugate of each sign. vellum. 110 ff. 22 x 14 cm. H/morocco. Prov.: John T. Beer; Hermann Suchier.—Cf. L. W. Riley, *op. cit.*, no. M9.

Lat. 51

SENECA. Tragoediae, with commentary by Nicholas Trivet. *England, ca. 1360–1370*, in a variety of hands.

Vellum. 154 ff. (few ff. missing). 25 x 17 cm. Contemp. vellum. [Library of E. H. W. Myerstein].

Lat. 52

CHARLES VIII, King of France. Orationes [fictae] legatorum Caroli VIII, regis francorum, 1495, with replies, ff.1–6.—*With* MARTINUS POLICH DE MELLERSTADT. Oratio pro recommendatione rectoris Georgii Dottanii habita, ff.6v–7.—PETRUS DE TUSSIGNANO. Recepte super nono Almansoris, ff.8–11. *Leipzig, 1500–1510.*

Paper. 12 ff. 20 x 15 cm. Boards.—*Orationes* printed in Hain-Cop. 12035. The second item appears unpublished, the third is a variant of GW 271, ff.45r–48v. Recipes, one against the plague, on blank space on ff. 7v, 11v and 12. Prov.: [Dr. Ernst Schulz].

Lat. 53

MONTEDOGLIO. Capitoli, esentioni et privilegii delli huomini et commune di Monte doglio . . . dalli Gran Duchi di Toscana confirmati. *Montedoglio, 1489–1698,* in various hands, in Latin and Italian.

Vellum. 25 ff. 23 x 16 cm. Contemp. leather. Signet of Montedoglio on ff.4v and 17r. Signatures of various notaries, the earliest document (ff.4v–10v) signed by Giovanni Battista Guidone de Guidoni.

Lat. 54

MONTEDOGLIO. Statuta et ordinamenta communis et hominum Montis Dolii. *Italy, 1490–1747,* various hands, in Latin and Italian.

Vellum. 76 ff. 28 x 21 cm. Later vellum binding. Original statutes, 87 chapters, ff.3–47, written by "Stefanus olim philippi et Stephani demaneriis . . ."

Montedoglio.   Statuta et ordinamenta.   Lat. 54.

Lat. 55

LIBER SCINTILLARUM etc.—1. LIBER SCINTILLARUM, ff.1–24v, *inc.:* De castitate et continentia.—2. SERMONES. Two incomplete sermons, ff.25–36v, the second (f.30) with *inc.:* Primum querite regnum dei et hec omnia adicientur vobis.—3. POENITENTIALE, ff.37–52v, *inc.:* In nomine Iesu Christi incipiunt interrogaciones que de scripturis sanctis et canonibus sacris in foro penitencie ad utilitatem confitencium fieri possunt et debent.—4. SERMONES. Two incomplete sermons, ff.53–58v, second (de penthecoste) with *inc.:* Effundam spiritum meum super omnem carnem.—5. Excerpts and glosses on Bible, f.59r.—6. DE PUGNA SPIRITUALI, f.59, *inc.:* Inter Ierusalem et Babyloniam nulla pax est sed guerra continua (Migne CLXXXIII, 761–5).—7. DE VITIIS, ff.59–61r, *inc.:* Forte die quadam avarus libidini obvians.—8. DE CONFESSIONE, f.61v, *inc.:* Ad habendum salutifere confessionis breviordinem.—9. LOTHARIUS DIACONUS (=Pope Innocent III), De contemptu mundi seu De

[12]

miseria conditionis humanae (excerpts), ff.62–70 (Migne CCXVII, 717–46).—10. QUINDECIM SIGNA xv dierum ante diem iudicii invenit sanctus Ieronimus in annalibus Hebreorum, f.70v (Migne XCIV, 555).—11. Two poems, f.72v: a. Tempus acceptabile, tempus est salutis (Walther 19171), and b. Sacerdotes mementote, nichil maius sacerdote (Walther 16999). *Germany, 13–14th cent.* (ff.59 et seq. are 13th cent.).

Vellum. 72 ff. 16 x 12 cm. Modern vellum over wooden boards. Fragment of larger collection which had presumably been bound together.

Lat. 56

QUAESTIONES DE ACCIDENTIBUS ANIME RATIONALIS libri tres. *Germany(?), first half 16th cent.*

Paper. 50 ff. 20 x 14 cm. Boards.

Lat. 57

[TERENCE]. Commentary on Andria and Eunuch. *Italy, ca. 1500.*

Paper. 10 ff. (incomplete at beginning). 22 x 15 cm. Boards.

Lat. 58

IVO OF CHARTRES. Panormia. *France, 12th cent.*

Vellum. 258 ff. (ff.237–254 misbound, following f.258). 28 x 19 cm. Initials in red and blue throughout and figurated initial on f.204v. Modern h/vellum over wooden boards. Phillipps ms. 7408.

Lat. 59

[ARISTOTLE]. Anonymous commentary on the Metaphysica, *inc.:* Omnes homines natura scire desiderant. Nam quaelibet res ferente natura appetit perfectionem . . . *Germany, 15th cent.*

Paper. 85 ff. 29 x 21 cm. Decorated initials. Vellum. Same commentary as ms.lat.49, possibly identical with that of Johannes Folsham (=Folsamus).—Cf. L. W. Riley, *op. cit.*, no. M6.

Lat. 60

WILLIAM OF AUXERRE. Summa aurea in quattuor libros sententiarum [of Petrus Lombardus]. *France(?), 14th cent.*

Vellum. 351 ff., double columns. 24 x 16 cm. Red and blue initials with ornamentation. H/morocco. Estate of E. Voynich (cf. De Ricci II, 1930).

Lat. 61

SERMONES de tempore, sanctis et variis causis, with the following interspersed tracts: 1. NOTABILIA de vitiis, ff.136r–141v.—2. BERNHARDUS, Ad Raymundum de cura rei familiaris epistola, ff.141–142.

Ad. Lat. 56: *Inc.:* An notitia et intellectus sint idem vel diversa.

—3. DESCRIPTIO FEMINARUM MALARUM, f.144.—4. TRACTATUS BONUS DE MORTUIS et eorum suffragiis (with reference to Waldensians, Wyclif and Hussites), ff.153v–158v.—5. TRACTATUS DE QUATTUOR VIRTUTIBUS cardinalibus, ff.188–207.— 6. TRACTATUS DE RESTITUTIONE, ff.222–234.—7. CHRISTIAN FUCHS, of Vienna, Sermo de excommunicatione, ff.235–245.— 8. Registrum, ff.247–248. *Austria, second half 15th cent.*

Paper. 249 ff. 21 x 15 cm. Contemp. calf over wooden boards. Item 3 is in verse and prose, compiled from Pseudo-Hildebert and other sources.

Lat. 62

ASTRONOMICAL FRAGMENTS. 1. *Inc.:* Primum regulares feriales unde oriantur videamus (f.1); *expl.:* . . . esse aliis dictum est (f.4v).— 2. PREVOSTIN, of Cremona. Fragment of the first book of his Summa theologica. *France, 13th cent.*

Vellum. 8 ff. Circular diagr. and table on f.1v. 22 x 14 cm. Modern vellum. Prov.: George Dunn.

Lat. 63

ST. AUGUSTINE and others: 1. ST. AUGUSTINE. De pastoribus, ff.1–9, first leaf missing(?).—2. IDEM. De ovibus, ff.9–23.—3. ST. AMBROSE. De laude et exhortatione viduitatis, ff.23–35.—4. ST. AUGUSTINE. Retractatio in libro ad Horosium contra Priscillianistas, f.36r.—5. OROSIUS. Commonitorium ad Sanctum Augustinum de Priscillianistis, ff.36–37.—6. ST. AUGUSTINE. Responsio ad Orosium de Priscillianistis et Origenis errore, ff.37–43.—7. IDEM. Retractatio in libro de correctione Donatistarum, ff.43–58.—8. IDEM. Retractatio in libro de fide et operibus, f.58r.—9. IDEM. De fide et operibus, ff.58–78.—10. IDEM. De dialectica, ff.79–87.—11. ARISTOTLE. Categoriae, tr. by St. Augustine, ff.87–102.—12. ST. AUGUSTINE. Commonitorium ad universam ecclesiam destinatum de Manicheis conversis, ff.102–104.—13. POPE JOHN II. Epistola de fide contra Euticianistas de duobus naturis in una persona Christi, ff.104–106.— 14. ST. AUGUSTINE. Collatio trinitatis . . . a se ipso ad semet ipsum, ff.106–109.—15. Catalogue of the works of St. Augustine, ff.109–112. *Germany, 12th cent.*

Vellum. 112 ff. 26 x 17 cm. Modern leather. Phillipps ms. 11901.

Lat. 64

BASLE, Council: 1. ANDREA DE PETRA. Oratio in congregatione generali, ff.1–9v.—2. JOHANNES, Abp. of Taranto. Oratio ad patres concilii Basiliensis, ff.9v–15r.—3. RESPONSIO SYNODALIS de

---

Ad. Lat. 61: On authorship of item 2, see B. Hauréau, *Notices et extraits de quelques manuscrits latins* (Paris, 1890), I, 334–7.

autoritate cuiuslibet consilii generalis supra papam, ff.15v–34v.—
4. JULIANUS CAESARINO. Oratio luculenta ad convertendum Bohemos, ff.35r–46v (incomplete). *Germany, first half of 15th cent.*

Paper. 46 ff. (2 ff. missing?) 28 x 20 cm. Modern boards. The texts have been identified in Mansi, XXIX, but do not follow his sequence.

Lat. 65

MAXIMUS STEINER. Institutionum dialecticarum sive prolusionum ad philosophiam rationalem tractatus tripartitus. On Aristotle's Organon; written by Andreas Ignatius Spahn (f.192 contains a list of 107 students of Steiner, of whom Spahn is the first). *Prague, 1641–1642.*

Paper. 197 ff. 19.5 x 15 cm. Contemp. vellum.—Cf. L. W. Riley, *op. cit.*, no. M35.

Lat. 66

D. ROUSSEL. Commentarius in universam Aristotelis Metaphysicam. *Paris, 1682.*

Paper. 2 ff., 523 pp. 22 x 16 cm. Contemp. red morocco.—Cf. L. W. Riley, *op. cit.*, no. M32. Name of student-scribe (De la Quint . . .) on engraved prel.f., followed by engr. portrait of Aristotle (Iollain exc.).

Lat. 67

MARCIANTONIUS GENUA. Lectiones super libros Physicorum Aristotelis, lectae anno 1549. *Italy, 1549.*

Paper. 207 ff. 29 x 20 cm. H/morocco.—Cf. L. W. Riley, *op. cit.*, no. M7.

Lat. 68

ALFONSO SPEZZANI. Commentary on books 3–7 of Aristotle's Physica. *Italy, 1591.*

Paper. 121 ff. 31 x 21 cm. H/morocco.—Cf. L. W. Riley, *op. cit.*, no. M33.

Lat. 69

HENRICUS SUSO. Horologium sapientie, incl. Cantica canticorum (ff.189–193). *Germany, first half 15th cent.*

Paper. 193 ff. 21.5 x 14 cm. Some decorated initials; two small faces drawn into capitals on ff.91v and 164v. Contemp. dyed kid over wooden boards. "Acquistato in Vienna dall' Antiquario della Biblioteca Imperiale in quella città e portato in dono al mio caro Cognato G. Ghizzi. Maggio. 1869." [sig.] Frangnani (?).—James H. Reddan, Venice, 1896 (ff.1v and 193v).

Lat. 70

CHRISTOPHER BRANDIS. Commentarius in universam Aristotelis Logicam . . . scriptus a Joanne Huober. *Dillingen, 1608–1609.*

Paper. 1050 pp. 19 x 15.5 cm. Contemp. stamped pigskin over wooden boards. Carthusian monastery, Buxheim. Owner's stamp: G.W.B.D.—Cf. L. W. Riley, *op. cit.*, no. M22.—Backer-Sommervogel, *op. cit.*, II, 85, B (same ms.?).

Lat. 71

CHRISTOPHER BRANDIS. Commentarius in octo libros Physicorum Aristotelis . . . scriptus a Joanne Huober. *Dillingen, 1609–1610.*

   Paper. 941 pp. 19 x 15.5 cm. Contemp. stamped pigskin (with initials G.W.B.D.) over wooden boards.—Cf. L. W. Riley, *op. cit.*, no. M23.—Backer-Sommervogel, *op. cit.*, II, 85, A (same ms.?).

Lat. 72

TERENCE. Comediae: Andria, ff.1–36.—Eunuchus, ff.37–72r.—Heautontimorumenos, ff.72v–106r.—Adelphi, ff.106v–137v.—Phormio, ff.138r–170v.—Hecyra, ff.171r–199r. *Germany, ca. 1500.*

   Paper. 200 ff. (last blank). 19 x 14 cm. Six illum. capitals. 17th-cent. stamped pigskin. With marginal and interlinear annotations.

Lat. 73

AD. CAIMUS. Imperialium institutionum libri IV (cum registro), auctore Ad. Rev. Dño. Caimo preposito ecc. par. S. Zenonis. *Austria(?), 1743.*

   Paper. 389 pp. 20 x 14 cm. Contemp. vellum. Title borders, vignettes and tail pieces drawn in pen-and-ink. Bookplate of M. D. Wilmersdoerffer, 1897.

Lat. 74

RICARDUS HESIUS. Epistolae latinae. Collection of model letters (some copies of actual letters?) in Latin, and 3 letters in Italian. The name of Hesius appears only in 6 letters at end. *Italy, 1598–1612.*

   Paper. 29 ff. (3 leaves removed). 20.5 x 14 cm. Contemp. boards.

Lat. 75

[ARISTOTLE]. On the De anima, incl. a section headed "Liber quintus de deo et angelis," *inc.:* Stemma philosophiae naturalis ab Aristotele descriptum et ab eiusdem schola nova restitutum. *South Germany, 17th cent.*

   Paper. 55–292 numb. ff., 85 ff. (actual count 315). 19.5 x 15 cm. Contemp. calf.—Cf. L. W. Riley, *op. cit.*, no. M12.

Lat. 76

GEORG KERN, STEPHEN WHITE and CHRISTOPHER BRANDIS. De praeceptis decalogi (commentary on Thomas Aquinas), written by Joa. Huober.—Summa controversiarum, written by same.—Prolegomena in universam philosophiam moralem Aristotelis, *inc.:* Antequam ad particulares materias descendamus quedam breviter. *Dillingen(?), 1608.*

Ad. Lat. 73: This is a commentary on the *Institutiones Iustiniani.*

Paper. 407 ff., blank ll., 37 ff., 1 blank l., 316 ff. 20.5 x 16.5 cm. Contemp. stamped pigskin. Carthusian monastery, Buxheim.—Cf. L. W. Riley, *op. cit.*, no. M14.—Backer-Sommervogel, IV, 1015–16 (Kern); VIII, 1093–98 (White); II, 85–86 (Brandis).

Lat. 77

ROMANUS RAUSCHER. Octo libri Physicorum [Aristotelis] ab Reverendo . . . Romano Rauscher ordinis S. Benedicti . . . traditi, a me Fratre Erasmo Altmanshausen monasterii Admontensis professo excepti.—*With* List of fathers and brothers "in convictu Salisburgensi," 1637–39.—Georg Berchtold Lorich, printed disputation.—Anonymous commentary on the De coelo. *Salzburg, 1638–1639.*

Paper. 4 ff., 525 pp., 6 ff., 352 (350) pp., diagrs., 1 folded sheet. 18.5 x 15 cm. Contemp. stamped pigskin.—Cf. L. W. Riley, *op. cit.*, no. M31.

Lat. 78

[ARISTOTLE]. On the Organon, Physica, and Metaphysica, *inc.* (Proemium): Fili, a iuventute tua excipe doctrinam, et usque ad canos invenies sapientias. *Germany, 17th cent.*

Paper. 258 ff. (a few blank). 19.5 x 15.5 cm. Contemp. vellum. Carthusian monastery, Buxheim.—Cf. L. W. Riley, *op. cit.*, no. M15.

Lat. 79

[ARISTOTLE]. On the Organon and Physica, written by Anselm, a Carthusian of Buxheim. *Buxheim, 1634–1635.*

Paper. 321 ff. 18 x 14 cm. Contemp. vellum. Carthusian monastery, Buxheim. The commentaries are the same as those in ms. lat. 78, but without commentary on the Metaphysica.—Cf. L. W. Riley, *op. cit.*, no. M18.

Lat. 80

PLACIDIUS AEGIDIUS MELANDER. On the De anima of Aristotle, *inc.*: Corpus naturale mixtum ut diximus in principio philosophiae aliud est perfectum aliud imperfectum. *Dillingen(?), 1621.*

Paper. 255 ff. 19 x 14 cm. Contemp. stamped pigskin (with initials P.P.M.A. and date 1621). Bound with various printed Aristotle dissertations; lists of doctoral candidates, Dillingen; etc.—Cf. L. W. Riley, *op. cit.*, no. M30.

Lat. 81

SUETONIUS TRANQUILLUS. De vita XII caesarum (extracts), ff.1–42.—*With* AUSONIUS, Versus de XII caesaribus, ff.42r–42v.—BENVENUTO DE RAMBALDIS, de Imola. Liber augustalis (extracts), ff.43–56v, with date of composition, 1385 (f.56v).—MACCABEES, 2nd book to death of Herod Agrippa (in Italian), ff.56–63, *inc.*: Qui se comensa lo secundo libro delli Machabei . . . Morto Simone quinto . . . *Italy, second half 15th cent.*

Paper. 63 ff. 22 x 14 cm. H/morocco.

Lat. 82*

13TH-CENT. NOTARIAL HANDBOOK. 1. JOHANNES DE BOLOGNA. Summa artis notariae, ff.1–25 (some leaves missing; cf. text in L. Rockinger, *Briefsteller und Formelbücher*, II, 603–712).— 2. EXEMPLA. Notarial examples derived from papal correspondence, ff.26–30.—3. ARNULFUS CANONICUS PARISIENSIS (Arnulf of Anagni). Summa 'Ut nos minores,' ff.31–43 (text contains dates 1250 [f.36r] and 1251 [f.37r]; apparently a better ms. than that used by J. Joosting for his ed. in *Zeitschrift der Savigny-Stiftung, Kan. Ab.*, XVII (1928), 153–223).—4. JOHANNES, praepositus Halberstadensis. Epistola, f.43v. *Italy?, second half 13th cent.*

Vellum. 43 ff. 23 x 17 cm. Contemp. h/pigskin over wooden boards, with guards taken from earlier ms.

Lat. 83

ST. BASIL, bishop of Caesarea. Epistola ad Gregorium theologum, ff.1–3.—*With* ST. JOHN CHRYSOSTOM. Contra iudeos sermones sex, ff.4–56.—IDEM. Adversus Anomoeos sermones quinque, ff.57–89. —IDEM. Ad Stagirium monacum libri tres, ff.89–139.—IDEM. Paradoxa, ff.140–149. *Italy, 15th cent.*

Paper. 150 ff. (last blank). 27 x 19 cm. Stamped leather with coat of arms. Phillipps ms. 9471.

Lat. 84

SERMONES ANONYMI: 1. Ecce rex tuus venit tibi pius . . . Si aliquis amicum . . . , ff.1–168.—2. Hora es iam nos de sompno surgere in hiis vitiis monet . . . , ff.170r–241v.—3. Sanctus Anshelmus longo tempore . . . , ff.243r–269v.—4. Liber et numerus . . . (commentary on Matthew), ff.270r–277r.—5. Honora deum et honorifica sacerdotes . . . , ff.278r–299r.—6. Benedictum est lignum, per quid sit iusticia . . . , ff.300r–311r.—7. Quotations from Bible, classics and fathers of the church, ff.312r–319r.—8. Ad laudem et gloriam omnipotentis dei . . . , ff.318r–322v. *Germany, 15th cent.*

Paper. 322 ff. 19 x 14 cm. Contemp. leather over wooden boards.

Lat. 85

WERNER ROLEWINCK. Fasciculus temporum. *Northern Italy, ca. 1470.*

Paper. 40 ff. 42 x 27 cm. Numerous drawings and diagrs., partly colored by hand. Contemp. stamped leather over wooden boards.

Lat. 86

FRANÇOIS DE MERLES (1480–1520). Memoirs and accounts. *France, late 15th and early 16th cent.*

Paper. 177 instead of 292 ff. (ff. 16–57 and 198–271 missing). 38 x 21 cm. Contemp. vellum. Contains report on studies in Pavia and Avignon; commentary on the plague, contemp. events, stay in Rome, and the Jews; various financial accounts; and detailed report on the construction of a residence.

Lat. 87

[ARISTOTLE]. On the Physica, De coelo, De generatione et corruptione, De anima, Metaphysica, Meteorologica, Organon, and Ethica Nicomachea. *Germany, 1670.*

Paper. 2 vols. 22.5 x 16 cm. 18th-cent. calf.—Cf. L. W. Riley, *op. cit.*, no. M19.

Lat. 88

ALEXANDER JOVIUS. Commentaria una cum quaestionibus in universam Aristotelis Logicam.—IDEM. Compendium in universam Aristotelis Logicam, collectum de lectione in lectionem per me Bernardum Berardum. *Italy, 1640–1641.*

Paper. 235 numb. ff., 21 ff., 69 numb. ff. 20 x 13.5 cm. Contemp. vellum.— Cf. L. W. Riley, *op. cit.*, no. M28.

Lat. 89*

ADAM. Summula de Summa Raymundi (verse abridgement of Raymondus de Pennaforte, cf. J. F. von Schulte, *Die Gesch. d. Quellen und d. Literatur des canonischen Rechts* <Stuttgart, 1875–80>, II, 427), ff.1–20v. —*With* Brief Bible dictionary, ff.20v–4. *France, 14th cent.*

Vellum. 24 ff. 17 x 10 cm. Gold stamped leather. Prov.: Luzarche collection, sold by auction, Paris, 1865; Stroehlin collection.

Lat. 90

ASCETIC MISCELLANY: 1. De arte bene moriendi, ff.1–13, *inc.:* Cum de presentis exilii miseria mortis . . . —2. POPE INNOCENT III. De miseria humane conditionis, ff.14–42.—3. Religious poetry: a. XV signa ante seculi consumationem fienda . . . , ff.42v–43v, *inc.:* Antequam iuditii dies metuenda . . . (H. Walther, *Versanfänge*, 1314); b. Altercatio animae et corporis . . . compilata per beatum Bernardum, ff.44r–50v, *inc.:* Vir quidam dum steterat velud heremita (variant of Walther 20421), cont. on f.44v: Iuxta corpus spiritus stetit et ploravit (Walther 10032: Visio Philiberti). *Italy, 15th cent.*

Paper. 56 ff. 23 x 16 cm. Illum. first page, with arms, and illum. capitals on ff. 14v and 24v. Modern gilt leather. Prov.: Ernesto Pagnoni, Milan.

Lat. 91

BARTHOLOMAEUS DE BREGANTIIS, Vicentinus. De venatione divini amoris, with two prologues, addressed to Hugh, cardinal bishop

---

Ad. Lat. 90, no. 1: Attributed to Matthew of Cracow.

of St. Sabina, O.P. (Hugh of Montrelais), and William, cardinal deacon of St. Eustachius (otherwise unknown). *Salzburg, 5 June 1453.*

Paper. 124 ff. 20 x 13 cm. H/morocco.—Cf. Quétif and Echard (1719), I, 258, no. 13.

Lat. 92

FIFTEENTH-CENTURY MISCELLANY: 1. JOHANNES GOLDNER. Sermones XXII de avaritia, ff.2–124r (written "per Johannem de prawnec [i.e. Brauneck]," 1470; apparently unpublished).—2. NICOLAUS DE DINKELSBÜHL. Von dem Vbel der aigenschafft die man hatt in den cloestern, ff.124–143v (sermon preached at the Univ. of Vienna; probably unpublished).—3. Extracts from Augustinus de Ancona and Bartholomaeus Pisanus, ff.143v–144v.—4. SIGISMUND, Holy Roman Emperor. Letter (in Czech) to his brother Wenceslaus, King of Bohemia, 4 Dec. 1418, f.145 (dated Vienna 1419, vero 1418; printed in F. Polacky, *Documenta Johannis Hus*, pp.682–6).—5. THOMAS (Palmerston) HIBERNICUS. De religione christiana, ff.146r–159v (dated 1421; cf. Hain 8544 and 13854).—6. PSEUDO-BERNARDUS. Epistola de cura domestica, ff.160r–162r (dated 1417). —7. Excerpts from ascetic writings, ff.162–164v.—8. CONSTANCE, Council. Conclusiones contra communionem populi sub utraque specie, ff.164v–167r (dated 1417).—9. PRAGUE, University. Determinatio super quibusdam erroneis articulis, 7 Feb. 1418, ff.167r–168r.—10. EPISTOLA CONTRA WICLEFISTAS et Husitas, known as "Eloquenti viro," but here without first sentence, *inc.:* Pro salutacione in Christo Jhesu domino nostro, ff.170r–193r. Followed on f.193r by poem "Dum de fide loquimur . . . ," 6 lines, and "Praga, modo doleas . . . ," 2 lines.—11. REMEDIA PRO CASIBUS CONTINGENTIBUS in divino officio, ff. 193v–194v.—12. COLLECTA DECRETI (excerpts from Gratian), ff.195–210.—13. STANISLAUS DE ZNOYMA. Tractatus contra articulos huscitorum et errores Johannis Wickleph, ff.210v–256v (dated 1420). *Bohemia, 15th cent.*

Paper. 257 ff. 20 x 15 cm. Stamped leather over wooden boards, ca. 1500. Prov.: "Liber iste Cenobii est Clarissarum Brixine commorancium" (inside front cover); "Elisabeth sancte in claustro me bibliotheca possideat . . ." (back cover).

Lat. 93

[FRANCISCANS OF METZ]. Letters and bulls of Pope Innocent VII, Pope Pius II, and Pope Sixtus IV respecting privileges of the Franciscan Order in Metz, brought together by Petrus de Vincentia (cf.

Ad. Lat. 92, no. 2: Published from other manuscripts by H. Menhardt in *Zeitschrift für deutsche Philologie*, LXXIII (1954), 1–39, 268–91. No. 6: Cf. note to Lat. 61.—No. 10: Attributed to Nicolaus de Dinkelsbühl.

Quétif and Echard, *op. cit.*, I, 880a), authenticity confirmed by the imperial notary Natalis Wassonius de Pontemontione (f.59). *Metz(?), 1489–1490.*

Vellum. 60 ff. (last blank). 13 x 8 cm. Contemp. blind-stamped leather over wooden boards. "Iste liber est de conventu fratrum minorum Sagunsium" (Saône?).

Lat. 94

TARTALEONI FAMILY. Copybook of financial transactions of the Tartaleoni brothers of Mantua, from 1565–1575. *Mantua, 1565–1575.*

Vellum. 42 ff. 24 x 16 cm. With notarial signets and signatures. Contemp. paper boards.

Lat. 95

STEPHANUS HUGONETI. Apparatus super constitutionibus Concilii Viennensis. *Northern Italy or S. France, early 14th cent.*

Vellum. 74 ff. 29 x 21 cm. 18th-cent. calf. An 18th-cent. inscription on f.1: "Carolus Maria Coo: a Pace."

Lat. 96

SERMONES DOMINICALES PER CIRCULUM ANNI, *inc.:* Tunc videbunt filium hominis. . . *France(?), 13th cent.*

Vellum. 65 ff. 20 x 14.5 cm. Boards.

Lat. 97

CATTANEI FAMILY. Will of Domina Georgeta, daughter of Marco Centurioni and widow of Jeronimo Cattanei, and legal proceedings about the inheritance involving primarily her grandson Sylvestro Cattanei and Isoltina, his brother Jeronimo's widow, dated 1548–1549, notarized by various officials of Genoa. Some earlier documents interspersed. *Genoa, 1536–1549,* in a variety of notarial hands.

Vellum. 46 ff. (last blank). 20.5 x 15 cm. Paper boards. On paper flyleaf at beginning: "Liberculus iste est Silvestri Cattanei."

Lat. 98

[ARISTOTLE]. Lecture notes containing questions & dispositions on the De coelo, De generatione et corruptione, and De anima, by a student at the "Collegium Callaritanum Sancti Josephi," a school of the "Poveri della Madre di Dio delle scuole pie." *Cagliari, Sardinia, 5 August 1695.*

Paper. 155, 2 ff. 21 x 15 cm. Contemp. vellum.—Cf. L. W. Riley, *Aristotle Texts and Commentaries to 1700 in the University of Pennsylvania Library* (publ. as monograph) (Philadelphia, 1961), M19A.

Ad. Lat. 95: Cf. Norman P. Zacour, "Stephanus Hugoneti and His 'Apparatus' on the Clementines," *Traditio*, XVII (1961), 527–30.—Ff. 21–30 misbound, actually sign. b to be placed between f.10 and 11.

Lat. 99

SEDULIUS. Carmen paschale, ff.1–47.—*With* Anonymous poems (none located in Walther): a. Contra superbos, f.47, *inc.:* Si quis materiam perpendat originis . . . b. Contra avaros, f.47v, *inc.:* Heu quos opes opibus cumulas, quod propria queris . . . c. Oratio quam dicitur edidisse Prudentius poeta. . . , f.48, *inc.:* O dee cunctipotens anime dator, o dee christe . . . d. Hymn Stelliferi conditor orbis, f.50v, *inc.:* Rapido coelum turbine versas. . .—Notes on the order of the liturgy, & verses in praise of monastic life, especially the Carthusian order (ff.59–65) and HISTORIA DE TRANSFIGURATIONE domini salvatoris (f.66). *Germany, second half 15th cent.*

Paper. 66 ff. (ff.52-58 blank). 14 x 10 cm. Boards.

Lat. 100

HENRICUS EENTHIUS(?). Notes on Aristotle's Logic, written by unnamed student.—*With* HENRICUS LOEFFLER. Tractatus primus De natura philosophiae, seu scientiae.—Theses logicae ex prolegomenis Weiroth, . . . Joannes Vogel, . . . Henricus Lofflerus, . . . Joannes Arnold, . . . Georgius Leinbauch, and others.—Defense of Joannes Vogel. *Germany, 1600.*

Paper. 393 ff. 19 x 16 cm. Contemp. vellum.—Cf. L. W. Riley, *op. cit.* (monograph), M16A.

Lat. 101

PSEUDO-ARISTOTLE. Secreta secretorum [extract]; text begins f.13v: Alexander cum sit corpus corruptibile. . . . *Germany, second half of 15th cent.*

Paper. 17 ff. 22 x 15 cm. Boards. Prov.: Charles W. Burr.—Cf. G. W. 2490. L. W. Riley, *op. cit.* (monograph), M7A.

Lat. 102

[ARISTOTLE]. Analysis librorum physicorum Aristotelis.—Preceded by GEOMETRIAE COMPENDIUM (7 ff.) and hand-colored drawings (on 2 ff.). *England, 1674–1675.*

Paper. 1 blank, 7, 2 ff., 385 pp. (pp.299-310 blank), 48 blank ff. 19.5 x 16 cm. 3 pp. with hand-colored primitive drawings, the 3rd on f.35 of the final blank section; geometrical drawings on ff.5-7. Prov.: Charles W. Burr.—Cf. L. W. Riley, *op. cit.* (monograph), M26A. Name Alexander Cunningham on p.92 is probably the name of a student-scribe, and not of the author.

Ad. Lat. 99: Poem c. published in Migne, *PL*, CI, 544.
Ad. Lat. 101: Cf. also Thorndike, *Incipits*, 2nd ed., col. 78.

Lat. 103

THEOLOGICAL MISCELLANY: 1. LEGENDE DELLA GLORIOSA VERGINE MARIA (in Italian), ff.2r–68r, *inc.:* Candor lucis eterne et speculum sine macula. Sapientia, secundo capitulo. Cosi como la luce corporale. . . .—2. TRACTATUS DE CIVITATE SANCTA JERUSALEM, ff.72r–163v, *inc.:* Videns Yesus civitatem flevit super illam dicens. . . .—3. QUAESTIONES DUO, f.164r, *inc.:* Quero de quo panno debet esse corruptibile. Respondet Alexander de Ales in tractatu de missa.—4. DOMINICA SEPTUAGESIMA, ff.165r–242v, *inc.:* Voca operationes et redde illud mercedem suam. . . .—5. DE CONFESSIONE, ff. 243r–350v, *inc.:* In omnibus qua confessionem pertinent. . . . *Italy, early 15th cent.*

Paper. 352 ff. (a few ff. blank). 9.5 x 7 cm. Modern red morocco.

Lat. 104

GASPARE CONTARINI. De Republica Veneta libri V. *Italy, mid-16th cent.*

Paper. 92 ff. (last blank). 20 x 14 cm. Unbound. From the Morbio library.

Lat. 105

JACOBUS DINETUS. Chrestomathy of Latin classics, ff.8–129, preceded by index and dedication.—Dicta astrologorum, ff.130–140r.—Carmen ex diversis Vergilii versibus . . . , ff.140v–162v. Dedicated by Jacobus Dinetus to his father Johannes, apparently as an account of his studies in Paris. *Paris, 1540.*

Paper. 162 ff. & 30 blank ff. 19 x 13 cm. 18th-cent. calf, with gold stamp of Plato & Dido on front and back.

Lat. 106

VAL D'AOSTA. Charters: 1. Confirmation made by Jean Carteron in favor of Ansermin of Pont d'Avix, Feb. 19, 1388 (1 f; 18 x 26 cm).—2. Charter of Agnes de Claustris concerning houses and land in the Val d'Aosta, Dec. 13, 1390 (1 f; 15 x 21 cm).—3. Exchange between Antoine Rolet and his nephew Antoine in the home of Jean Trousse of Annecy, 1399 (1 f; 39 x 26 cm).—4. Agreement between the bishop of Aosta and Gregory de Chastellar and Jean Thomasset de Chastellar concerning some rents, 1423 (1 f; 43 x 30 cm).—5. Feudal sentence concerning the fief of Pin, between William of Carreria and Boniface Boneri, Châtillon, Sept. 24, 1439 (1 f; 32 x 60 cm).—6. Agreement between G. Girardi and J. Chasson, 1478 (1 f; 20 x 19 cm). *Val d'Aosta, 1388–1478.*

Vellum. 6 ff. Unbound.

Lat. 107

ALBERTANUS CAUSIDICUS Brixiensis.—1. Liber de doctrina loquendi et tacendi, ff.1–7.—2. IDEM. Liber consolationis et consilii, ff.7–32 (includes the "Tale of Melibeus," cf. E. P. Goldschmidt, *Medieval Texts*, [London, 1943], pp.7–9).—3. IDEM. Liber de amore et dilectione, ff.23–56r. Expl. gives date of composition, 1263 [sic].—4. IDEM. Five sermons, ff.56v–68r, *inc.:* Congregatio nostra sit in nomine domini. . . .—5. PETRUS DAMIANUS. Rhythmos ad diversos mundi status, f.68r and v. *Northern Italy, late 14th cent.*

Vellum. 68 ff. 25.5 x 19 cm. Historiated initial I (knight with shield) and illum. border, slightly later (f.2r). 19th-cent. calf.

Lat. 108

GUILLELMUS DURANTUS. Rationale divinorum officiorum, ff.1–81v.—2. BENEDICTIONES ornamentorum ecclesiae, ff.82r–86v. —3. THOMMASO PORCACCHI (or Porcacci). Sonetti . . . per li psalmi del rev. padre . . . Bonaventura, sonnet by Francesco Pancera and Vergilius Hierardi, and epigram by Francisco Pegasi (in Ital.), ff.87r–88v.—4. PAROLE DEVOTE de l'anima di Jesu, riposte dell'anima [e] di Messer Jesu Christo (in Ital.), ff.89r–98r.—5. Letter from Johannes Aloisius Tuscanus (auditor of the papal camera) to Petrus "cardinalis Firasonensis," ff.98v–99v.—6. VERSUS DE MORTE, and other poems, ff.100r–102v.—7. Letter from "Frater Johannes" to his Carthusian brethren at Padova, "De humilitate interiori et patientia vera," f.103.—8. EXCOMMUNICATIO vel potius excommunicationis intimatio in die ramis palmarum (in Ital.), ff.104r–106v.—9. MODUS ABSOLVENDI ab excommunicatione maiori, f.107.—10. EXORTATIONE ET INTERROGATIONE che si ha da fare in colloquio delli monaci quando si ha da dar' la cappa ad alcun' novitio, (in Ital.), ff.108r–109v.—11. VERSUS . . . ac sobrie et caute legendi, ff.110r–115v.—12. CONCLUSIO huius operis, f.116.—13. Letter from "Frater Johannes" to his Carthusian brethren, "De humilitate," f.117. *Bologna, late 16th cent.*

Paper. 118 ff. The entire work written by Domnus Severinus (cf. ff.81v and 117v). 21 x 15 cm. Contemp. vellum.

Lat. 109

MONCELESE (Territory of Venice). Book of deeds to various territorial acquisitions from 1508 to 1631 (some of the later ones in Italian). *Venice(?), 16th and early 17th cent.*

Vellum. 3 unnumb., 83 numb., 3 blank ff. 26 x 19 cm. Notarial signets and signatures. 17th-cent. morocco. From the library of Morbio.

Lat. 110

SALELLES and LIMOU. Reconoychenssas [Reconnaissances] de Salelas e de Lemosis.—*With* CASTRES. Reconoychenssas de Casthans.

—PRADES. Reconoychenssas de Pradelas. Surveys of possessions and fiefs of King Charles VI of France through Johannes de Claromonte, 1397–1398, with notarizations. *Southern France, 1397–1398.*

Vellum. 140, 57, 4 ff., 1 blank f. 35 x 28 cm. Few figurated initials. Stamped calf over wooden boards.

Lat. 111
GUILLAUME DE MONTLAUZUN. Apparatus; commentary on the Clementines, *inc.:* Magnifice bonitatis mireque pietatis viro domino Iohanni. *Southern France or Spain, middle of 14th cent.*

Vellum. 52 ff. 41 x 27 cm. Portfolio.

Lat. 112
PETRUS DE RIGA. Aurora. *France, middle of 13th cent.*

Vellum. 154 ff. 25 x 15 cm. Faint sketch of the Virgin on f.125. Modern binding in imitation of old h/leather over wooden boards with old guards (two vellum incunable leaves, probably printed by Peter Schöffer of Mainz, of a canonical text with commentary).

Lat. 113*
CLEMENTINES. With *Glossa ord.* of Johannes Andreae and additional glosses (among these: Paulus de Liazariis, Guillaume de Montlauzun, Jesselin de Cassagnes), f.1–46v.—2. The const. 'Exivi de paradiso' (Clem. 5.11.1) is, as usual, without glosses, and is placed outside the corpus of the Clementines, f.47–49r.—3. DINUS DE MUGELLO, *Commentary on the Regulae iuris,* f.49v–63v. *Avignon(?), 14th cent.*

Vellum. 63 ff. 38 x 25 cm. H/leather.

Lat. 114*
BERNARDUS RAYMUNDI. Apparatus in sexto libro Decretalium [of Boniface VIII], *inc.:* Bonifacius, id est bonum faciens . . . . (No such work listed in Schulte, *op. cit.,* II, 505). *Avignon (?), 14th cent.*

Vellum. 34 ff. 41 x 25 cm. Portfolio.

Lat. 115*
GUILLAUME DE MANDAGOUT. Libellus super electionibus faciendis et earum ordinandis, with Mandagout's own gloss on his work (cf. P. Viollet in *Hist. litt. de la France* <Paris, 1865 ff.>, XXXIV, 25). *Avignon (?), early 14th cent.*

Vellum. 24 ff. 41 x 26.5 cm. Illuminated initial V, with figure of a monk, reading or writing, with drollery showing rabbit playing the bagpipes. Portfolio.

Lat. 116
DICTIONARY OF SYNONYMS (frequently with German equivalents), ff.2–51r.—*With* Tracts on various theological subjects, derived

from St. Thomas Aquinas (cf. f.192r: sic ergo patent ista que excerpta sunt hic breviter De summa fratris Thome contra gentiles) with index, ff.51v–240.—AUCTORITATES DE DECRETO, *inc.:* Nicholaus papa. Mala consuetudo, ff.241–245. *Germany, ca. 1400.*

Vellum. 245 ff. 11 x 8 cm. Vellum. A brief description attached to the flyleaf signed Schrauf, and dated 4 Oct., 1876.

Lat. 117

MAPHEUS VEGIUS. De educatione liberorum et eorum claris morbis. Annotations in the margins. *Rome, December 24, 1443* (f.138v).

Paper. 138 ff. (ff.77-80, between books III and IV are blank). 20 x 14 cm. Decorated initial and faded coat of arms (f.1). 18th-cent. calf.

Lat. 118*

SACRAMENTAL HANDBOOK. 1. JOANNES FRIBURGENSIS. Summa confessorum (cf. Schulte, *op. cit.*, II, 421), ff.1–18r.—2. VERSE in hexameters, f. 18r, *inc.:* Aures versifice.—3. VERSUS de facetia mensae (Walther 7497), f.18v.—4. ANDREAS DE ESCOBAR. Modus confitendi (cf. Schulte, *op. cit.*, II, 440).—5. Two poems, the first beginning "Primum est docere ignorantem," the second, "O homo qui velox es ad mensam," f.37r–v.—6. QUESTIO, ff.37v–9v, *inc.:* Queritur utrum pena mortis diminuat. . . . —7. SEX DOCUMENTA homini morituro multum necessaria et utilia, ff.39v–43r.—8. Unidentified text, ff.113v–4r, *inc.:* Vocavit multos.—9. HERMANNUS DE SCHILDIS (=de Alemannia). Speculum manuale sacerdotum (Schulte, *op. cit.*, II, 431), ff.45–52.—10. TRACTATUS DE SACRAMENTIS, ff.53–82, *inc.:* Quaeritur primum quid sit signum.—11. BERENGARIUS. Summa poenitentialis (cf. J. A. Fabricius, *Bibl. lat. med. et inf. aet.* <ed. 1754>, I, 214, and Schulte, *op. cit.*, II, 531, n. 45), ff.84–123.—12. HERMANNUS DE SCHILDIS. Speculum manuale sacerdotum (different portion from no. 9), ff.124–33.—13. SERMONES de B. Maria, ff.135–43, *inc.:* Que est ista. . . . [Cant.6:9]. Hec est vox.— 14. DE MENSIBUS ANNI, ff.144–6, *inc.:* Hic narrat primo de mense (cf. Thorndike, *Incipits*, 2nd ed., col. 623).—15. SERMONES, ff.147–88, *inc.:* Considera quod hodie . . . [Deut.31:15]. Verba.—16. DE DECEM PRECEPTIS, ff.189–211, *inc.:* Sacra scriptura continet deesse [*recte* decem] precepta.—17. PREAMBULA COMMUNICATIONIS, f.211, *inc.:* Qui digne vult communicari.—18. DE VI SIGNORUM, ff.211v–14, *inc.* (introd.): In inter cetera; (text): Aries capilli multi (not in Thorndike).—19. SOMPNIALES DANIELIS prophete, ff.214v–7, *inc.:* Quot fecit in Babylonia, with prayer in German.—20. SERMONES varii et exempla, ff.218–54, beginning with De dedicatione, *inc.:* Salus huic domui [Luc.19:9]. Solempnitas hodierne.—21. FUNDAMENTUM PUERORUM [by Thomas of

Erfurt?], ff.255-64, *inc.:* Eusebius scribit (scribe's name is Ulricus; cf. f.264v).—22. COMPOTUS ECCLESIASTICUS [commentary by a student at Paris?], ff.265-78, *inc.:* Puer natus est nobis [Is.9:6]. . . . Sed hoc tempus (scribe's name is Johannes; cf. f.278v).—23. SERMONES, ff.279-88, *inc.:* Venit rex in templum [Dan.14:9]. In principio huius sermonis.—24. QUESTIO, ff.289-91, *inc.:* Queritur utrum pena purgatorii infligatur animalibus.—25. NOTABILIA VARIA et sermones, ff.296-306. *Germany, 14th-15th cent.,* in several hands.

Paper. 306 ff. 21 x 15 cm. Contemp. h/pigskin over boards. Belonged to the Carthusians in Buxheim; part of the ms. apparently belonged to Johannis Wigg, rector of the church of "Witenowe"(?) (f.254v); from the library of J. W. Six.

Lat. 119

PADUA, S. Luca. Fourteen notarial documents, concerning sales, financial transactions, etc. Among names are Johannes a Prato, Aycha Bangi, Johannes d'Este, Vitalianus Galvani, Mascara de Mascaris. *Padua, 1291-1302.*

Vellum. 14 ff. Various sizes (folded), the tallest 81 cm. long. 19th-cent. h/morocco.

Lat. 120

CISTERCIAN ORDER. Registrum ordinis Cysterciensis (f.17v) preceded by poem Tu Jesus in Missa (cf. Walther 19484), Calendarium, Ad te levavi populus (Walther 460), index to Registrum, Quo ordine libri in refectorio . . . leguntur, *inc.:* Disce per hoc scriptum . . . (Walther 4536), and followed by table of Sunday calendar letters.— With DIRECTORIUM divini officii secundum usum Cisterciensium. *Germany, 15th cent.* (The Directorium written in a 17th-cent. hand on paper).

120 ff. vellum and 17 ff. paper. 17 x 12 cm. 16th-cent. stamped pigskin over wooden boards.

Lat. 121

PETRUS DE BRACO (or Bracho). Repertorium juris canonici secundum ordinem alphabeticum. Last 3 leaves contain: Repudium ambitionis contra miseros cardinalium servitores. *Germany, 15th cent.*

Paper (but outer sheets of first sign. vellum). 338 ff. 42.5 x 39 cm. Illum. first page, with arms. Repaired original tooled calf over wooden boards. Prov.: Part of deed of Johannes Zomernaet to the Carthusian monastery, Marie Castri (Marienburg(?), which acc. to Cottineau II, 1751 was an Augustinian monastery), 1493.—Cf. I.A. Fabricius, *Bibl. lat. med. et inf. aetatis* (1734), II, 728.

Lat. 122*

FRANCISCAN MISCELLANY. 1. ST. AUGUSTINE. De meditationibus, ff.1-9, *inc.:* Hic confitetur homo miseriam suam.—2. PETRUS

JOHANNIS OLIVI. De forma vite regularis fratrum minorum, ff.9v–15v.—3. COMPASSIO Beatae Mariae, f.15v (Chevalier 8012).— 4. BARTHOLOMEUS ALBICIUS PISANUS. Liber conformitatum S. Francisci (excerpt), ff.16–56.—5. Short quotations from St. Bernard, St. Augustine, St. John Cassian, St. Jerome, etc., ff.66–7.— 6. ST. BONAVENTURA. Itinerarium mentis in se ipsum, ff.68–74.—7. PETRUS JOHANNIS OLIVI. Decem gradus humilitatis, ff.74v–5, *inc.:* Non est dubium.—8. NOTABILIS SPECIALIS ad contemplationes, ff.75v–8, *inc.:* Ut divinorum preceptorum.—9. JACOBUS DE TUDERTO. Brief commentary on the beatitudes, f.78v.—10. HUGO DE SANCTO VICTORE. De arrha anime (Migne CLXXVI, 951–70), ff.79–84.—11. Unidentified fragment (some leaves missing); verses on ff.88–9, including: Christi, fili summi patris (Chevalier 24399).— 12. ST. BERNARDUS. Meditationes de humana conditione (Migne CLXXXIV, 485–508), ff.90v–108v.—13. IDEM. Jubilus (variant of Migne CLXXXIV, 1317–20), ff.108v–9v.—14. ST. AUGUSTINE. Oratio in tribulatione, ff.109v–11.—15. ST. BONAVENTURA. Regula novitiorum, ff.112–32.—16. [ST. BERNARDUS?]. De passione, ff.132v–35, *inc.:* Intuere o homo.—17. EUGENIUS IV, Pope. Bull subjecting the Poor Clares and Tertiaries to the vicar general of the Franciscan Order (scribe's name is Pellotus notarius. Publ. in *Bullarium franciscanum*, N.S., I <1929>, no. 1045), ff.136–8.—18. ORDO in missa privata et feriali, ff.140–3.—19. NICHOLAS IV, Pope. Bull approving the Franciscan rule for the Tertiary Order (Potthast 23044), ff.144–55.—20. VITAE PATRUM, extracts, ff.156–99.—21. CURA NOVITIORUM, ff.204–5. *Italy, ca. 1460–1510.* Various hands.

Paper (ff.144-155 vellum). 206 ff. (ff.57-65, 85-86, 200-203 blank). 14 x 10 cm. Contemp. calf.

Lat. 123

BIBLIOPHILE HANDBOOK of the 17th century, including a catalogue of a small, predominantly classical library, with historical and literary information. *Italy(?), 17th cent.*

Paper. 65 ff. 12 x 7 cm. Title and vignettes in pen-and-ink drawings. Contemp. paper. Inscription of Franciscus Mancini, f.1; dedication to Franciscus Vitelius, archb. of Thessalonica, apostolic nuncio at Venice, f.13.

Lat. 124

PROPHECY, *inc.:* (Omnes ad praeda venient) More certe venatorum scilicet Julii post obitum, in conclaui quisque cardinalium . . . ; f.2r: Ad Reverendissimum Cardinalem Senense [Giovanni Tedeschini Piccolomini], and *expl.* (f.4v): Per quatuor vacuae erunt sedes superbi et tirranni. Ego Dominus. *Italy, ca. 1523.*

Paper. 4 ff. 20 x 15 cm. Two pen-and-ink drawings: Hand extending from clouds, with pointed finger (f.4r) and figure on horseback with lion in foreground, tiara and crowns of the Holy Roman Emperor and the King of France in background; inscription over rider *Ju*[lius] *car*[dinalis] (Giulio de' Medici?) and *Leo* (Pope Leo?) above the lion, and legend beneath *Dolus: dolosuī* [?] *insequitur.* Modern boards. Orginally part of larger volume? Top margin of f.1r. bears letter "g" (signature?).—Cf. Lynn Thorndike, *A History of Magic and Experimental Science,* V, 476; VI, 160, 236, etc.

Lat. 125

CRISPUS SALLUSTIUS. Historia atque oratoris clarissimi vita.—IDEM. De coniuratione Catilinae.—IDEM. De bello Jugurthino.—DISTICHON MARTIALIS in Sallustium.—PSEUDO-SALLUSTIUS. In Marcum Tullium Ciceronem invectiva.—PSEUDO-CICERO. Responsio seu invectiva. *Spain, late 15th cent.*

Paper. 149 ff. 22 x 15 cm. H/calf over defective wooden boards.

Lat. 126

ALPHABETICAL DICTIONARY of legal and theological matters (to the letter M), with "The Degrees of marriages" on verso of f.193. *England, late 16th cent.*

Paper. 194 ff. 29.5 x 19.5 cm. Contemp. vellum.

Lat. 127

GEORGIUS PONGRACZ (bp. of Waitzen, d. 1676). Informatio de statu Episcopatus Vaciensis. *With* folded colored map of the diocese of Waitzen. Report on the bishopric of Waitzen under Turkish rule. *Austria, ca. 1670.*

Paper. 22 ff., 1 folded map. 29 x 19 cm. (map, 43.5 x 59 cm). 18th-cent. red silk over paper boards.

Lat. 128

LUDOVICUS HELIANUS (or LOUIS HÉLIAN). Oratio de bello suscipiendo adversus Venetianos et Turcas gratio Maximiliano . . . in Conventu presulum, electorum et civitatum Romani Imperii dicta in Augusta Vindelica quarta Idus Aprilis Anno . . . 1510, ff.1–16. (This speech was printed in Augsburg in the same year, 1510, cf. British Museum cat. and cat. of the Bibliothèque nationale).—IDEM. Venatio leonum (?), ff.17–24. Poem of 142 elegiac couplets, seemingly unpublished. *Southern Germany, ca. 1510.*

Paper. 30 ff. (last 6 blank). 20 x 13.5 cm. Paper.

Lat. 129

BOETHIUS. De consolatione philosophiae, ff.2–86, with marginal and interlinear notes.—List of 20 books taken by an unnamed owner to

Salamanca in 1471, among them various Aristotle items, Boethius and Seneca, f.87v. *Spain, before 1466.* "MCCCCLXVI" added at end in hand resembling that of commentator.

Paper. 88 ff. (first damaged, 1 leaf missing). 29 x 21.5 cm. Contemp. red vellum.

Lat. 130

AUGUSTINUS DE LEONISSA. Moralia super figuris utriusque testamenti, ff.1–249v.—IDEM. Sermo ad clerum in festo Johannis Evangeliste quem fecit frater Augustinus de Leonissa in Concilio basiliensi anno 1433, ff.249v–254. *Germany(?), ca. 1450.*

Paper. 4 prel., 255 ff. (4 prel., ff.25, 195 and 255 blank). 30.5 x 21.5 cm. Contemp. blind stamped calf over wooden boards. Augustinus de Leonissa is listed by Chevalier who simply quotes information supplied by Copinger, *Supplement to Hain's Repertorium,* II(1), no.3546, where Augustinus is identified as a member of the Hermits of St. Augustine and the author of "Sermones super oratione dominica."

Lat. 131

PIERRE BERSUIRE. Reductorium moralis in quo moralisantur omnes figure Biblie et caetera. In 16 books. *Avignon, 1409(?).*

Paper. 349 ff. 29 x 22 cm. Contemp. h/leather over wooden boards. Manuscript notation at end: "quod Avinnione fuit factum Parissiis vero correctum et ablatum anno domini M°CCCC°9°."

Lat. 132

HYMNS AND PRAYERS, in Latin, with interlinear German, and in part I each hymn or prayer followed by complete German translation. Part I, beginning "Conditor alme siderum" ("O Du hailiger schöpffer der gestirn"), contains 86 hymns and prayers, a longer inserted version of Sedulius' "A solis ortus cardine" in a different hand, and on the last three leaves (f.10v–12r) "Ave praeclara maris stella" in a somewhat later hand.—Part II (sig.glv), beginning "Almi prophete progenies," written in different hand and on different paper, contains 30 hymns. This part has numerical notations over words in the text, and commentary in the margins. *Germany, late 15th cent.*

Paper. 86 ff. (last blank). 21 x 15 cm. Initials in red, rubricated. 16th-cent. h/pigskin over wooden boards. "Ex dono R. D. Jo. Heussii . . . 1603," and "Residentiae e Societatis Jesu. . . ." For identification of hymns see F. J. Mone, *Lateinische Hymnen des Mittelalters* (Freiburg, 1835-55).

Lat. 133

MEDICAL, GEOMETRICAL AND OPTICAL TREATISES: 1. BREVIS DESCRIPTIO ANATOMICA corporis humani, 1644 (three treatises on the three "cavities" of the human body), ff.1–18.—

2. DE QUATUOR HUMORIBUS, f.21.—3. SUPPLEMENTA QUEDAM ANATOMICA, f.22.—4. DE PARTIBUS MULIERUM [ex Caspar] Bauhino, Feb. 15, 1644, ff.23-27.—5. PERUTILES QUEDAM OBSERVATIONES ex libro primo pathologiae Jo. Fernelii De morborum differentiis, 1645, ff.27-43.—6. JOHN LINDIE. Historia universalis syntagma . . . in Accademia regia universitatis abredonensis . . . , ff.61-68.—7. DE MENSURIS, ff.70-108.—8. OPTICA, Feb. 6, 1646, ff.111-117. *Aberdeen(?), 1644-1646.*

Paper. 129 ff. (various ff. blank). 18.5 x 14 cm. Diagrs. in 7 and 8. Contemp. vellum. Name of Anselmus de Boot, 1636 (sic) on f.129v. Bookplate of Robert William Duff; signed by Jane Clerk Duff, 1858.

Lat. 134

[ARISTOTLE]. 1. WILHELM FROELICH. Commentationes philosophicae in Organum Aristotelis dictatae, compositae, et explicatae ab admodum Reverendo Patre Guilhelmo Froelich, Societatis Jesu, anno MDCLXIV, vii octobris, ff. 1-136. (This is, in fact, a miscellany of lecture notes which are often incomplete, and in very confused order). —2. IDEM. Compendium Physicae in Communi Breslae, ff.137-179.— 3. C. W. L. B. VON NOSTIZ. Commentationes in quatuor libros Aristotelis De coelo et mundo Christ. Wenc. L. B. de Nostiz, ff.181-199. —4. WILHELM FROELICH. Disputationes philosophicae in octo libros Physicorum Aristotelis traditae ab admodum Reverendo Patre Guilielmo Froelich, Vrateslaviae, viii Augusti anno MDCLXV, ff.203-522.—5. GEORGIUS GIO. Ius privatum quod mihi dictavit Mussiponti . . . D. D. Georgius Gio ibidem professor ordinarius, 2 May 1667. A. M. D. G. B. V. H., ff.523-606.—6. A Treatise on papal authority in Italy, etc. (in Italian, incomplete), ff.607-632. *Various places, 1664-1667.*

Paper. 632 ff. 19 x 16.5 cm. Contemp. vellum; title on spine: Philosophia et Ius privat: script: à C. W. S. R. J. C. de N. . . R. Bookplate of C. W. G. von Nostiz. Not in L. W. Riley, *op. cit.*

Lat. 135

JOHANN JONSTON. Naturae constantia et diatribe. *ca. 1632* (Ms. copy of imprint: Amsterdam, G. Blaeu, 1632).

Paper. 114 ff. 19.5 x 16 cm. Contemp. h/vellum. Bookplate of C. W. G. von Nostitz.

Lat. 136

FLORENCE, Universitas Mercatorum et Artificium. Statuta (Latin and Italian). *Florence, 1516-1547.*

Paper. 247 ff. 28 x 21.5 cm. Contemp. h/leather.—Cf. Italy, Senate. *Catalogo della raccolta di statuti*, III, p.160.—Contains list of members, index to the statutes, the statutes proper as revised and written by Roberto Celio degli Oricoli in February 1519, followed by various additions up to the year 1547.

Lat. 137

SIENA. Raccolta di imbreviature notarili, 1499–1585, with notarial signatures "Antonius Campano olim Nicolai Tophani filius," "Alexander olim Ansani," "Alexander olim Joannis Cristophori de Boninsignis," "Franciscus quondam Joannes Simonius," "Franciscus olim Petri Cosmus," etc. Most of these "imbreviature" are concerned with various business transactions, especially those of Bartholomeus Boninsigne (or Buoninsegni) de Boninsignis (1520–1585). *Siena, 1499–1585* (with some later additions).

Vellum. 2 blank ff., 94 ff., 25 blank ff. 24 x 16.5 cm. Signets of notaries, some of the later ones stamped in. Contemp. full leather over wooden boards, blind stamped, with brass buckles and clasps.

Lat. 138

SOCIETAS SANCTAE ANNAE, Malogoscz, Catalogus fratrum Societatis Sanctae Annae in Malogoscz, 1595 [–1833].—Catalogus fratrum ex hac in illam vitam commigrantium, 1600 [–1822].—Catalogus sororum Societatis Sanctae Annae, 1595 [–1832]. *Malogoscz (Ruthenia), 1595–1833.*

Paper. 19, 2, and 10 ff. (on 36 ff; bound with the foundation charter of the chapter in Malogoscz and Statutes of the Societas Sanctę Annę per Poloniam, Lithuaniam, Russiam . . . Cracow, 1590). 30 x 19 cm. Contemp. (i.e. late 16th cent.) vellum.

Lat. 139

[SPANISH FRAGMENT consisting of ff.XXIV–XXXIII, XLIII–XLIV, and XLVI of a codex]:—1. Clausule testamenti Reverendissimi . . . domini Lupi . . . archiepiscopi caesaraugustensis . . . 1382, ff.XXIVr–XXIXv.—2. Copia executorie sententie quam capellanus maior obtinuit contra vicarium sedis super responsione ducentorum quinquaginta solidorum singulis annis eydem capellano maiori sedis praedicti solvendorum [addressed to King Alfonso of Aragon], ff.XXXr–XXXIIIv.—3. Eugenius IV, pope, 1383–1447. [Document directed against the conciliarists at Basle and Felix V (Amadeus VIII, duke of Savoy) and concerned with various benefices, Rome, Oct. 29, 1444], ff.XLIIIr–XLIVv.—4. [Document read and published in the presence of Eugenius IV, Nov. 19, 1443], f.XLVIv. *Spain, 15th cent.*

Paper. 13 ff. 29.5 x 22.5 cm. Unbound.

Lat. 140

GUILELMUS PARALDUS. Summa de vitiis, ff.1–113v.—*With* De singulis vitiis (et virtutibus), ff.113v–122v, *inc.:* Arrogantia est gloriari Deo quod non acceperis placendi cupiditate. *Germany, second half of 15th cent.*

Paper. 124 ff. (last two blank). 28 x 21.5 cm. Contemp. leather over wooden boards, with guards from 14th-cent. ms.—15th-cent. inscription (f.122r): "Iste liber est monasterii Sancti Pancratii in Ranshofen."—Leaf pasted on inside back cover contains recipes.

Lat. 141

MARTINELLUS, BLASIUS. Ex libris Paris de Grassis Bononiensis, magistri ceremoniarum, qui pontificatum Leonis decimi ab anno 1513 usque ad annum 1521 scripsit . . . [and continued to the year 1538]. *Italy, second half of 16th cent.*

Paper. 78 ff. 27.5 x 20 cm. Contemp. boards.—Pastor quotes exhaustively from this text, using the original in the Vatican Archives (cf. v.XII of the *Geschichte der Päpste*).

Lat. 142

VOCABULARIUS EX QUO, Latin—Low German, *inc.:* Ex quo vocabularii autentici varii sunt in numero scilicet Huguccio, Breviloquus, Papyas, aliique codices . . . (the incipit and the ending differ from the five 15th-cent. printed editions described by C. Borchling and B. Claussen, *Niederdeutsche Bibliographie*, nos. 10, 19, 65, 100 and 154). *Aachen(?), second half of 15th cent.*

Paper. 230 ff. (ff.104 and 217 cut out without loss of text; 10 ff. at beginning and 2 ff. at end with notes on grammar, letter writing, etc.) 20.5 x 16 cm. Colored, decorated initial "E". Contemp. blind-stamped calf over wooden boards.

Lat. 143

VITAE EPISCOPORUM et patriarcharum aquilensium a primo christianae aerae seculo usque ad annum MCCCLVIII. *Venice(?), second half of 15th cent.* (ff.1–3 and 14–15 in a 16th cent. hand).

Paper. 42 ff. (ff.5-13 and 16–42 numbered xvii-lii in a contemp. hand). 20 x 15 cm. H/leather.—Prov.: Walter Sneyd; C. W. Previté-Orton; A. N. L. Munby.—Variant text printed in Muratori, v.16.

Lat. 144

[PAPAL STATES]. Collection of documents relating to Aspra, Carbi and Forli, and a two-leaf fragment of a philosophical treatise. Among the subjects of the documents are: local government regulations, fixing of meat prices, safety and defense, sales, salt taxes, wills. *Italy, 1500–1548* (one document at beginning dated 1660).

Paper. 60 ff. Various sizes, bound in one vol. (31 x 22.5 cm). Boards.

Lat. 145

[PIACENZA]. 16 documents dealing with real estate, elections, wills, etc., from the years 1457–1546, all notarized and with notarial signets. *Piacenza, 1494–1546.*

Vellum. 5, 3, 8, 2, 4, 4, 4, 6, 4, 4, 4, 6, 2, 4, 2, 6 = 68 ff. Various sizes in 1 vol. (27 x 20 cm.). Boards.

Lat. 146

1. ALBERTO CATTANI (or Chatanus, de Cathanis). Jus civile; lectures delivered in Siena 1467-1468, probably taken down by a Rafael Cumanus (f.1, upper right-hand margin).—2. IDEM(?) Clausularum . . . tractatus.—3. JOHANNES DE GRASSIS (Giovanni Grassi). Tractatus (on civil law), lectures delivered at Pavia in 1466; undeciphered cryptic signature at end.—4. ALBERTO CATTANI. Violantes, etc., beginning with 18 lines of poetry, followed by 78 ff. dealing in part with Cattani's relationship with an unidentified admired lady Violante. *Siena and Pavia, 1466-1468.*

Paper. 228 ff. (without 20 ff. cut out at beginning; various numbering, all but the first contemp.: 88 ff., numbered 1-87, 1 blank f.; table of contents, 27 ff., 1 blank f.; table of contents, 29 ff., 1 blank f.; 77 ff., 1 [2] blank ff.) 33.5 x 23.5 cm. Contemp. h/leather over wooden boards, front largely missing.—Prov.: Marques de Barbera y de la Manresa.

Cryptic signature

Lat. 147

[LITURGY]. 1. Officium dicendum in ecclesia supra illos, qui damnati sunt ad mortem.—2. LITANIAE B. M. V., quae in sacro aede lauretana canuntur.—3. 2 ff. later additions. *Bologna(?), ca. 1600.*

Vellum. 10 ff. (last blank). 23 x 16 cm. Contemp. vellum, with painted medallions in center of covers (almost entirely rubbed off).

Lat. 148

BERNARDO CANAL. Manuale Bernardi Canal notarii de Rippis; notarial entries made in Ripas between April 1351 and March 1351 (i.e. 1352). Most entries are cancelled, without affecting legibility. *Ripas (Catalonia), 1351-1352.*

Paper. 80 ff. 22 x 14 cm. Contemp. vellum.

Lat. 149

ERNST, archduke of Austria. Signed letter to Pope Clement VIII, recommending the selection of the archbishop of Naples [Hannibal of Capua] as cardinal. With seal. *Prague, Sept. 13, 1593.*

Vellum. 1 folded f. 36 x 22.5 cm. In folder.

Lat. 150

[TOMMASO DE VIO, called GAETANO (or Caietano, Cajetano)]. De restitutione Caietani sumula. Anonymous commentary, in Latin and Spanish, on Cardinal Gaetano's "Restitutio" which is part of his *Summula.* — 2. AVISOS PARA CONFESSORES sacados de diversos doctores, containing section "De los cavalleros y nobles," "De hombres de letras," and "De mercadores." *Spain, early 17th cent.*

Paper. 6 blank, 64, 6 blank, 13, 1 blank ff. 21.5 x 16 cm. Contemp. vellum.

Lat. 151

LEGAL DOCUMENTS (fragment). *Manresa (Catalonia), 1320–1321.*

Paper. 12 ff. (badly wormed and fringed). 30 x 21 cm. In folder.

Lat. 152

TEBALDUS (Theobaldus) PLACENTINUS. Regulae de longis et brevibus syllabis, in verse, ff.1r–13r, *inc.:* Ante per exemplum soliti cognoscere verbum . . . (cf. Manitius, *Gesch. d. lat. Literatur des Mittelalters*, III, 734–35 mentions four mss., all less complete than the present), with marginal and interlinear commentary. — *With* Treatise on Prosody, ff.13r–15r, *inc.:* Ut ad metricam facultatem cungruum posimus sortiri exordium sciendum est, quod literarum alie sunt vocales. . . . (Similar text in the Marciana, Venice, cod. Nanianus CXXV of the 14th cent., and Trivulziana, Milan, cod. misc. 760 of the 15th cent.). *Northern Italy, ca. 1200.*

Vellum. 15 ff. 17 x 12 cm. Boards.—Prov.: Paulo Nicelli, son of Petro, erased date 1275(?) on line 1 of f.15v; see also earlier ownership reference to the same Paulo Nicelli but without date on lines 17-20 of f.15v.—Commentary on upper margin of f.1, line 3 (etc.) reads: Materia tebaldi est in hoc libro omnis prima sillaba que ante suum tempus non poterat cognosci nisi per exemplum. Sua intencio est in eodem libro tradere versalem regulam qualiter omnis vocalis posita antecedens omnem consonantem in principio sillabe possit cognosci utrum sit brevis vel longa. . . .

Lat. 153

BERNARDINO STEFONIO. Flavia Tragedia. (Text in Latin, prologue in Italian.) *Italy, ca. 1620.*

Paper. 2 ff., 10 pp., 1 blank f., pp. 11–147, 147–331. 10 x 7 cm. Title within engraved figurated medallion. Contemp. calf, gold tooled with initials F.C. on front and back.—Bookplate of Hans Hauser and "Ex libris Fairbridge."—Cf. A. de Backer and C. Sommervogel, *op. cit.*, vol. VII, col. 1529, no. 4.

Lat. 154

PSALTER, for use in the daily offices of the Franciscans of Avignon. *Avignon, 15th cent.*

[35]

Vellum. 166 ff. 15 x 10 cm. 18th-cent. calf.—Arms of Michel de Léon, treasurer of France at Marseilles (1727–1800) on spine; monogram of Charles Kothen (1814–1880), a Finnish nobleman who was a refugee in Marseilles.

Lat. 155

[ARISTOTLE]. Disputationes in duos libros Aristotelis De generatione et corruptione, nec non De universa metaphysica et morali philosophia eiusdem. Addito etiam Tractatus [reverendi patris Salvaterra, qui dictabat] de horologiis solaribus. . . . Pesciettus Jacobus Maria scribebat Genuae. *Genoa, 1680.*

Paper. 283 ff. 21 x 15 cm. Contemp. vellum.—Acquired after the publication of L. W. Riley, comp., *Aristotle Texts (op.cit.)*

Lat. 156

PROPHETIA ANONYMI. Versus reperti Hierosolimae in Capella sepulcri domini nostri Jesu Christi in quodam muro antiquissimo cum prophetia sequenti sub anno domini 1470 die prima mensis Thebet 1. Januarii. . . . Sequitur prophetia. Audire verbum domini principes sodomorum. . . . (Predicts conquest of Milan, conflagration in Brescia, destruction of Bologna and Ferrara, pestilence, and the delivery of Jerusalem from the Saracens between 1484 and 1509.) *Germany, ca. 1484.*

Paper. 2 ff. 20.5 x 14 cm. Boards.—Small bookplate "Homo Hominibus, 1874."

Lat. 157

ANGELUS (CARLETUS) DE CLAVASIO. Act concerning the Franciscan monastery San Spirito near Reggio, notarized by "Jeronymus filius . . . Ludovici de Favallibus" [or Fanallibus?]. *San Spirito?, 16 July 1491.*

Vellum. 1 f. (39 lines). 50 x 40 cm. Large figurated initial I, in colors, representing an angel standing on a column. In folder.—Clavasio names Joannes de Caligariis; Albertus, son of Nicolaus de Fontanella; Franciscus, son of Gabriele de Pradonerio; and Christophorus, son of Antonius de Luca to be charged with responsibilities for the secular affairs of the monastery.

Lat. 158

SERMONES VARII. 1. PEREGRINUS POLONUS. Sermones de tempore, ff.1-82, *inc.*: Ecce rex tuus venit tibi. In hiis verbis . . . , followed by 1 p. (f.82v) of text dealing with conciliar matters and mentioning the Hussites and the date 1433, the name Conradus Hillin [?] on upper margin.—2. Anonymous sermon, ff.83r-122r, *inc.*: Dicite filie Syon ecce rex tuus venit.—3. DEMON JEIUNANDI, ff.122v-128v, *inc.*: Cum jeiunatus. . . .—4. AUCTORITATES SCRIPTORUM de . . . viciis peccatorum, ff.128v-130v.—5. Anonymous sermons, ff.131r-142v, *inc.*: Erunt quasi angeli dei.—6. ASSUMPTIO BEATAE VIRGINIS, etc., ff.143r-167v, *inc.* (143r): Surge domine in requiem tuam (by Bernard of Siena?, cf. Little, p.244); (f.155r): In omnibus requiem; (f.158r): Nativitas tua. . . . —7. DE ASSUMPTIONE MAIORE, ff.168v-180r, *inc.*: Adest, fratres diletissimi dies. . . . (With contemporary marginal notes and corrections, especially in the Peregrinus.) *Southern Germany, 1432–35* (dated 1432 on ff.120v and 122r; 1433 on f.82r; 1435 on ff.142v, 157v and 160v).

Paper. 180 ff. (ff.178–179 [cut to half size] blank, f.180 pasted against back cover [correction or emendation to the text], 1 f. in 8vo inserted between ff.134 and 135). 29.5 x 21 cm. Contemp. pigskin over wooden boards, with back and front-cover label, largely unreadable. Part of front-cover title: Flores Jacobi.—Prov.: Carthusian monastery, Buxheim; part of earlier owner's note on f.179v: ". . . Ich Herr Hans von Vallen. . . ."

Lat. 160

ANDREA GRITTI. Instructions to Nicolaus Theupulo on his appointment by the Doge of Venice to govern Brescia for one year. With table of contents. *Venice, 10th day (no month indicated), 1525;* written by notary Petrus Grafoldarius.

Vellum. 31 ff. 22.5 x 15.5 cm. Initial page (f.2) with illum. lion of St. Mark and coat of arms. Modern h/calf.

Lat. 161

JOHANNES TOSTIUS. Johannis Tostii Vratislaviensis Silesii poetae coronatae clarissimorum Witebergensium professorum descriptio, qui anno 1582 floruerunt, et publice in Academia magna cum fructu docuerunt. Witebergae, excudebat Matthäus Welack, anno M.D.LXXXII. (Copy or autograph?) *Wittenberg?, ca. 1582.*

Paper. 8 ff. (ff.5–8 blank). 20 x 16 cm. Boards.—Matthäus Welack printed in Wittenberg 1578–1593. It was not ascertained whether these poems were actually printed.

Lat. 162

[HISTORIA NATURALIS]. Compilation (possibly lecture notes) covering astronomy, cosmography, geography, geology, physics and biology (incl. psychology), with references to Copernicus, Tycho de Brahe, Gassendi, Descartes, etc. Incl. chapters on fossils, magnets, vacuum, anatomy. Inscription on f.49v: Hactenus P. Ricci (lecturer, student or scribe?), the entire ms. in one hand. *Italy, ca. 1700.*

Paper. 205 ff. (ff.197–205 blank). 18 x 14 cm. Illus. Contemp. boards.—Prov.: Conte Antonio Ancini, conditore nel Collegio de'Nobili di Modena, 1730.

Lat. 163

PSEUDO-ARISTOTLE. De regimine principum [excerpt from the Secreta secretorum] with commentary, ff.2r-17r, *inc.*: (text) Cum sit corpus corruptibile eique accidat . . . ; (commentary): Ordo vivendi phisice secundum Aristotelem sequitur hic. . . . Iste liber principali sua divisione . . . , *expl.*: Explicit modus vivendi phisice secundum Aristotelem, editus per Johannem Hispaniensem, De observatione diete et corporis extractus a quodam libro de arabico qui latine liber dicitur Secreta secretorum.—*With* MARCUS TULLIUS CICERO Liber de vera amicitia, 215 lines of verse, ff.17v-20v, *inc.*: Nil iucundius est viro dum vivit amico/Cum consorte dulcius sapit omne bonum/ . . . . *Germany, 15th cent.*

Paper. 21.5 x 15.5 cm. 20 ff. Vellum. Concerning the Pseudo-Aristotle text see *Gesamtkatalog der Wiegendrucke*, no. 2490; Lynn Thorndike, *A History of Magic and Experimental Science*, II, 268–270; Robert Steel, *Opera hactenus inedita Rogeri Baconi*, V, xvi–xviii; John of Spain's transl. was published by H. Souchier, *Denkmäler provenzal. Lit. u. Sprache*, (Halle, 1883), I, 473 ff. The commentary has not been identified. Not in L. W. Riley, *Aristotle Texts* (*op. cit.*).—The incipit of the versified *De amicitia* not in H. Walther, *Initia Carminum* (*op.cit.*).

Lat. 164*

ADAM. Summula de summa Raymundi (cf. Lat. 89), with extensive anonymous commentary, *inc.*: Omnem scientiam et disciplinam sacra scriptura transcendit. *Southern Germany or Austria, 1422*, by a scribe Johannes Kemp [?, name crossed out, cf. f.173v].

Paper. 175 ff. 29 x 21 cm. Colored initials, some with faces in pen-and-ink. Contemp. blind-stamped sheepskin over wooden boards (rebacked), new guards.—Same scribe as ms. Lat. 165.

Lat. 165*

SUMMA METRICA (cf. Schulte, *op. cit.*, II, 528). With extensive prose commentary (*inc.*: Hora est iam nos de somno surgere). *Southern Germany or Austria, 1422*, by a scribe Johannes (cf. f.40r).

Paper. 41 ff. (ff.38v, 39r, 40v and 41 blank). 29 x 21.5 cm. Colored initials at beginning of text and commentary. H/calf.—Same scribe as ms. Lat. 164. Both mss. give the place where the ms. was written, deciphered (correctly?) as Brunslock; no such place could be identified in the usual gazetteers.

Lat. 166

[ROVIGO]. Raccolta di leggi ad uso della Podestà di Rovigo. (Title missing, text in Latin with a few sections in Italian), *inc.*: De modo administrationis Policinii. Probe sis mentis. . . . (The main part of the ms., dated 1546, signed by Hieronymus Murionius, secretarius, p.167.) *Rovigo, 1546.*

Vellum. 173 pp. (f.1 missing). 23.5 x 16.5 cm. Paper.—Prov.: Johannes Betrus Ravenoldus; Gabriel Michieli, Bassano, 1723 [?] (cf.p.173).—List of known mss. of statutes of Rovigo in L. Fontana, *Bibliografia degli statuti*, (Turin, 1907), vol.2, pp.500–502.

Lat. 167

CHARLES V, Emperor of the Holy Roman Empire. Collection of laws, edicts, proclamations, etc., prepared for the use of the notary L. Panagathus, in Lombardy, incl. decree against the smuggling of arms to the Turks, for the arrest of followers of Luther, privileges for the "Collegium germanicum" at Bologna, establishment of a medical faculty at Milan, "facultas creandi doctores, poetas," etc. *Lombardy, after 1530.*

Paper. 4 blank, 133, 9 ff. 30.5 x 21 cm. Contemp. vellum.—Prov.: L. Panagathus.—The fact that one document is in French and that the notarial hand shows French characteristics, also the inclusion of some items relating to Switzerland (incl. one to Lausanne) make it appear likely that this ms. was executed in the northwest of Lombardy.—On last f. prayer against the plague.

Lat. 168

DOMENICUS DE TAPARELLIS. Testament of Domenico Taparelli of Savigliano concerning his burial, donations to various churches, disposal of property to his wife and children, etc. Executed by the imperial notary Vincentius de Alba. *Savigliano, 19 March 1395.*

Vellum. 1 f. Ca. 40 x 37 cm. In folder.

Lat. 169

CHRONICLE (incomplete), begins with the year 28 A.D. (*inc.*: Pontius Pilatus procurator Iudee mittitur a Tiberio) and ends 1448; a few corrections and emendations, and additions in a different hand with the last date 1476. *Florence?, ca. 1464–1476.*

Paper. 57 ff. (ff. 1–2 lacking). 21 x 14.5 cm. Boards.—Though a world chronicle, Italian political history (especially Florence, Milan, Genoa and Venice) is stressed. Important events in Italian literary history as well as natural phenomena are mentioned.

Lat. 170

[ARISTOTLE]. 1. IN ARISTOTELIS LIBROS De generatione et corruptione, *inc.*: Post octo libros physicorum, ff.1r-183r.—2. DISPUTATIO in libros Aristotelis De anima, *inc.*: Ordo disputationis exigit . . . , ff.183r-303r.—3. QUAESTIONES de ente possibili, *inc.*: Tribus questionibus absolvent, ff.305-315. *Italy, late 16th or early 17th cent.*

Paper. 317 ff. (ff.316–317 blank). 20.5 x 15.5 cm. Contemp. vellum.— Acquired after publ. of L. W. Riley, comp., *Aristotle Texts (op.cit.).*

Lat. 171

[ARISTOTLE]. Metaphisica, De anima et Meteorologia [et De physionomia]. (Anonymous commentary.) *Italy, 17th cent.*

Paper. 6 ff., 67 pp., 1 blank, 5 ff., 71 pp., 15 ff., 112 pp., 19 ff., 87 pp., 1 f. 11.5 x 7.5 cm. Full-page pen-and-ink drawing on f.2 and at beginning of each of the 3 following parts; figurated title border; vignette at end. Cloth.—"Ad usum F. Bened. M. Stellati, in memoriam J. Casimiri Panza ipsi donatus in conventu S. Mariae super Taburrum [?], die XVIII augusti 1730; Philippus Rosanus (at beginning of Problemata meteorologica); Josephi . . . crossed out on title page; stamp R. S. on inside back cover.—Acquired after publ. of L. W. Riley, comp., *Aristotle Texts* (*op.cit.*).

Lat. 172

[ARISTOTLE]. 1. In universam Aristotelis Physicam, ff.1r-163v.—2. Ad quatuor libros: De mundo et coelo; duo De generatione; quatuor De meteoris; et Aristotelicos tractatus qui Mundus dicitur, disputatio, ff.163v-289v.—3. Ad quatuor Libros meteorologicos Aristotelis, ff.291r-309r.—4. Ad libros tres De anima et ea quae vulgo dicuntur Parva naturalia tractatus, ff.313r-422v. (With marginal additions in different ink, but by the same scribe.) *France, 16th cent.*

Paper. 422 ff. (f.K12 removed, without loss of text; a few ff. blank). 22.5 x 17 cm. Contemp. leather, with name "CL. DECHAMP HEV." on front cover.—Acquired after publ. of L. W. Riley, comp., *Aristotle Texts* (*op.cit.*).

Lat. 173

ANTONIUS BERALDUS. Document of Beraldus, canon of the Cathedral of Cahors, etc., in which he makes known to the clergy of the diocese a letter from Pope Clement VII, of March 15, 1531, ordering the return of property, titles, belongings, and money of Guillaume and Géraud of Figeac, heirs of François Grana, under penalty of excommunication for those who unrightfully retain such property, etc. *Cahors, 1532.*

Vellum. 1 f. Ca. 35.5 x 26 cm. (folded to 13.5 x 12 cm.). In folder.

Lat. 174

RABANUS ANGLICUS. Liber Rabani [corrected from Babani] Horoscopo [sic] intitulatus, translatus de Hebraico in Latinum a Dandalo Ylardensi ad instantiam abbatis P. de Visula, ff.1r-26v, *inc.*: Rerum omnipotens opifex.—*With* COM[M]ENTUM super predi[c]-tionum [sic] Rabani Anglici factum per . . . [name crossed out, unreadable], ff.29r-99v, *inc.*: Rerum omnipotens &c. Quanta diligentia voluerit.—JOACHIM DE FIORE. Liber summorum pontificum incipit ab Innocentio 4º [=Vaticinia], ff.101r-123v.—COM[M]ENTARIUM florum pontificum, ff.125v-168v, *inc.*: Domus est cooperimentum.—ST. CYRILLUS (general of the Carmelites). Oraculum [with the Expositio of Joachim de Fiore], ff.170r-268r.—IDEM. Revelatio, ff.268v-272v. *Italy, ca. 1600*, in several hands.

Paper. 272 ff. (ff.27-28, 100, 124, 169, 234-242 blank, these last with omission of text). 20 x 14 cm. Contemp. vellum.—"Hunc librum invenit Gregorius de Gregoriis in bello Pontificis Urbani VIII anno 1644. . . ."—None of the incipits in L. Thorndike, *op.cit.*

Lat. 175

SIMON FYRBAS. In libros Aristotelis De anima et Metaphysicos commentarii, dictati a reverendo et doctissimo Patre Simone Fyrbas, monacho schyrensi, conscripti a religoso Fr. Dominico Blatt, eiusdem ordin. et monasterii professo. *Scheyern, 1632.*

Paper. 1 f., 501, 13 pp. 19.5 x 15 cm. Illus. title border. Contemp. calf, with blind-pressed initials F.D.B. (Domenicus Blatt) S. and date 1632.—Letter from Isaac Husek on this ms. tipped in at beginning. Not in L. W. Riley, comp., *Aristotle Texts (op.cit.).*

Lat. 176

[VENICE]. Copy of document contesting the rights to the property of Francesco and Giovanni di Leone, "cives ferrarienses," in the district of Rovigo, made in behalf of Venice by Antonius Ferro, 1485. *Lombardy, late 15th cent.(?).*

Paper. 10 ff. (last blank). 31.5 x 21 cm. In folder.

Lat. 177

JACOBUS BALBI. Notarial document. Jacobus Balbi, acting on behalf of the associates "Marco Zorzi, Jacomo and Piero Balbi" of Venice, appoints Marco Giorgio to collect amounts due to them from Venturinus de Pinzonibus. Notarized by Petrus Arivabenus. *Venice, 22 September 1472.*

Vellum. 1 f. Ca. 34.5 x 14.5 cm. Notarial signet. In folder.—With stamp of the "Archives de l'Ordre de Malthe."

Lat. 178

CASTELNAU-DE-LÉVIS (Tarn). Terrier of the "seigneurie de Castelnau," or survey of property by exact location, rent, name of tenant, mentioning many strips of land and vineyards. *Tarn, 1309.*

Paper. 1 unnumb., 59 ff. 31.5 x 23 cm. In folder (14th cent. document).— Unsigned 18th cent. owners' descr. fastened to vellum wrapper: Livre en papier . . . contenant un état des tenanciers des fiefs de Castelnau, St<u>e</u> Croix, St. Sernin et la Bastide, et de la vente qu'ils font, fait en l'an 1309.—Castelnau = Castelnau-de-Bonafous, near Albi.

Ad. Lat. 178: The text of a charter of 1343, now badly faded, is written on the back of the final folio.—On the provenance of the ms., see Maurice Greslé-Bouignol, "Le chartrier des seigneurs de Graulhet-Castelnau-de-Lévis aux Archives du Tarn," *Annales du Midi*, LXXII (1960), 89-98.

Lat. 179

DENIS FAUCHER (Dionysius Faucherius). Poetry (with prefatory matter in prose) largely, if not entirely, by Denis Faucher, *inc.* (f.1r): Monachus est afflictus et moerens animus . . . , followed (f.1v) by an almost full-page miniature (a nun on the cross) with poem "Ad scholasticam" below (*inc.*: Coelesti ut valeas sponso . . .); *inc.* (prose on f.2r): Vera sanctimonialis illa est, quae amore . . . ; miniature representing skull on f.3r; the main part begins on f.3v with De contemptu mortis . . . carmen Dionysii, followed by his De contemptu mundi et amore dei epistola ad scholasticam [in verse]; Ad eandem epistola . . . ad abnegationem propriae voluntatis; Ad Antonium Rorincum discipulum ut Christi suave iugum accepiat; Hymnus in laudem divae Katherinae [hymn ascribed to Faucher by Chevalier]; Ad scholasticam discipulam de adventu Christi; Animae divino amore languentis deprecatio; Carmen saphicum; Ode dicolos tetrastrophos, dialogus quo homo pius . . . consolatur; Hortatur scholastica; ending with Italian "Himno de l'amore divino." *Italy, ca. 1530–50.*

Paper. 16 ff. (in front of printed Henricus de Herpf) and 16 ff. (after printed text) = 32 ff. 14.5 x 10 cm. Morocco (ca. 1700).—Prov.: Ballesden.—Bound with printed HENRICUS DE HERPF, Speculum perfectionis, (Venice, de Sabio, 1524) and shelved as NC. H3948.524.

Lat. 180

ALBERTUS MAGNUS (PSEUDO-). Secreta mulierum et virorum, ff.2r-54r, *inc.* (text): Dilectissimo sibi in Christo . . . , (commentary): Circa initium libri aliqua preambula sunt notanda . . . (the incipit of the text differs slightly from Thorndike, *op. cit.*, and early printed eds.; that of the commentary does not appear in Thorndike); *expl.* (text): . . . qui in deo patre vivit et regnat per omnia secula seculorum, (commentary): . . . vita eterna ad quam deus omnipotens gloriosus et magnificus nos perducat qui cum deo patre et filio et spiritu sancto vivit . . . The Secreta are preceded by 1 f. (fragment of a larger work?) with three texts: 1. De coitu, *inc.*: Item ex quo multa vitia continguntur ex inordinatu coytu . . . (47 lines); 2. Artes mulierum (17 lines); 3. De meretrice, *inc.*: Item meretrix sic diffinitur . . . (11 lines). (None of these could be identified in Thorndike). *Germany?, 15th cent.*

Paper. 54 ff. 21 x 14 cm. H/vellum.

Lat. 181

LUCIUS AENNEUS SENECA. Liber epistolarum ad Lucilium [Lucillum in *inc.* of ms.] (Fragment, letters 1–26 only). *Northern Italy, late 14th cent.*

Paper. 12 ff. 21 x 14.5 cm. Boards.—Letter 26 icplt.

Lat. 182*
AEGIDIUS DE FUSCARARIIS. Ordo judicarius (cf. Schulte, *op. cit.*, II, 141). *Italy, first half 14th cent.*

Vellum. 20 ff. 46.5 x 29 cm. Vellum. The two signatures (A^{12}, B^8) written by two different hands; the second scribe ends: Qui scripsit scribat; semper cum domino vivat. Amen.

Lat. 183
[CHRISTIAN FRIEDRICH ANDERS]. 1. Philopinacium (i.e. liber amicorum with entries on ff.71, 81–2, 87, 91–2, 94, 96, 106–8, 110–1, 131, 161, 180–1, 183, 185, 188–9, 192, 195–8, in Latin, Greek, French, German, English and Slavic), ff.3r-220r.—Latin quotations, ff.220v-251v. *Zittau, 1731–1733.*

Paper. 251 ff. (most ff. blank). 12 x 17 cm. Title within illus. border, full-page illus. tipped in between ff.108–9, bookplate on verso of f.180. Contem. gilt red morocco. Prov.: Bechstein collection.

Lat. 184
JEAN PASSERAT. 1. Conjecturarum et opinionum libri IV (with index of words explained, and index of Latin authors), ff.1r-96v.—2. Conjecturarum liber I (second redaction), ff.97r-104v.—3. *Idem* (third redaction as printed after Passerat's death, Paris, C. Morel, 1612), ff.105r-114v.—4. Veterum poematum qua divulsa ad lacera supersunt, tomus alter. Auctorum nomina Lucilius et Naevius (fragments of Lucilius and Naevius, with references to authors quoted), ff.117r-180v. (Autograph manuscript, largely unpublished). *Paris, ca. 1572–1600.*

Paper. 181 ff. (ff.5–7 and blank f.45 wanting; ff.46–7, 115–6, 158 and 181 blank). 32.5 x 22.5 cm. 18th cent. morocco.

Lat. 185°
GRECISMUS CORNUTUS, *inc.:* [C]espitat [or Despitat?] inphaler[is] ypos blactaque supinus/Glossa velud themeto labat hemus ineffatuato/ . . . , *expl.:* Finit cornutus graphos non est solutus avesque. (105 lines of verse, agreeing in most part with the [Pseudo-?]Johannes de Garlandia's Cornutus, with numerous interlinear notes explaining the meaning of words, e.g. line 1 over Cespitat: fucillat vel dubitat; inphaler: est inornatus; ypos: equus; etc. For discussion of authorship see Hans Liebl, *Die Disticha Cornuti* [Straubing, 1888] [Programm—Studienanstalt, Straubing]). Pasted in front of the "Graecismus" is a table "Littere grecorum" and a list with commentary "Grecorum dipthongi proprie sex sunt." *Leipzig or Erfurt?, late 15th cent.*

Paper. 1, 4 ff. 20.5 x 15.5 cm. Boards (bound with Rudolf Agricola, *Historia periucunda sanctissime matris Anne*, Leipzig, Thanner, 1507, and shelved with printed book).—A possible clue to the author may be found in the explicit which differs from the Liebl text; "avesque" following the "non est solutus," possibly referring to a name like Vögel, Fögel?

Lat. 186°

NICOLAS CHORIER (pseud.: Joannes Meursius). Elegantiae latini sermonis [seu Aloisia Sigaea De arcanis amoris et veneris]. (Dialogues I–V. Lat. and Ital. in parallel columns). With contemp. ms. corrections. *Italy?, ca. 1700.*

    Paper. 1 f., 37 pp. 31.5 x 21.5 cm. Boards.—Prov.: "Archiv. Campo/anpiero—Maldura."

Lat. 187°

DE SEPTEM PECCATIS MORTALIBUS, *inc.*: Est sciendum quod ista sunt septem peccata mortalia . . . *Germany, ca. 1500.*

    Paper. 10 ff. 20 x 14.5 cm. Boards. Bound and shelved with *De continentia sacerdotum*, Nürnberg, Weissenberger, 1510.

Lat. 188°

HARTMANN SCHOPPER. Ars artium, sive ars magna cabalistica auctore Hartman Scoppero Novoforensi Norico pars secunda, Francofurti apud Moenum, MDLXIX. (Supposedly a posthumous work, this text deals primarily with numbers. A first dedication, undated, bears the name Joannes Theodorus de Bry, Argentinensis, civisque Oppenehimensis, possibly the scribe of this ms. The second, original, dedication by Schopper, is dated 1564). *Germany, 17th cent.*

    Paper. 2 blank, 1, 45, 4 blank ff. 37 x 26 cm. Schematic drawings. Contemp. boards.

Lat. 189°

[AUGUSTINIANS]. Privilegia (compiled probably at the request of, and for, the Augustinian Hermits of Rouen, containing copies of all pertinent documents issued by Clement V, Urban VI, Boniface IX, Alexander V, Martin V, Eugene IV, Nicholas V and Sixtus IV, including a letter by the cardinal protector of the order, Guillaume de Estouteville, and notarized by Marco Marzio Saxoferratensis), *inc.*: Guilielmus miseratione divina episcopus . . . . *Italy, soon after March 29, 1475.*

    Vellum. 32 ff. (last f. pasted against back cover, ff.30-2 blank, 2 ff. fragment of lectionary used as prel. fly-leaves). 16 x 13 cm. Contemp. doeskin.

Lat. 190°

[VALENCIA, Universidad]. Copy of privileges granted by Alexander VI in 1501 [wrongly dated 1510]; "extracta a libro privilegiorum insignis civitatis Valencie" by the notary Jacobus Benedictus Eximeno, with postscript, May, 1560. *Valencia, 16th cent.*

    Paper. 6 ff. (ff.5-6 blank). 31 x 22 cm. Notarial signet. In folder. See also Ms. Sp. 38 ff.

Lat. 191°

[LOUVAIN]. Lecture notes taken by Petrus S. Langevelt, 1646–1648. 1. ARNOLD MENNEKEN. Prior Physicae aristotelicae, vol. 1, ff.2r-156v.—2. JOANNES PAULI. Posterior Physicae sermocinalis, ff.159r-293r.—3 ARNOLD MENNEKEN. Commentarius in universam Aristotelis Physicam, vol. 2, ff.3-105r.—4. [IDEM?]. Commentarius in Spheram Joannis de Sacrobosco, ff.109r-135r.—5. JOANNES PAULI. Explanatio librorum De caelo [Aristotelis], ff.137r-183r.—6. [IDEM?]. De generatione et corruptione [Aristotelis], ff.183r-215v.—7. [IDEM?]. Liber metheororum ff.216r-243r.—8. ARNOLD MENNEKEN. Metaphysica aristotelica universa, ff.244r-329.—9. [IDEM?]. Libri de anima, ff.330r-383r. *Louvain, 1646–48.*

Paper. 2 vols. 20 x 16 cm. Engr. title pages (v. 2, f.3 signed Pet. Rucholle fec.; f.137 Q. Boel fec., I. G. exc.) 2 engr. bound in with vol. 2, few schematic drawings. Contemp. calf.—Prov.: P. S. Langevelt.— Biblioth. Aelsen [?]—Acquired after the publication of L. W. Riley, *op. cit.*

Lat. 192°

GAMALIEL [cf. cover-title, i.e. JAKOB HERMANN OBEREIT?, cf. *Deutscher Gesamtkatalog*, where Abaris Gamaliel is listed as pseud. of Obereit]. Physica generalis observatoria intima ex sensu experimentali aquè ac intellectuali harmoniae physicae universi anglicae cum Leibnitianâ collatae ad fundamenta radicitus perspicua systematis naturae anglici ac regiminis mundi ethico-physici per physicam originis intimae omnium revolutionum ad perfectionem usque summam centralem ex primitiva simplicitate in formas physicas actualiter characteristicas septempliciter elementares sponte resolutâ [added in different ink] à Fratre Violae Crucis Gamaliele. (Caption-title: Comparatio praerogativa monadologiae et harmoniae physicae . . . cum Leibnitianâ ad fundamenta a priori systematis naturae Newtoniani et Clarkiani . . .). With corrections and emendations throughout. *Switzerland?, late 18th cent.*

Paper. 80 pp. 23.5 x 18 cm. In portfolio. This ms. and Ms. Fr. 95 are apparently in the same hand. Berthold Zehme, *Jakob Hermann Obereit* (Lindau, 1920) does not mention this title.

Lat. 193°

[ARISTOTLE]. Libri animalium notata supra librum animalium Aristotelis [cf. f.52v]. (Unidentified fragmentary commentary on books 4–7 and 10 of the De historia animalium, on books 11[?]–14 [i.e. probably 1?–4] of the De partibus animalium, and on book 16 etc. [i.e. probably book 2 etc.] of the De generatione animalium.—Partial list of *incipits:* Lib. 5, f.6r, *inc.:* Iam narravimus superius; lib. 6, f.8r, *inc.:* Et oportet cum eo quod diximus; lib. 7, f.14r, *inc.:* Natura animalium et generationis [?] eorum; lib. 10, f.16r, *inc.:* Forte autem accidit quibusdam viris; lib. 12 [or 11?], f.17r, *inc.:* Illorum [?] omni opinione nobili [?]; Lib. 12 [?], f.19r, *inc.:* . . . declaravimus superius membra; lib. 13, f.29r, *inc.:* Sequitur dicere [?] de naturis dentium; lib. 14, f.42v, *inc.:* Et iam declaravimus superius dispositionem membrorum, f.43r: Et cum tam scivimus; lib. 16, f.48r, *inc.:* Iam declaravimus virtutes. *Southern France?, first half 14th cent.*

Vellum. 52 ff. 32.5 x 22 cm. Portfolio.—Acquired after publication of L. W. Riley, *op. cit.*

Lat. 194°

REIMS. Two-leaf fragment of ledger, f.1r Recepta domorum et stallorum; f.2r Computus . . . ; f.2v Expensa, incl. "Hospitale beate Marie." *Reims, 14th cent.*

Vellum. 2 ff. 37.5 x 27 cm. In folder.

Lat. 195°

FRATER GEORGIUS (= George Martinuzzi), Ser^{mi} Regis Hungarię thesaurarius. Copy of intelligence report to Ferdinand I on the sultan, Turkish troops, etc., "datum Varadini 16 mensis Augusti . . . 1538." *Hungary?, ca. 1540.*

Paper. 4 pp. (last p. blank). 29.5 x 22 cm. In folder. This report was printed in *Codex epistolaris Fratris Georgii* . . . (Budapest, 1881), pp. 15–17, identically, except for several slightly different readings.

Lat. 196°

THEOLOGICAL MISCELLANY. 1. Biblical references, ff.1r-4v.— 2. DE FIDE CATHOLICA, ff.6r-93v. (Commentary on text of the De fide <Fourth Lateran Council, cf. Mansi XXII, 982>, prefaced by an index <ff.6r-8v>, followed by the text of the De fide <ff.8v-9r>; the commentary proper begins on f.9r, *inc.:* Firmiter credimus et simpliciter con[fitemur] et fidem ortodoxam . . . ; see also Lat. 10).—3. DISTINCTIONES magistri [?] super quattuor libros sententiarum [Petri Lombardi], ff.94r-153r, *inc.:* Veteris ac Novi Testamenti . . . . (Not in Stegmüller, *Repertorium comm. in Sententias P. Lombardi* <Würzburg, 1947>).—4. DE VIRTUTIBUS et vitiis variis, ff.154r-185v, *inc.:* De paradiso et gaudiis.—5. JORDANUS DE QUEDLINBURG. Postilla, ff.186r-187v, *inc.:* Si quis diligit . . . . (Sermon preached on Pentecost, cf. R. Lievens, *Jordanus van Quedlinburg,* <Ghent, 1958>, Sermon no. 317, "Lat. initia," p.404).—6. QUAESTIONES PULCHRE de contritione, ff.187v-188v, *inc.:* Prima quaestio utrum de necessitate salutis. . . .—7. Sermons, or Commentary, on the Gospels, ff.189r-283v, *inc.:* Missus est Gabriel angelus . . . Quia nec lex nec jus.— 8. SERMONES QUADRAGESIMALES, ff.283v-297r, *inc.:* Parari lucernam Christo. . . . —9. ST. BONAVENTURA. 4 short extracts, one assigned to St. Bonaventura, ff.297v-298r.—10. ROBERT HOLKOT. Super sapientam, ff.298r-299r, *inc.*: Sancti et devoti. . . . —11. JORDANUS DE QUEDLINBURG. Sermo, ff.299v-302v., *inc.*: Erunt signa in sole . . . , (to Luc. 22, 25; R. Lievens, *op. cit.*, Sermon no. 6).—12. JOANNES DE SEGOVIA. Sermo in consilio basiliensi de contemplatione [?] . . . , 1434, ff.302v-307v, *inc.*: Nota pulcra est amica . . . .—13. JORDANUS DE QUEDLINBURG. [Sermo] in sexagesima . . . , ff.307v-308v, *inc.*: Nota IX utilitates. . . . (Name Jordanus at end; not identified in R. Lievens, *op. cit.*)— 14. IDEM. Sermo, ff.308v-310r, *inc.*: Qui facit voluntatem. . . . (R. Lievens, *op. cit.*, Sermon no. 260).—15. Commentary on Robert Holkot, f.310r-v, *inc.*: Holcot movet quaestiones. . . .—16. UTRUM PECCATA dismissa redeantur, f.310v, *inc.*: Secundum [?] Reymundus [de Pennaforte] . . . .—17. PASSIO JESU CHRISTI, ff.311r-321r, *inc.*: Egressus Jhesus . . . .—18. Extract from Robert Holkot, ff.321v-322r, *inc.*: Nomen secundum Holkot . . . .—19. RAYMUNDUS DE PENNAFORTE. Extract, f.322r-v, *inc.*: Septem sunt cause. *Germany, ca. 1450?, in several different hands.*

Paper. 322 ff. 29–31 x 21 cm. Contemp. red calf over wooden boards.

Lat. 197°

[ARISTOTLE]. 1. DISPUTATIONES in Metaphysicam Aristotelis, ff.1-82, *with* DISPUTATIO de 4 intelligentiis, ff.83-95.—2. DISPUTATIONES in 10 libros Aristotelis [Ethica] ad Nicomachum, [second numbering] ff.1-67, *with* DISPUTATIO de virtute morali in communi, ff.68-94. *N.p., second half 17th cent.?, written in several hands.*

Paper. 1, 95, 1 blank, 67, 3 blank ff., ff.68-94, 1, 34 blank ff. Ca. 18 x 12.5 cm. Boards. Acquired after publ. of L. W. Riley, *op. cit.*

Lat. 198°

NICOLAUS GERBEL. Letter to Joachim Camerarius, then prof. of Greek at Tübingen, transmitting a copy of his edition of Arrianus [De expeditione Alexandri, graece, Basle, R. Winter, 1539]. *Strasbourg, 9 April, 1539.*

Paper. 1 f. 19.5 x 16.5 cm. In folder.

Dutch 1

PSALTERIUM cum canticis, beginning with a table of the seven penitential psalms (ff.1v-2r), followed by the calendar, with two stanzas of verses (4 lines each) at the end of each month (ff.3r-14v), *inc.* (verse at end of January): Snijt vleys voer onsen coninck ian; *expl.* (December): Leest wel wildy ewich vrolick wesen; table of psalms 21, 43, 45, 49, 53,

59, 62, 66, 69, 71, 78, 81, 82, 93, 108 (ff.15r-16v), *inc.*: Om te vinden die xv psalmen die men leset voer alle gheloinghe sielen; text of psalms, translated from the vulgate, with initial Latin words, and marginal notes showing variations from Hebrew (ff.17r-127v), *inc.*: Davids eersten psalm. Beatus vir. Alich is die man die niet gegaen en is in den raet der ongodliker; canticles, litanies and collects (ff.127v-139r), *inc.*: Dat Canticum van Ezechias den coninc van iuda doen hy sieck lach vander pestilentien, *expl.*: god ewelick sonder eynde. Amen (ff.127v-139r). *Netherlands, 15th cent.*

Vellum. 143 ff. (unnumb. f. between ff. 101 and 102). 11.5 x 16 cm. Red and blue capitals and rubrics. Vellum.

Dutch 2

FRANEKER, Academy. Resolutions of the governing body, relating to appointments of professors and other official matters, 1683–1709. *Franeker, 1683–1709.*

Paper. 81 ff. 32 x 20.5 cm. Contemp. vellum.

Dutch 3

RIJNLAND, Heemraad. Privilegiën der Heemraad van Rijnland, 1255–1658. *Netherlands, early 18th cent.*

Paper. 3 blank, 110, 4 blank ff. 26 x 20.5 cm. Contemp. calf with gilt arms of Rijnland.

Dutch 4

LANTRECHT van Zallant, van Twenthe, van Vullenhoe, van Drenthe, mit anderen privilegen des landes van Oberijssell. *Netherlands, ca. 1546* (date of the last item, "Reformatie van soven articulen in den lantrechte," f.90r).

Vellum. 93 ff. (preceded and followed by single blank f.) 22 x 15 cm. Contemp. vellum.—Detailed contents, with bibliogr. references, by the archivist of Drenthe, dated 1895, laid in.

Flemish 1

BOOK OF HOURS, *inc.* (f.11r): Hier begint onser wrouwen ghetide. *Low Countries, 15th cent.*

Vellum. 158 ff. 16 x 10.5 cm. Seven illum. historiated initials, illum. borders. Contemp. blind-stamped calf over wooden boards.—Bookplates of James Laurie and Paul-Louis Feiss.

Flemish 2

[ANTWERP]. Memorie op de Costumen van Antwerpen . . . 1608. *Antwerp, early 17th cent.*

Paper. 5 blank ff., 598 pp. (text), 1 blank f., 2 ff. (index in a 19th-cent. hand), 5 blank ff. 31.5 x 21.5 cm. Contemp. blind-stamped calf.—Prov.: M. N. Nanteuil; A. Renson.

Flemish 3

[FRANÇOIS VLAEMYNCK]. Detailed inventory of landed property situated in Eastern Flanders; the properties are numbered by sections, "folio" i–xxxv (xxix in two parts, ii has been removed); *inc.*: Dit naervolghende es den Landtsprocht [?] . . . van Fransoys Vlaemijnck. . . . *Flanders, 1559.*

Paper. 231 ff. (ff. 1, 14–16, 18, 25–6, 28, 32–5, 38, 40–5, 49–51, 55–61, 67–8, 73–5, 82–3, 87, 91, 95, 97–9, 102, 108, 116–20, 123–6, 128–30, 132–3, 135–6, 138–40, 144–46, 150–1, 153–61, 164–5, 167–8, 170, 172–7, 179–81, 183–87, 190–231 blank; ff. 154–7, blank, removed). 21.5 x 15.5 cm. Few notarial signets. Contemp. blind-stamped calf.—Prov.: Bibliothèque du Château de Villetard; Bibl. d'H.de Backer (sales cat., no. 3112).

Eng. 1

ENGLISH RELIGIOUS POEMS.—1. SEVEN PENITENTIAL PSALMS (ascribed variously to Richard Maydestone and Richard Rolle), ff.1r–13v (J. E. Wells, *A Manual of the Writings in Middle English* ([New Haven, 1916], pp. 403–5).—2. RICHARD ROLLE. The Pricke of Conscience, ff.14r–118r (*ibid.*, pp. 447–9).—3. The LAMENTATION OF ST. ANSELM, ff.118v–120v. *England, ca. 1400.*

Vellum. 120 ff. (imperfect, the following ff. known to be wanting: one before f.1, one between ff.7 & 8, one between ff.12 & 13, two between ff.14 & 15, eight between ff.25 & 26, one between ff.49 & 50, one between ff.78 & 79 and one between ff.91 & 92). 25 x 17 cm. Illum. initials. Morocco (Sangorski & Sutcliffe).—Prov.: Richard Halter & Francis Quawden (ms. inscription, f.77r, XVth cent.?); Gilbert Ireland Blackburne of Hale Hall, 1934.—Cf. Bruce Dickins, "The Ireland Blackburne Manuscript of Seven Penitential Psalms, The Pricke of Conscience and Lamentacio Sancti Anselmi," *Leeds Studies in English and Kindred Languages*, III (1934), 30-36.

Eng. 2

WYCLIFITE HOMILIES, a treatise on the Love of God and How One Should Attain to It. *England, first half of 15th cent.*, ff. 146–148 in a somewhat later hand.

Vellum. 148 ff. (imperfect, 8 ff. at beginning, one between ff.128 & 129 and one between ff.146 & 147 known to be wanting). 12 x 7 cm. Pen-and-ink marginal drawings (3v, 8v, 24v, 37v, etc.) 17th-cent. calf. [Harmsworth Trust Library].

Eng. 3

MIRROR (OR MYRRUR) TO LEWDE MEN AND WYMMEN. *England, early 15th cent.*

Vellum. 168 ff. 26 x 18 cm. Illum. letters, and border on f.1. 18th-cent. calf.—Cf. E. V. Stover's note on this ms. in *Library Chronicle*, XVI (1949-50), 81-86.

Eng. 4

MICHELL ARCHER (pref. signed "Mighell Archar"). A Dream of Bounden Dutie (Poem in seven parts, 224 verses of seven lines each, dedicated to Queen Elizabeth). *England, ca. 1580.*

Vellum. 61 ff. 13 x 15 cm. 17th-cent. green velvet.

Eng. 5

JOHN DAVENANT, bp. of Salisbury. Animaduersions upon a Treatise Latelie Published and Intituled The Loue of God to Mankind. *England, between 1633 and 1641.*

Paper. 109 ff. 31 x 20 cm. 17th-cent. calf, rebacked.—Prov.: Algernon Capell, Earl of Essex, Viscount Maldon & Baron Capell of Hadham, 1701 (bookplate); James Everett (1784-1872).—Ms. of Davenant's book, printed in London, 1641 (Wing D314) and abridged in the same year (Wing D315).—In the front of the book, in pencil, is written "An original Manuscript of Bishop Davenant"; under this is written, in another hand, "The above is in the autograph of Adam Clarke LLC."

Eng. 6

BIBLE, N. T., in the translation of John Wyclif, the "intermediate" version. *England, early 15th cent.*

Vellum. 239 ff. 19 x 12 cm. 16th-cent. calf.—Prov.: Gilbert, Bishop of Bath and Wells (autograph on fly leaf).—*A Catalogue of the T. Edward Ross Collection of Bibles Presented to the University of Pennsylvania Library* (Philadelphia, 1947), pp.27-28.

Eng. 7

FRANÇOIS MARIE AROUET DE VOLTAIRE. La Pucelle, or the Maid of Orleans, a Poem in XXI Cantos from the French of Mr. Voltaire, with the Author's Preface and Original Notes (cantos 1–4 only, transcribed from the privately printed 1796–97 translation). With ms. annotations and corrections in ink and pencil. *England, ca. 1796.*

Paper. 6, 126, 8 blank ff. 37 x 24 cm. Contemp. h/calf over marbled boards.

Eng. 8

FOUR ENGLISH DEVOTIONAL WORKS.—1. WALTER HILTON. The Scale of Perfection or Scala perfectionis, Bk.1, ch.21–93, Bk.2, ch.1–46, ff.1r–77v, (J. E. Wells, *A Manual* [New Haven, 1916], pp.460-1).—2. ST. BONAVENTURA. Stimulus amoris, or Prickying of Love translated by Walter Hilton, ff.77v–127v.—3. Amor dei or Love of God, ff.127v–146v.—4. RICHARD ROLLE. The Prick of Conscience, ff.147r–159v, (Wells, *op.cit.*, pp. 447–9). *England, early 15th cent.*

Vellum. 159 ff. (imperfect at beginning and end). 40 x 26 cm. 15th-cent. calf, rebacked.—Prov.: Samuel Bauter, XVII cent.; John Butlar, 1764; Thomas Stonor, 3rd Lord Camoys, 1870.—*Second Report of the Royal Commission on Historical Manuscripts, Appendix* (London, 1871) p.33.

Eng. 9

MRS. RANDALL. Receipts from a Mr. Randall, and others, and accounts of expenditures, 1778–1785. *London, 1778–1785.*

Paper. 99 ff. (first 4, and last 25 ff. blank). 20 x 16 cm. Vellum.

Eng. 10

[ENGLAND, Ledger]. A state of the revenue of excise from Michaelmas 1662 to Midsummer 1674[–1765]. "Hereditary and temporary excise," "Imported liquors," "Farm rent," "Lottery," "Numbers of distillers," 1736–1765, "Number of common brewers," 1684–1765, "Cyder, vinegar, strong waters, mead and coffee charged," 1684–1765, "Duties on malt," "Duty on candles," "Sope, paper . . . silver wire, starch," "Hides," "Coffee," "Tea," "Chocolate," "Glass, coaches, Silk & linnen," details of duties and the amount they produced, numbers of brewers, etc. *London, 1765.*

Paper. 4 ff., 218 pp. (many left blank). 36 x 26.5 cm. Contemp. red morocco.

Eng. 11

A SYSTEM OF PHYSICKS. Comments on astronomy, meteorology, mineralogy, metallurgy, and physiology, by an unidentified author. *England, 1688–1689.*

Paper. 2 vols. (362 pp., numbered 1-189, 1-173). 18 x 12 cm. Schematic drawings. Contemp. mottled calf.—C. Fitzwalter inside front cover of v.2.

Eng. 14

HENRY MACKENZIE, 1745–1831. La Roche [a tale]. *Edinburgh, 1779.*

Paper. 55 ff. of text, with 2 ff. of verse on Tickell. 18.5 x 12 cm. Contemp. calf. First published in the *Mirror; A Periodical Paper*, (Edinburgh, 1779-1780), in three successive issues, no. 42-44, June 19-26, 1779. The text follows the printed version, including the explanatory note and the first words of the story. It was later published in: [Leigh Hunt], *Classic tales, serious and lively* . . . (London, Hunt and Reynell, 1807). In the text the introductory matter is omitted, and the first sentence of the story is changed.

Eng. 15

SCOTLAND. Some Acts of Exchequer Concerning the Annuities. *Edinburgh, 1642 or soon after;* signed: J. Durhame.

Paper. 3 ff. (last leaf blank). 27 x 19 cm. Unbound.

Eng. 18

MARY ISHERWOOD. A general atlas being a collection of maps of the world and quarters with a geographical clock and mariners compass. *England, ca. 1770.*

Paper. 34 ff. (last blank) and 30 ff. (maps). 34 x 27 cm. 24 colored maps. Contemp. boards.

Eng. 19

[JAMES TURNER]. Report of the Privy Council respecting Sir James Turner together with his petition to the King, his letters to the Duke of Lauderdale and his narrative of the rebellion. Copied from the originals in the library of Dawson Turner, Esq., 1664–1680. *England or Scotland, 1830.*

Paper. xx, 1 blank, 72 ff. 32 x 20 cm. H/vellum.—Letter, dated 1874, by Curt Deedes indicates that this vol. is supposed to come from the library of F. Madan; presented to William Stubbs; American Congregational Assoc.

Eng. 20

THE DIVINE POLITICKS, or a modell of Gods kingdome shewinge out of the Holy Scripture how God doth order man into His eternall estate. Autograph[?] ms., with corrections. *England, 17th cent.*

Paper. 338 ff. (first signature misbound). 19 x 15 cm. Contemp. calf.—Prov.: William Humphri [Humphry?].

Eng. 21

ROBERT WILLIAMS. Notes concerning trade, collected by Robert Williams. (Deals with money, measures, weights, various commodities, beginning with London, 1632, and continuing with a variety of places, incl. Tunis, Madrid, Genoa, Rome, Florence, Leghorn, Venice, Naples, Smyrna, Constantinople, Alexandria, Moscow, Hamburg, Antwerp; at the end more information on trade in Leghorn, and list of books to be kept by a merchant.) *Leghorn, 1632–54.*

Paper. 1 f., 90 pp. 20.5 x 14 cm. Contemp. vellum, with initials R. W. on front cover.—According to entry cn f.1r Robert Williams died in Turkey on Feb. 21, 1660 (61); Colwell Library.

Eng. 22

H.M.S. SEA HORSE. Log book of the armed British vessel under the command of Captain Charles Cathcart Grant (succeeding a Capt. Smith, about Jan. 11–14, 1761) travelling from Plymouth to the Cape of Good Hope and back to the Scilly Islands. *Various places (on board ship), 8 January 1761–3 April 1762.*

Paper. 86 ff. 19.5 x 16 cm. Contemp. vellum.—Prov.: Charles Mason (blank f. following f.86).—A copy of the same log book is in the British Record Office (ADM.51/882). Ms.Eng.22 is presumably Captain Grant's personal copy, acc. to information supplied by the Secretary of the Publ.Rec.Office.

Ad. Eng. 19: The original documents, copied in this ms., belonged in 1830 to W. S. Fitch of Ipswich, and evicently came from the papers of the Duke of Lauderdale. They supplement Turner's *Memoirs* published by the Bannatyne Club in 1829.

Ad. Eng. 21: These notes are extracts from Lewis Roberts, *Merchants Map of Commerce*, first published in 1638.

Eng. 23

N. SANDERSON. A treatise of fluxions. *Cambridge?, ca. 1725.*

Paper. 2 ff., 128 pp.—8 folded tables, announcement of his mathematics lectures bound in at end. 18.5 x 12 cm. Cloth.—Prov.: E. Otis Kendall.

Eng. 24

PETRUS DE ABANO. Heptameron, or a work of seven days, being the elements of practical magick. . . . With an appendix of twenty-seven forms of fortifications, serving for all times, only with an alteration of the horary angel and his seal, by Isaac Jevon, Philomath. 1724/5. *England, ca. 1725.*

Paper. 74 pp. 32.5 x 21 cm. Illus. Cloth.

Eng. 25

LETTERS HISTORICAL AND GALLANT from two ladies of quality to each other, one of whom was in Paris and the other in the country. By Madam de C***. Containing curious and diverting accounts of the manners, customs and curiosities of several parts of France. . . . Done from the French. . . . *England, 1740–41.*

Paper. 6 vols. in 1 (430 pp.) 32.5 x 20.5 cm. Cloth.—Prov.: James Hingston.

Eng. 26

RÉNÉ DE CERIZIERS. Jonathan, or, The true friend, written originally in French, done into English by . . . [Sir William Lower; this reading is pencilled on title-page and verso of prel. f. The name blocked out is practically unreadable, but seems not to be that of Lower]. Autograph?, with numerous corrections in a contemp. hand. *England, ca. 1660* [cf. date on title page].

Paper. 2 ff., 163 pp., 3 ff. 20.5 x 15.5 cm. H/cloth.

Eng. 28°

LATIN-ENGLISH MISCELLANY. 1. [TERTULLIAN]. Commentary to Tertullian "Edit. Lutetiae M.D.C.34. Sumptibus Mathurini Du Puis" [cf. prel. f.2r], 4 ff., pp. 1–54. —[Beginning on opposite end of vol.:] 2. BIBLE. Extracts and commentary, Eng. and Lat., "Mr. Gibbon at Gregor. Nov. 26–29" [reverse f.1r], ff.1–17.—3. THOMAS FLATMAN. Miscellanies "ex interiori templo Londini sic imperantibus fatis, Nov. 9, 1661, ff.18–38. (24 pieces of verse, acc. to dealer's descr. largely published in his *Poems and songs*, printed in 1676, etc.) *England, 17th cent.*

Paper. 4 ff., 54 pp., 18 blank ff., 38 ff. 13 x 7 cm. Calf. Bookplate J. Fr. Cosent; J. Milford, 1850; D.D.R.H. Groowe (?). Originally classified as 821/F61.1.

Ad. Eng. 25: The author of the French text is Anne Marguerite Petit du Noyer.

Eng. 29°

GILES FARNABY. The Psalmes of David [etc.], to fower parts, for viols and voyce, the first booke doricke mottoes, the second, divine canzonets, . . . with a prelud, before the Psalmes, cromaticke. (With dedication to Henry King . . . cheife prebend of the Cathdirall [sic] Church of Saint Paul. *England, first half 17th cent.*

Paper. 2 ff., 136 pp. music (soprano part), 18 ruled, 3 blank ff. 13.5 x 19 cm. Contemp. calf.—Prov.: Oliver Hopkinson; gift of Edward Hopkinson, Jr. Cf. O. E. Albrecht, *Census of European Music Manuscripts* (Philadelphia, 1951), p. 117, and his article in *Musical Quarterly*, XXXXI (1945), especially p. 498.

Giles Farnaby. Eng. 29, p. 54.

Fr. 1

GUILLAUME DE LORRIS and JEHAN DE MEUNG. Le Roman de la rose. *France, middle of 15th cent.*

Paper. 340 ff. 30 x 21 cm. Rubricated in red and yellow. Blind-stamped contemp. calf, rebacked.—18th-cent. inscription "Delaplanches" at beginning and earlier inscription "Marcel"(?) on inside front cover. On blank leaf, preceding text, are pasted verses 64-73, written apparently in the same hand as the ms.

Fr. 2*

MARC-ANTOINE MILLOTET, fils. Extrait des mémoires servant à l'histoire des choses, que se sont passées en Bourgogne pendant la première et la seconde guerre civile [1650-1668]. *Burgundy, 17th cent.*

Paper. 122 pp. 29 x 20 cm. Contemp. vellum.—Prov.: "p[re] Charvin ainé, de St. Loup de Varennes, près Chalon-sur-Saône, 1808," and unidentified later bookplate T I R C inside front cover.—The ms. is a summary of the *Mémoire*, published by Charles Muteau, Dijon, 1866.

[54]

Fr. 3*

MÉMOIRE SUR L'ÉTAT POLITIQUE DES PAÏS BAS et La constitution tant externe qu'interne des Provinces. *France, ca. 1757.*

Paper. 2 blank, 236 unnumbered, 7 blank ff. 25.5 x 23 cm. Gilded contemp. morocco, with arms on sides. Publ. in 1784 as *Mémoires historiques et politiques des Pays-Bas autrichiens;* later editions name the author, Patrice-Mac de Nény.

Fr. 4

VERGILIUS MARO. Le livre des Eneydes, *inc.:* [J]ay entrepris de coucher en mes vers/Le cas de Troye qui fut alenuers/. . . . *France, 15th cent.*

Vellum. 161 ff., written in "lettres bâtardes" in two columns. Large spaces left blank at beginning of each book, obviously for the illuminator. 37 x 29 cm. 17th-cent. red morocco.—Prov.: Louis César de La Baume-Leblanc and Duc de La Vallière.—*Catalogue des livres de la Bibliothèque de feu M. Le Duc de la Vallière. . . par Guillaume de Bure* (Paris, 1783), II, no.2459; Parke-Bernet *Catalogue no.1282* (Gabriel Wells), 1951, no.562.—According to the description of this ms. in the sales catalogue "this translation of Virgil's Aeneid, written in decasyllabic couplets, is neither the very free adaptation that was written in the 12th century and printed at Lyons . . . in 1482, nor the version by Octavien de Saint-Gelais which Vérard printed in 1509."

Fr. 5

FRANÇOIS DE LA FOSSE. Poésies de François de La Fosse, Ecuyer Sr: de Valpendant, valet de garderobe du Roy, ordinaire de Monseigneur le Duc de Bourgogne, et valet de chambre de Madame la Duchesse de Bourgogne. *France, between 1707 and 1721.*

Paper. 578 pp., 2 ff., 560 pp., 10 ff. (last blank). 23.5 x 18 cm. Bound in contemp. calf.—Prov.: M. de Noircourt.—After the introduction follows on pp.1-177 "Histoire fée et autrement," largely in prose. The poems, often quite free, incl. "Version de la seconde épode d'Horace, Beatus ille qui procul . . ." (p.194-197), "Plainte sur la Mort du Grand Roy [Louis XIV] (p.240), a satire in verse "Damon" (pp.256-265), transcripts of poems by François Villon, Du Bellay, Ronsard, Baïf, Sarazin, Scarron, and others (pp.298-335), poems about Jansenists and Jesuits "Portrait de Rabelais," pp.547-551.

Fr. 8

DESVIGNES(?). Le trésor du royaume des cieux. *Paris, 1701.*

Paper. 12 ff., 105 numbered pp. 18 x 12 cm. Contemp. calf. Religious poems dedicated to Samuel Bernard (1651-1739).

Fr. 9

GIOVANNI BOCCACIO. Decameron, translated into French by Laurens de Premierfait. *France, 15th cent.*

Paper. 658 ff. 28 x 19.5 cm. Illum. initials. 17th-cent. vellum.—Prov.: P. R. Lyell.—Cf. R. Bossuat, *Manuel bibl. de la litt. franç.* (Melun, 1951), no.5972.

Fr. 10

ROBERT (a Monk of the XVth century). Le château périlleux, f.1–85v.—*With* LE PELERINAGE DE DAMOISELLE SAPIENCE. *Northern France, ca. 1450–1460.*

Paper. 95 ff. 20 x 14 cm. H/calf, dated 1813.—Prov.: J. A. J. Delignières de Bommy d'Abbéville; M. Victor Advielle d'Arras (1889).—Discussion of this work and other existing mss. may be found in Groeber, *Grundriss d. roman. Philol.* II, pt. 1, p.1166. Account of Passion interpolated on ff.51r-63v.

Fr. 11

CHRONIQUE VERSIFIÉE de la ville de Metz (to 1575). *Metz(?), ca. 1580.*

Paper. Ff. 8, 7, [9], 10-14, 29-126, 129-161 [i.e. ff.1-6, 15-28, 127-28 missing] =139 ff. 20 x 15.5 cm. 19th-cent. calf.—Prov.: Hermann Suchier.

Fr. 12

1. [ST. BERNARD OF CLAIRVAUX]. Les lamentations, ff.1–8.—2. JACQUES MILLET (or MILET). La destruction de Troye, ff.9–448r.—3. LE MYSTÈRE DE LA PASSION de Notre Sauveur Jesus Christ, ff.448r–486r, *inc.*: [A] la louenge dieu de la vierge souveraine de tous saines et de toutes sainctes et a la requeste de tres excellante et redoubte dame et puissant princesse dame Ysabel de Baviere reyne de France j'ai translate ceste passion . . . l'an de grace mil troys cens quatre vingtz et dishuit. . . . [*France*], *1450.*

Paper. 30 x 21 cm. 486 ff. H/leather on original wooden boards. 1. Wrongly attributed to St. Bernard.—2. Bossuat, *op. cit.*, p.567 "mystère composé entre 1450 et 1453;" L. Petit de Julleville, *Les mystères* (Paris, 1880), II, 569 ff. lists mss. and printed eds.—3. Cf. G. Frank, *Mediaeval French Drama* (Oxford, 1954), pp.184-186 and E. Roy, *Mystère de la Passion en France du XIV*ᵉ *au XVI*ᵉ *siècle* (Paris, 1903), pp.252 ff., with list of mss. This text, written in 1398 for Isabelle of Bavaria, was the model for later mysteries, incl. the Passion of Greban.

Fr. 13

EXAMEN DU SYSTÈME des cours de Vienne, de Petersbourg et de Berlin, concernant le démembrement de la Pologne. 1773. *Austria(?), 1773–1774.*

Paper. 28 pp. 24.5 x 18.5 cm. Boards.

Fr. 14

1. SEPT SAGES. Roman des sept sages de Rome, ff.1–34 (R. Bossuat, *op cit.*, pp.132-133).—2. MARQUES DE ROME. Roman de Mark de Rome, ff.39–141 (*ibid.*). *France, ca. 1350.*

Ad. Fr. 13: Cf. Ludwik Finkel, *Bibliografia Historii Polskiej* (Warsaw, 1955), no. 5007.

Vellum. Fragment of 130 ff; earlier numbering, ff.1, 3-22, 26-29, 24-25, 30-34, 39-66, 69-73, 73-91, 93-100, 100-110, 112-117, 119-141, incorrect; several ff. are missing and others are torn. 18.4 x 11.7 cm. 19th-cent. boards.—Phillipps Collection, ms.3679.

Fr. 15

CHANSONNIER. 310 poems by Guillaume de Machaut, Oton de Grandson, Brisebarre de Douai, Eustache Deschamps, and others. *France, ca. 1400.*

Vellum. 101 ff, double columns. 30 x 24.2 cm. Red morocco.—Prov.: L. S. Olschki.—Cf. G. Bertoni in *Arch. romanicum*, XVI (1933), 1-20, who gives a not entirely accurate description, reproduces 304 incipits, and reprints 7 poems. Inscription of f.1r: "Droit est ferme," (Isabelle of Bavaria?).

Fr. 16

LIBER FORTUNAE. *France, ca. 1450.*

Paper. 98 ff. (incorrectly numbered pp.1-192). 17.4 x 12.5 cm. 18th-cent. calf.—Arms of Vicomte de Villiers du Terrage on binding.—Cf. J. L. Grigsby, *Romania*, LXXX(1960), 447-460.

Fr. 17

SAINT-MICHEL, Order of the Knights of. Statutes and Constitution. *France, 1476.*

Vellum. 45 ff. 20 x 14.7 cm. Illum. initial "L" on f.1. 19th-cent. gilt red morocco.

Fr. 18

CONSEIL au Roy Francois I[er] concernant les finances. *Inc.:* Lemoulument cler et vray concernant lauctorite du Roy, le prouffit de ses affaires. . . . *France, ca. 1522.*

Vellum. 16 ff. (last two blank). One of two preliminary ff. (title?) removed. 17.2 x 11.7 cm. Illum. initials in alternate blue and gold, and red and gold. Contemp. sheepskin.—Prov.: Xaraquemada. Madrid, 1753; J.M.A. 1835.—Cf. M. Wolfe and N. Zacour, "The Growing Pains of French Finance, 1522-1523," *Library Chronicle*, XXII (1956), 58-83.

Fr. 20

HONORÉ BONNET. L'arbre des batailles (Bossuat, *op.cit.*, p.542). *France, 15th cent.*

Paper. 126 ff. 20 x 13 cm. 19th-cent. calf.—Prov.: George Poulin (ca. 1500); Alexandre de Keller (19th-cent.).

Fr. 21

ADRIEN DE SAINT-GELAIS and others. Collection of 16th-century French poetry, containing Les troys buccines . . . foy, charite et esperance, pp.1–42; Le moyen d'avoir paix en France.—6 rondeaux, by Anne de Graville, André de la Vigne, Richard de la Porte, Jean Marot, etc.—2 ballads, one ascribed to François Villon or Alain Chartier.—14 other pieces in verse and prose incl. a prophecy by Paul Paradiso. *Rouen, first half of the 16th cent.;* additions which seem to be in the hand of Robert de la Porte, son of the original possessor Richard de la Porte, bear terminal date 1552.

Paper. 152 pp. 20 x 14 cm. 19th-cent. calf.—Prov.: Family La Porte (16th cent.), Baron Jérome Pichon.—Cf. V. L. Saulnier, *Bulletin de bibliophile*, 1952, nos.3-5.

Fr. 22

BLANCANDIN et l'Orgueilleuse d'amour, verses 415–6135. *France, late 13th or early 14th cent.*

Vellum. 136 ff. (beginning and end missing). 15.5 x 12 cm. Morocco.—Cf. Franklin P. Sweeter, *Blancandin; the University of Pennsylvania ms.* (unpubl. Ph.D. thesis, 1956) and his edition *Blancandin . . .* , Geneva, 1964. (*Textes littéraires français*, v. 112).

Fr. 23

SYDRACH, la Fontaine de toute science. *France, 1457* (f.1r).

Paper. 218 ff. (ff.1-2 blank; incomplete at end, 2 ff. or more missing). 28.5 x 20.5 cm. 15th-cent. blind-stamped calf, repaired and rebacked.

Fr. 24

BENOIT DE ST. MAURE. Roman de Troie, (fragment containing verses 6658–7024). *France, ca. 1300.*

Vellum. 2 ff. 29 x 20.5 cm. Boards.

Fr. 25

PARIS, Chambre des Comptes. Noms de tous les officiers . . . qui ont possédés une même charge avec la datte de leurs réceptions. Extrait des mémoriaux de la Chambre des Comptes de Paris contenant les noms, et la succession chronologique de tous les présidens, maîtres, correcteurs, et auditeurs, avocats, et procureurs, généraux, tant ordinaires qu'extra-ordinaires, greffiers en chef, anciens et alternatifs, et premiers huissiers de la ditte chambre; suivant l'ordre de leurs receptions [1304–1759] (f.2).—Table alphabetique (pp.424–552). *Paris, written by "Gerardin"* (cf. title). *1756–1759.*

Paper. 558 pp. (pp.553-558 blank). 35.5 x 23 cm. Contemp. calf.

Fr. 26

NICOLAS DE NEUFVILLE (Seigneur de Villeroi, 1542–1617). Mémoires. *Villeroy, 8 April 1589* (*f.53v*) *and later.*

Paper. 174 ff. 30 x 20 cm. 17th-cent. calf.—Prov.: J. Sotheby 1685 (f.1).

Ad. Fr. 24: Published by S. Pellegrini in *Archivum romanicum*, XII (1928) 515–29.
Ad. Fr. 26: Cf. *Mémoires de Villeroy et de Saucey*, ed. Auguste Poirson (Paris, 1868).

Fr. 27

RECUEIL DE POËSIE. Collection of French poetry and songs (largely love songs) of the late seventeenth and early eighteenth centuries, with table of contents. *France, ca. 1675–1725.*

Paper. 391 ff. (ff.378-384 removed). 25 x 19 cm. Contemp. calf.

Fr. 28

PARIS, Parlement. Extrait raisonné des registres du Parlament de Paris, redigé par titres, chapitres, paragraphes, règlemens et mémoires, selon l'ordre de l'alphabet, des tems et des matières depuis 1254 usqu'en 1655. *France, 17th cent.*

Paper. 9 vols. of 12 (vols.IV, V and XI missing). 33 x 27 cm. Contemp. calf.

Fr. 29

RECUEIL DE POËSIE (incl. "Le lutrin vivant" and "Vertvert" of Gresset, epitaphs of the duc de Villars and Molière, an ode to Voltaire). *France, 18th cent.*

Paper. 604, 11 pp. 18 x 14 cm. Contemp. calf.—Bookplates of Paul Lacroix ("Jacob Bibliophile" with monogram PL) and Frédéric Lachèvre.

Fr. 30

VAUD, France. Le Coutumier du païs de Vaud, appartenant au très noble généreux Seigneur Ballif George Nicolas Reiff des Romont. . . . *Fribourg(?), early 18th cent. (?)*, with later additions (ff.156).

Paper. 1, 165, 16, 1 ff. 33 x 21 cm. Contemp. calf.—Prov.: George Nicolas Reyff 1739; bookplate of E. Chatoney.—These are the customs confirmed by the council of the town of Fribourg in Jan. 1649, and published in June 1650 (f.163). The title (possibly later) is dated 1747.

Fr. 31

HONORÉ GABRIEL RIQUETI MIRABEAU. Discourse (fragment) on the necessity of abolishing the negro slave trade. *Paris(?), 1790.*

Paper. 4 ff. 23 x 18 cm. Unbound.—Written in a secretarial hand, but with corrections which are probably in the hand of Count Mirabeau.

Fr. 32*

FRÈRE LAURENT. Somme le Roi (cf. Bossuat, *op. cit.*, pp. 335–6), ff.1–63 and 84.—*With* MIROIR DES BONNES FEMMES, ff.64–83. *France, ca. 1300.*

Vellum. 85 ff. (misbound: ff.1–4 belong after f.29, f.84 belongs after f.63). The leaf between ff.23 and 24 is unnumbered; some leaves are missing. 19.8 x 13.8 cm. The ms. is discussed and the text of the *Miroir* analysed by John L. Grigsby, "Miroir des bonnes femmes," *Romania*, LXXXII (1961), 458–81; LXXXIII (1962), 30–51.

Fr. 33

DITS MORAUX DES PHILOSOPHES. French translation by Guillaume de Tignonville of the Dicta philosophorum. *France, 15th cent.*

Vellum. 100 ff. 25 x 17 cm. Initials in gold and blue. 19th-cent. stamped calf.—Notice of sale "chez le duc de la Vallière," 1788. Inscription on flyleaf indicates a later owner named Muraire.

Fr. 34

PIERRE QUIROT. Extrait des coustumes génerallles et particulières de France et des Gaulles en ce qui concerne les servitudes réelles, les édifices et bastiments et le fait des rapports des jurés en toutes matières . . . par le Sieur Pierre Quirot, architecte du Roy, expert juré, bourgeois à Paris. 1709 (pp.1–370); Ordonnances and arrêts (pp. 370bis–611). *France, after 1732.*

Paper. 14 ff., pp.1-134, ff.134bis-136bis, pp.137-370, ff.370bis-371, pp.371 tertio-382, ff.382bis-383, pp.383-408, f.408, pp.409-443, 3 unnumbered ff., f.444, pp.445-446, 3 printed pp., pp 447-614(last 3 blank), 28 ff. index. 37 x 23 cm. 18th-cent. calf.—With few exceptions the "coutumes" here extracted belong to the 16th century.

Fr. 35

PROVENCE. Explication des statuts de Provence. [Title on spine:] Application des statuts sur les droits seigneuriaux. *Provence, 17th–18th cent.*

Paper. Title, 2 ff. contents, 1 vol. of documents in different hands, with corrections and emendations, numbered separately and also ff.1-534. Contemp. vellum

Fr. 36

JESUITS. 1. DIALOGUES DES MORTS, between Varade and Barrière, pp.1–48.—2. LE FRANC. Dialogues des morts modernes, ou entretiens des âmes de Louis XIV . . ., 1741, pp.49–129.—3. CHANSON D'UN INCONNU . . . ou Histoire véritable arrivée à l'endroit d'un R.R.P. de la Compagnie de Jésus, pp.131–265.—4. MÉMOIRE D'UNE CRUAUTÉ INOUÏE commise en la ville de Munau par les RR. PP. Jésuites de Liège en France, 1736, pp.269–285.—5. CHANSON DE PARADE, pp.286–290.—6. Treatise on the brewing of beer, pp.288–290. *France, 18th cent.*

Paper. 290 pp. 24 x 18 cm. Contemp. vellum.—Not identified in A. de Backer and C. Sommervogel, *Bibl. de la Compagnie de Jésus* (Paris, 1890-1909).

Fr. 37

[FRIEDRICH AUGUST I, Elector of Saxony (AUGUST II, King of Poland), surnamed August der Starke]. Le portrait de la cour de Saxe. Highly critical account of important members of the court of "August

[60]

the Strong." Acc. to the "Avertissement", compiled for the King (with his signature [?] on f.91v) in this unique (!) copy. *Saxony(?), early 18th cent.*

Paper. 1 and 93 ff. 20 x 32 cm. 18th-cent. boards. Among the portraits are those of J. R. Patkul, H. H. Flemming, L. G. Hoym, Minister Bose, Treasurer Brewentowsky, Chamberlain Miltitz, etc.

Fr. 38

GUEFFIER, chargé d'affaires du Roi de France (Louis XIV). Dépêches depuis le 29e Novembre 1649 jusqu'au Juin 1660. *France, 18th cent.*

Paper. 7 vols. 37 x 23 cm. Contemp. calf, coat of arms of Gabriel Bernard de Rieux, president of the second Chambre des enquêtes of the Parlement of Paris (d.1745).—Prov.: Gabriel Bernard de Rieux; Thomas Phillipps, ms.3175.— *Catalogue de la bibliothèque de feu M. le Président Bernard de Rieux* (Paris, Barrois, 1747).

Fr. 40

[ARTOIS]. Hebert [conseiller] Sur Artois. . . . Rémarques faites sur plusieurs articles de la coutume d'Artois et sur quelques question[s] de droit et de pratique, par feu monsieur le conseiller Hebert. With alphabetical table of contents, pp.715–759. *France, early 18th cent.*

Paper. 759 pp. 32 x 20 cm. Contemp. calf.—Prov.: Sr. Le Fran, greffier de l'abbaye de St. Vaast.

Fr. 41

L'EVANGILE DE L'ENFANCE, ff.12–42r, *inc.:* Cy commancent les enfances notre sire et partye des miracles qu'il fist en son enfance et si commancerat en la maniere qui ensuyt par vers rimes translatez de latin en françois par le roy charles.vi^e . . . [verse 1]: DIre vous vueil si et retrawe/Chose qui a tous pourra plaire. . . .—2. La Passion de Notre Sauveur Jesus Christ, ff.41v–98r, *inc.:* CY ensient la passion de notre doulx Sauueur Jhesucrist en Romans. lequel nous doint viure en cest siecle en telle maniere [text begins:] Au temps que Jhesucrist prist mort. . . .—3. [Moral precepts in 48 Latin distichs, all but three followed by French quatrains], ff.100r–105v, *inc.:* Inter convivas fac sis sermone modestus/Ne dicare loquax dum vis bonus ipse videri/ Attempre toy quant tu seras a table/Que ne parles trop de vray ne de fable/ . . . *France, second half of 15th cent.* Lettre bâtarde.

Ad. Fr. 37: Attributed to Johann Friedrich von Wolfframsdorf and edited from another ms. by R. Pekrun, *Hof und Politik Augusts d. Starken im Lichte d. Portrait de la Cour de Pologne*, Friedland, 1914–15.

Ad. Fr. 38: Gueffier was "resident de France" at Rome; cf. the detailed description of a similar collection in the catalogue of Paris, Bibl. nat., *Coll. des 500 de Colbert*, mss. 356–63.

Paper. 106 ff. (first, f.99, and last two blank). 28.5 x 20.5 cm. Ornamented initials, some with grotesque faces drawn in pen-and-ink. 18th-cent.(?) velvet.— "Ex libris Congregationis Oratorii à [Place undeciphered]. . . 1674." 1. The same incipit, but in considerably earlier spelling is found in Langfors, *Les incipits des poèmes français*, p.99; see also Bonnard, *Les traductions de la Bible in vers*, p.238, listing the same first line, but otherwise different rendering attributed to Jean Baynzford.—2. Prose version of the apocryphal gospel.—3. Not in Langfors.

Fr. 42
DOUAI. Compte des biens, rentes et reuenues de le liuree du commun des chapellains de leglise saint Ame [St. Amé] en Douay et des biens des chapelles . . . fait et rendu par m[o]y Jullien Geruais . . . *Douai, 1496.*

Vellum. 18 ff.(last blank). 32 x 23.5 cm. Unbound.

L'Evangile de L'Enfance—French 41

Fr. 43
URBAIN CHEVREAU, 1613–1701. Chevraeana. The published edition of 1697–1700 with numerous interleaved and marginal additions and corrections by Chevreau in preparation for a new edition, which never appeared. Bound in are some notes by two owners: Nicolas Boindin and Gustave Mouravit. *N.p., ca. 1700.*

Paper. 2 vols. 17.5 x 10 cm. Full, ornamented gilt morocco, by David. Large paper copy, with some leaves from another copy inserted.—Prov.: N. Boindin; A. de La Fizelière; G. Mouravit.—Cf. *Bulletin du Bibliophile*, XIII série (1858), pp.1058-1065, where a ms. addition from v.2, p.288 is published.

Fr. 44

GEORGES CHASTELLAIN, 1405(?)–1475. Declaration de tous les haulx fais et glorieuses aventures du Duc Philippe de Bourgongne. Éloge, ff.3r–12r.—IDEM. Éloge de Charles le Hardy, ff.12r–19v. These texts are preceded by 1 page of poetry ("Bien est il vray que pour eulx arengier, En mon service ils passent maint dangier, . . . "), 2 pages of prose ("Au trop considerer l'orreur de la puissance que cupide s'attribue) and 1 page with arms inscribed "BROESSGER DA GELAS." *France, ca. 1470.* Lettre bâtarde.

Paper. 22 ff. (last three blank, except for brief inscriptions of ff. 21-22). 28.5 x 22 cm. Contemp.(?) leather cover. "Dis boeck hoost for Janne [? suprascription over blacked out name] Rombouts."—Text found on ff.3-19 of this ms. has been printed from other mss. in Kervyn de Lettenhove, *Oeuvres de Georges Chastellain,* (Bruxelles, 1865), VII 213-236.

Fr. 45
(Provençal)

CANCON en Agenais (Lot-et-Garonne). Cens, rentes, revenues droiz et devoirs deubz a la recepte de Cancon, *inc.:* JHS. Segonse los que an reconogut al noble senhor Johan de Verdu senhor dela peria e de canquo per las gens et habitans de Canquo et al hunorable senhor mosseu Ramon dela faga son procurayre. . . . *Cancon(?), 1463–1470.*

Paper. 26 ff. 29 x 22 cm. Vellum (document in Provençal, 1374).—Signed by notary Petrus de Copertone (ff.1-13 and 26). Documents on ff.14-23 are in Old French.

Fr. 46

CANCON en Agenais (Lot-et-Garonne). Registre des marches passes pour la reconstruction et les restaurations du chateau de Cancon. *Cancon(?), 1544–1547.*

Paper. 41 ff. (ff.27-28 missing; blank [?] ff. at end removed). 27.5 x 19.5 cm. Contemp. blind-stamped leather (badly worn).—Cf. L. Massip, *Hist. de la ville et des seigneurs de Cancon* (Cancon, 1891), pp.138-140. Signed in various places by the notary Antoine Robert. The castle belonged to Marie de Verdun and her husband Charles de Montferrat.

Ad. Fr. 44: M. Octave Le Maire of Brussels clarified the provenance. The arms are those of the Rombouts family, glass painters at Brussels in the 15th and 16th cent.; BROESSGER DAT GELAS ("more fragile than glass") apparently alludes to the family profession. Infra-red photography reveals that the original statement of ownership reads "Die boeck hoost for Claes Rombouts"; we may conclude that the ms. first belonged to Claes Rombouts and was inherited either by his son or a member of his brother's family.—Line 7: DA *read* DAT. Line 10: Dis *read* Die.

Fr. 47

[DUTCH EAST AND WEST INDIES COMPANY]. Démonstration de l'injuste et chimérique prétention que les directeurs de la Compagnie des Indes en Hollande forment, afin de faire révoquer, ou du moins rendre inutile l'octroy que sa Majesté Impériale et Catholique a accordé à ses sujets des Pays-Bas autrichiens pour l'établissement d'une Compagnie de Commerce et de Navigation aux Indes Orientales et Occidentales, dediée à Messeigneurs les États Généraux des Provinces Unies. *Belgium(?), 18th cent.*

Paper. 51 pp. 23 x 19.5 cm. Unbound.

Fr. 48

FRANÇOIS JOSEPH LA GRANGE—CHANCEL. Les philippiques et autres pièces, avec des notes historiques et critiques. *France, second half of 18th cent.*

Paper. 1, 69 ff. 18 x 10.5 cm. Contemp. calf.

Fr. 49

[DAILLON, Comtes du Lude]. Histoire généalogique de la maison des Seigneurs de Daillon, Comtes du Lude, depuis l'année 1364. *France, ca. 1710–1725.*

Paper. 1 f., 92 pp. (pp.76-78, 83-92 blank). 18.5 x 14 cm. Contemp. calf.—Thomas Phillipps (ms.3965); John Townley.

Fr. 50

AYMÉ BERTIN. Oeuvres académiques. *Lyons, 1734–1749[–52].*

Paper. 4 ff., 437 pp. 28 x 19 cm. Diagrs. Contemp. calf. Contains papers read by Aymé Bertin before the academies of Lyons and Villefranche on such varied subjects as Amazons, Rhodes, canon law ("purgations canoniques"), history of the French language, etc. Added are "Discours par M. Annibal Claret de Flurieux, en réponse à celuy de M. l'abbé de Pusignieux," pp.245-57 and several essays by A. Bertin, incl. a treatise "sur la géometrie pratique", pp.265-437.

Fr. 51

[LOUIS XV, King of France]. Traité des droits du domaine du Roy, leur origine, comme aussi le préjudice que Sa Majesté se fait en surchargeant ses sujets avec des impôts. *France, 1755* (cf. p.14, line 1–2).

Paper. 202 pp. 29.5 x 20 cm. H/vellum.

Fr. 52

LOUIS SANLECQUE, abbé. Satyre sur la direction (en vers; contre les confesseurs, directeurs de conscience). *Paris, ca. 1690.*

Paper. 6 ff. 22 x 16.5 cm. in vol. (26 x 18.5 cm.). H/cloth.—Prov.: Dumont de Villeneuve.

Fr. 53

WYNANTS, G. A. de. Mémoire contenant des notions générales de tout ce qui concerne le gouvernement des Pays-Bas autrichiens.—État général de tous les revenus et de toutes les charges des Pays Bas autrichiens. *Belgium, ca. 1730.*

Paper. 503, 136 pp. 33.5 x 20.5 cm. Portrait of de Wynants, engraved by E. Pilsen after I. P. Sauvage, bound at beginning. H/calf.—Prov.: J. Timmers. —Contemp. copy; the original is in the University Library, Ghent.

Fr. 54

COMPAGNIE DE COMMERCE DE LORRAINE. Collection of documents and a few printed items, relating to the Company (which was founded by Duke Leopold, partly to protect commerce in the Duchy against the crisis evoked by Law) and Claude Regnault. These documents date largely from the years 1724 to 1791, though also included is the marriage contract of Claude Regnault, 1694. *France, 1694–1791.*

Paper, a few documents on vellum. Several hundred pieces in various sizes. Boxed.

Fr. 55

[GRAF LUDWIG and PHILIPP COBENZL]. Dossier of 105 letters and documents, 1786–1806, mostly addressed to Ludwig von Cobenzl (for 20 years Austrian ambassador to Russia) and Philipp von Cobenzl (one-time vice chancellor of Austria). Most items have bearing on political and diplomatic matters, especially relations between Austria, Russia, Prussia, and France. The letters were written by F. J. J. N. von Dietrichstein, Johann von Thugut, Ferdinand von Trauttmansdorf, K. T. A. M. von Dalberg, Mme. Bernier de Villers, Baron Giusti, K. R. von Buol-Schauenstein, Prince N. V. Repnin, Baron Limon-Hallewin, Count Panin, Peter von Herbert, W. W. Grenville, Archduke Ferdinand of Austria, Archduke Josef of Hungary, Prince Karl Auersperg, Prince Ferdinand of Wuerttemberg, J. P. K. J. von Stadion, Karl von Finkenstein, Andreas Razumovski, Ludwig von Lebzeltern, and a few others. *Various places, 1786–1806.*

Paper. 213 ff. (a few blank). Various sizes. Boxed.

Fr. 56

JOHN THAYER. Rélation de la conversion de M^r. Jean Thayer, ministre protestant de Boston . . . , converti à la réligion catholique à Rome le 23 mai 1783. Écrite par lui-même avec une lettre à son frère, en réponse à quelques objections sur le parti qu'il a pris . . . , 66 pp.— *With* RÉFLEXIONS sur la souvérainnetté, le serment de liberté, d'égalité et la constitution civile du clergé, 175 pp. *England?, ca. 1800* (cf. note on prel. f.2r: "du Diocese de Coutances, Reading").

Paper. 2 ff., 66 pp., 1 blank f., 96 pp., 4 ff. (last blank), pp. 97–175. 16 x 10 cm. Contemp. boards.—Prov.: G. V. Digard (f.2v).—For J. Thayer, see J. Sabin, *Bibl. Amer.*, (New York, 1934), XXV, 98, etc.—Bound with several printed pamphlets: RECIT des traitements, (London, 1797); TABLEAU des horreurs de la Révolution française, (n.p.d.); DE LA HARPE, Lettres . . . en faveur de la religion, (London, 1797).

Fr. 57

[OPERA COMIQUES]. 1. LA BEQUILLE du bon homme Barnabas, pp.1–32.—2. LE MAGAZIN des modernes, pp.33–65.—3. VAUDEVILLE pantomime, pp.65–72.—4. L'INFIDÉLITÉ PUNIE, pp.73–97.—5. VAUDEVILLE, pp.97–8. *France, 18th cent.*

Paper. 98 pp. 30 x 19 cm. Contemp. vellum.

Fr. 58

BALTHASARD FRANÇOIS DE MERLES, Marquis de BEAUCHAMP. Des mathématiques.—Astronomie (Des cercles du premier mobile ou seconds cercles; Des divers point[s] du ciel; Des cieux et du nombre d'iceux; Du mouvement des cieux; De la figure du monde; De la solidité des cieux; Des divers systèmes du monde). Autograph ms. with corrections. *France, second half 17th cent.*

Paper. 10 ff. 28 x 19.5 cm. Astronomical figures. In folder.

Fr. 59

[GENOA, 1684]. Lettre de résponçe sur les hostilitéz que les François ont fait contre Gennes, escritte de la dite ville par Mons. N. à Mons. N. à Turin. *Genoa, 2 June, 1684.*

Paper. 26 ff., last blank. 24 x 17.5 cm. In folder.

Fr. 61

PHILLIPE EMMANUEL DE COULANGES. Relation de mon voyage d'Allemagne et d'Italie es années mille six cent cinquante sept et cinquante huit, 409 pp.—*With* IDEM. Conclaves d'Alexandre VIII et d'Innocent XII es années 1689 et 1691, 218 pp.—BIOGRAPHIE de P. E. de Coulanges, pp.219–229. *France, ca. 1746.*

Paper. 409 pp., 2 blank ff., title, 229 pp., 9 blank ff. 31 x 20 cm. Contemp. calf with the arms of A. Le Fevre d'Ormesson on front and back cover and initials DO on spine.—Copied for André François d'Ormesson from the autograph ms. (f.227).—The memoirs of Coulanges as published by Monmerque in 1820 contain a very incomplete text.

Fr. 62

NOAILLES FAMILY. Correspondance de Noailles (incl. les Gontaut, Biron, Pibrac, etc.), 1539–1634. (Copied by and for Theodore de Gontaut-Biron from originals, largely in the Bibliothèque nationale, Paris.) *Paris, third quarter 19th cent.*

Paper. 2 vols. 27.5 x 20.5 cm. H/morocco. Bookplate of Theodore de Gontaut-Biron.—Genealogy of the family Noailles, 1386–1700, at beginning of vol. 1.

Fr. 63

CHANSONS HISTORIQUES et gaillardes. (Political satirical songs of the 17th and early 18th century, incl. songs by Blot, Benserade, Boussy-Rabutin, Coulanges, etc. With musical notations on ff.1r, 9v, 11v, 13r, 15r, 27r, 31r, 38v, 61r.—Added at end: Inees de Castro, tragédie du S. de La Motte Houdart, ff.170–180.) *France, ca. 1723–30*, with annotations and corrections in a contemp. hand.

Paper. 182 ff., (f.181 loose, f.182 blank). 36.5 x 23 cm. Drawing of whale on f.160. Contemp. calf, with arms of Bonnier de la Mosson on front cover and name on back cover.—Ex libris Viollet Le Duc.

Fr. 64

[PASCAL FAMILY]. 1. (Cover-title:) JOURNAL d'annotation, (caption-title:) GENEALOGIE de la maison Pascal divisée en trois branches, comme il sera detaillé y après [Pascal de la Rochette; Pascal de Longpra; Pascal de l'Ertegne]. The genealogy of the Pascal de Longpra incl. an original document concerning Jean Pascal, dated 1555. The genealogy of the branch of La Rochette extends to 1776.—2. Various documents, accounts, letters, etc., mainly of family members residing at St. Geoire (near Grenoble), mostly of the second half 18th cent. *St. Geoire (etc.), 1555–1796*.

Paper. 1: 12 ff. (ff.3–4 blank); 34.5 x 23 cm.—2: 15 items, of various length and size. 1: Contemp. boards.—The entire dossier in folder.

Fr. 65
(Provençal)

BORDEAUX, Confrerie de Sainte-Euladie et de Saint-Gênes. Fragment of the statutes and membership lists, as follows: Aqueste presente confrairia fut instituide et levade l'an de grace 1321, with renewal, dated 1530 (f.1r).—List of members, with addition up to the year 1581, but lacking end of letter A, all of B–F, beginning of G, end of I, L, end of M, N–O and end of P (f.1v and 6 ff.)—Au nom deu pay et du filh et deu saint esperit . . . asso son lous stablimens . . . per lous confraires et confrairesses de las confrairies establidas en la gleise Sainct Euladie de Bourdeu 1321 (4 ff., end missing). *Bordeaux, ca. 1530*.

Vellum. 11 ff. 34.5 x 26.5 cm. Historiated initial A (f.1v) and other decorated initials. In folder.

Fr. 66

JEAN MAROT. La vray-disant, advocate des dames. (This ms. is incomplete, lacking one or more ff. at the beginning. The text begins on f.2r with line 15 of the "Envoy," i.e. with "La concubine adultere excusa." The work is dedicated to Anne de Bretagne, queen of France.) *France, ca. 1506.*

Vellum. 10 ff. (first blank). It is likely that the missing part at the beginning contained an illum. dedication or a miniature, and possibly the prel. "rondeaux" printed in Clement Marot, *Oeuvres*, (The Hague, 1731), V, 283-96. 21 x 13.5 cm. Capitals and line endings illum. Modern vellum.—Prov.: "Ce livre est à moy/ Jane Gaillarde."—Prel. collation indicates variant readings of some consequence from the text publ. in 1731. On the text tradition and the few extant mss. see the preface by Lenglet Dufresnoy in the *Oeuvres* (*op. cit.*), V, 278-82; L. Theureau, . . . *Jean Marot*, (Caen, 1873), 92-103 and 185; A. Ehrlich, *Jean Marots Leben u. Werke*, (Leipzig, 1902), 18-24 and 97.—The ms. has suffered from damp, but is legible throughout with the help of an ultraviolet lamp. It must have been, at one time, a ms. "de luxe," destined for a person of distinction.

Fr. 67
[FRIEDRICH AUGUST I, Elector of Saxony (August II, King of Poland), surnamed August der Starke]. Le portrait de la cour de Pologne. (The text of this ms. of which supposedly "il n'y a que cet exemplaire au monde," is identical with ms.fr.37, Le portrait de la cour de Saxe).—*With* BREVE RAGGUAGLIO delle [24] famiglie più antiche e più nobili romane. *Saxony?, 18th cent.*

Paper. 244, 138 pp., 1 f. 19 x 15 and 19 x 13.5 cm. Contemp. h/calf.

Fr. 68
DESCRIPTION HISTORIQUE de toutes les cérémonies qui se font à Rome depuis la mort du pape jusqu'à la fin du repas que son successeur donne à tous les cardinaux pour son heureux avènement au pontificat. *France, ca. 1730.*

Paper. 84 ff. (last 2 blank). 23 x 17.5 cm. Contemp. boards.

Fr. 69
ABRÉGÉ CRONOLOGIQUE de l'histoire de la maison royale de Savoie [de Berold, premier comte de Savoie, à Victor Amédée III, roi de Sardaigne, Cypre, Jerusalem, duc de Savoie]. With corrections and cancellations in a contemp. hand. *Savoy, ca. 1773.*

Paper. Title, 2 blank, 103 ff. 19 x 12 cm. Paper.

Fr. 70
CAHIER DE CHANSONS, romances, ariettes, et autres mis en ordre par D. B. . . . pour Mademoiselle de la Barre (Brin de Jonc) l'an 1783. *France, 1783.*

Paper. 212 pp. (pp.203-5 blank, pp.206-12 "Table"). 20 x 14.5 cm. Contemp. calf.—Bookplate on title removed.

Ad. Fr. 67: Cf. note to Fr. 37.

Fr. 71

MEMOIRE sur la province de Bretagne. *France, ca. 1697.*

Paper. 126, 4 blank ff. 25 x 18.5 cm. H/morocco.—Ms. copy of a treatise compiled by Pommereu, intendant of Brittany at the request of the Duke de Beauvilliers, governor of the Duke of Burgundy, to be used in instructing his royal pupil, acc. to information supplied by dealer, without bibliogr. ref.

Fr. 72

JEAN BAYARD. Disposition of extensive property to institutions, etc., recorded before Claude de Gaudet in "St. Geoyre" (i.e. St. Geoire, cf. ms. Fr. 64), signed and witnessed at beginning, Feb. 27, 1586, and again at end, 3 [?] May 1592, the main part dated 1586. *St. Geoyre, 1586–92.*

Paper. 30 ff. (ff.29–30 blank; old foliation 241–270). 29.5 x 19 cm. Boards.

Fr. 73

PARLAMENT DE PARIS. Arrêt du Parlament de Paris relatif aux dettes [1,500,000 livres] de feue Marie Charlotte de Meusnier, femme de Guillaume Bernard de Rezay, conseiller au Parlament de Paris, represented by Louis de Moret, seigneur de Bournonville. *Paris, 1752.*

Vellum. 68 ff. 26.5 x 19.5 cm. Cloth.—G. D. Paris/ Greff./ 20.sols.; I.A.B. and one undeciphered symbol stamped on many pages.

Fr. 74

JEAN-BAPTISTE LINGAUD. Papers from, or related to, the "secrétaire-greffier de l'hotel-de-ville" of Limoges, May 1, 1777—Jan. 1, 1813 (incl. family papers, correspondence of Cérésier, Léonard-Honoré Gay-Vernon, etc.), illustrating especially the period of the French Revolution in the Department of Limousin. *Limoges and various other places, 1777–1813.*

Paper. 471 pieces of mss. (1212 pp. of text). Various sizes. 4 boxes. Detailed descr. of contents filed with collection (9 ff.mimeogr.)

Fr. 78

NICOLAS MALEBRANCHE (apocryphal). Traité de l'infini creé. *France, 18th cent.*

Paper. 86 ff. (last blank). 21 x 16 cm. Contemp. h/leather.—Prov.: Jules [?] Thierry.

Fr. 79

DE LA PHILOSOPHIE et des philosophes. *France, 18th cent.*

Paper. 245 ff. 24.5 x 18.5 cm. Figures in text. Contemp. vellum.—Prov.: Frederick North, Earl of Guilford.

Fr. 80
(Provençal)

[ARLES]. Lo registre del peage d'Arle. (Register of tolls of the city of Arles, incl. list of "li segnors de la partidate," among them the archbishop, Rainant Portellet de Senas, Raymon de Villa Nova, Imbert Dardier, etc.) *Arles, first half 15th cent.*

Vellum. 17 ff. 26 x 18.5 cm. Contemp. blind-stamped vellum.—Letters "EE" on front cover.

Fr. 81

ORAISONS [et confessions] extraict[s] de plusieurs livres bien devote[s], incl. prayers for all occasions, e.g. "pour les malades," "quand on veult voyager," an "oraison pour la paix de l'eglise" (ff.56r-60v), paraphrases of several psalms (e.g. ff.68v-75r) and 3 prayers in German (ff.93-95). *Belgium, middle 16th cent.*

Paper. 128 ff. (text beginning on f.9; ff.92–128 blank). 15.5 x 10.5 cm. Contemp. blind-stamped calf.—Prov. [entries]: Espoir comforte, Antoinne de Harnin; N'espoir ne craincte, Max. de Borsele, 1571 (f.3r); Ac lede synd croijs, contre fortune. . . . Ariere de Fosses, 1571 (f.5r); Soufrir pour parvenir, Richard de Merode, 1573 (f.6r).

Fr. 82

VAL SECRET, Abbaye de Nôtre Dame (Aisne). Terrier, or survey of property in the area of "Saussoy" (near Château-Thierry) by size, rent and name of tenant, for its owner, abbot Jehan d'Anizy. *Val Secret, 1324.*

Vellum. Originally presumably in the form of a roll, measuring ca. 107 x 25 cm., now in two pieces, used on recto and verso. In folder.

Fr. 83

ORDRE DE LA NEF (also called ORDRE DU NAVIRE, or ORDRE DES ARGONAUTES DE ST. NICOLAS). Statutes of the order, created by Charles III, King of Jerusalem, Sicily and Naples, Duke of Durazzo; prologue (f.1r) *inc.*: Cy com[m]ence le prologu [!] de l'ordre de la nef. Le pere et le fils et le saint esperit . . . ; text (f.2r) *inc.*: Cy com[m]encent les chapitres de l'ordre. . . . *Naples, 1 December 1381.*

Vellum. 21 ff. (of 24; 3 ff. at end, probably blank ⟨since 21v is also blank⟩ removed). 32.5 x 23 cm. Illum. initial "L" (ship held by angels, ca. 7 x 8 cm.) and coat of arms of Charles III. 18th-cent. vellum.—Prov.: Copy prepared for Charles III(?); Matteo Luigi Conanici (1726–1805); Walter Sneyd (purchased in 1835).

Fr. 84

LOUIS XI, King of France. Letter to the king's cousin Antoine, Sire de Craon, commander of the army in Germany, concerning the campaign against Charles le Témeraire, Duke of Burgundy. Signed "par le Roy,

Orsome," "donne a Herlande le XI⁰ jour de juillet l'an de grace mil CCCC soixante quinze." *Herland, 1475.*

Vellum. 1 f. Ca. 25.5 x 15.5 cm. Mounted on vellum strip, in folder. Signature (of Louis XI?) removed.

Fr. 85

[DE LORNAY]. Account of payments "tant pour luy [le capitaine de Lornay] que aux gens estans soubz sa charge," June–October, 1490. De Lornay was in charge of "chevaucheurs de la . . . campaignie d'Alemans et Picartz soubz le dict [de Lornay] et Jehannot des Près," supposedly in the pay of Anne de Bretagne. *France?, 1490.*

Vellum. 1 f. (text on both sides, f.viii of an account book). 37.5 x 22.5 cm. (inner margin trimmed with loss of text). In folder.

Fr. 86

ST. JEAN de Jerusalem (ordre). Anciens et nouveaux statuts . . . traduits [de l'Italien] sur l'édition de Borgeforte [i.e. Borgo Novo] de 1676. De l'ordonnance du Chapitre du Grand Prieuré de France, (213 pp.)—*With* IDEM. Ordonnances du Chapitre general tenu l'an 1631, par . . . frère Antoine de Paule, (134 pp.)—Followed by "Table" for the statutes (14 pp.) and the ordonnances, (2 pp.) *France, ca. 1700.*

Paper. Title, 213 pp., 1 blank f., 134, 14, 2 pp. 30 x 20 cm. Contemp. calf.— One f., presumably naming former owner, and bookplate removed.

Fr. 87
(Provençal)

[JOHAM (JEAN) DE VERNOILS]. Ensegon se las recognoyssenssas et fieux novels appertenens al noble Joham de Vernoils, seigneur de Peyrat et coseigneur de Pompinhan an los locs de Pompinhan et de Gresolas, preses e resobus p[er] me Peyre Racier capella e notary del loc de Canals . . . MCCCCLXVII (1467–1472), followed by additions concerning Pompignan, Grisoles, etc., to 1567, ff.44v-46r in a later hand. *Tarn et Garonne, 1467–1567.*

Paper. 2, 89 ff. (ff.10, 13, 17, 22, 35–43, 49, 52, 54, 59–66, 75, 79 blank), 2 ff. 30 x 22 cm. Notarial signets. Contemp. vellum.—Prov.: Comte Chappaz de la Prat.

Fr. 88

[CARNATIC REGION, India]. Moeurs et coutumes des gentils à la Côte Coromandel. *France?, 18th cent.*

Paper. 54 ff. (last blank). 34 x 24 cm. Boards.

Fr. 89

DOUTES et questions sue le traité de Versailles du premier may 1756 entre le roi [de France] et l'imperatrice [de l'Allemagne], reine de

Hongrie. Ce manuscrit a été presenté dans les premiers jours do mois d'août 1756 et par consequence avant l'entrée du roi de Prusse en Saxe et en Bohême. (The anonymous author argues that the treaty is detrimental to the interests of France.) *France, ca. 1756–1757.*

Paper. 34 ff. (last blank). 33 x 22 cm. Boards.

Fr. 90

JEAN BAPTISTE COLBERT CORRESPONDENCE. 34 autograph letters and 42 letters with Colbert's signature, addressed to the president of police of Paris De la Reynie, 1665, 1667, 1672, 1675, 1677, and 1678. The letters deal with a variety of subjects, e.g. trade regulations (incl. censorship), licensing, taxes, imprisonment. *Paris, etc., 1655–1678.*

Paper. Various sizes. In folder.

Jean Baptiste Colbert Correspondence.

Ad. Fr. 89: This tract, written by Jean Louis Favier, was published in London in 1778.—Line 1: sue *read* sur; may *read* mai.

[72]

Fr. 91

MATTHIEU D'ESCOUCHY. Chroniques de Charles VII (ff.1-170), followed by "Les epitaphes touchant le regne . . . du Roy Charles de France, 7ᵉ de ce nom," (ca. 700 lines of verse). *France, second half 16th cent.*

   Paper. 177 ff. 34 x 21.5 cm. Calf. Comparison with printed edition indicates considerable variants; the "epitaphes" were not included in the printed edition (ed.: DuFresne de Beaucourt, *Soc. de l'histoire de France*, 1863–64).

Fr. 92
(Provençal)°

BATIE ROLAND, Seigniory. Liber tasthiarum domini Batide Rolandi et Polafoli (Les taysthes que prent le noble Guillaume de Belmont senheur de la Bastye Roland et de Pelafol audit lieu de la Bastie, f.2r). Two later entries (1515) on f.1r. *Dauphiné, late 15th cent.*

   Paper. 12 ff. (ff.9–10 blank). 29 x 10.5 cm. Contemp. vellum.

Fr. 93°

[ALENÇON]. Collection of documents relating to Alençon and nearby territories, in seven vols. 1. Inventories of the estates or possessions of Louis Edet, avocat (1685); Pierre Demante, chapelier (1706); Nicolas Beslaut, marchand (1710); René Morel, marchand (1710); Louis de St. Denis, écuyer (1711); Gaspard Marchand, marchand étamier (1715); Isaac Enjubault, procureur (1712); Jean Guernon, guarde (1712); Louis du Hamel, prêtre (1715); Jacques Pavard, chandellier (1715); Jacques Prodhomme, marchand (1716); Paul François Hebert, marchand (1718); inventaire des prisonniers criminels et civils (1724); Nicolas Cherbonnier, greffier (1725); Isaye Boullay, marchand (1724); Thomas Renier, drapier (1726).—2. Inventories . . . of René Bidon, drapier (1738); Françoise Langlois, veuve de Thomas Yvon, drapier (1730); François de Montigny, president-trésorier (1730); Nicolas Poullais, conseiller du roi (1731); Marie Anthoinette de Marseille, veuve de René Marais, trésorier (1732); Julien Clouet, avocat (1732).—3. Inventories . . . of Elisabeth Thérèse Perrin, veuve de Pierre Gabriel de Vilbois, écuyer (1742); Michel Auger, aubergiste (1745); Jean Pierre Leguay, vitrier (1745); Louis François Caillet, prêtre (1746); François Chesnel, menulsier (1746); François de Boiville, sieur de la Laudelle (1747); Jean Vautoullon, lieutenant hollandais, prisonnier de guerre (1747); François Thirault, marchand de toiles (1747); Vincent Lebrec, cordager (1747); Grégoire Charles de Bougis, écuyer (1747); Louise Marie Thérèse Vandarmeulin (1747); Pierre Roussel, serrurier (1747); François Lesureul, avocat (1748); Alexis Rozé, laboureur (1748); François Jolly, journalier (1748); Joseph Lesage, conseiller et avocat (1748); René Alleaume, laboureur (1748); Nicolas Chevrel, au bureau des finances (1754).—4. Miscellaneous documents: (a) relating to the family Basire (1657–1720)—(b) legal, e.g. contre Charles Verrier; biens des religionnaires fugitifs; wills; rents; guardianships; trials (1685–1776) —(c) commercial, i.e. sales of property, incl. printing establishment (1694–1789)—(d) marriage contracts (1695–1726) and (e) contract "relatif à la guérison d'un cancer" (1649), together 37 items.—5. Miscellaneous documents: (a) trial Agon-Gobillet (1786)—(b) docs. concerning properties at Agon; Coutainville; Blainville; Neuilly-le-Bisson; Beauvain; Alençon proper; etc. (1601–1803)—(c) group relating to "métiers" (1700–1732)—(d) financial, incl. "taxe pour la nourriture des pauvres" (1662–1723)—(e) marriage contracts (17th cent.–1743), etc., together 52 documents.—6. Mainly historical documents, incl. letters of Henri d'Orléans (1658) and the Duke de Longueville, relating to treaty with England (1656); arrêt du Parlement de Rouen (1756); docs. relating to the seigneuries (fiefs) of Coutainville; Fontaine-Ettouppefour; Fontenay; Fresneau; Lonray; Montreuil; Ravigny; Houssemain (1641–1786); dépenses relatives au passage des gens de guerre, 10157 livres (1653); fief des curés, paroisse de la Mesnière (1624); several docs. relating to the French Revolution in the dept. Orne; nomination of Jehan de Beaumont "à l'office de bailli de Montigny" (1615); inventories of estates (1646–1719); marriage contract (François de Matignon, 1631), etc., together 42 documents of which one is printed.—7. Papers relating to the seignory of Montmartin-en-Oranges, incl. copies of land titles from 1359 on. *Alençon, etc., 1601–1803.*

Paper (and vellum in v. 4–5). 7 v. Various sizes. 19th cent. vellum.

Fr. 94°

POETRY MISCELLANY. 12 sheets of poetry (incl. Sur la prise du Maréchal de Villeroy, Le Berger et les chiens, Description de la ville de Madrid, Le pape presentant aux puissances le general des . . . <fringed, word missing>, Vers sur les Jesuites, Chanson faite aux Jesuites, Chanson de Monsieur Baffry) by different writers, and 1 printed "Epigramme contre M. l'Avocat xxx," *inc.:* Quoi, vous me reprochez un trait qui fait honneur . . . *France, 18th cent.*

Paper. 13 items. Various sizes. In folder.

Fr. 95°

ABARIS, SUISSE, du lac de Constance [cf. f.33r, i.e. JAKOB HERMANN OBEREIT?, cf. *Deutscher Gesamtkatalog:* Abaris Gamaliel. Name F. Armand and "du lac de Constance" crossed out]. La balance cosmopolitique du ciel de l'humanité à la Newton; un supplément social de Rousseau par Abaris et Diogène. (In form of dialogue, with corrections and emendations throughout. Political-philosophical discussion, probably written during the early years of the French Revolution, with reference on f.29 to "Philadelphie de la Pensylvanie, la source de la liberté sobrement republicaine . . . libre à la Franklin"). *Switzerland?, late 18th cent.*

Paper. 34 ff., last blank (f.28v–29r blank). 21.5 x 18 cm. In portfolio. This ms. and ms. Lat. 192 are apparently in the same hand. Berthold Zehme, *Jakob Hermann Obereit* (Lindau, 1920) does not mention this title, and none in French.

Fr. 97°

[FLANDERS]. Comptes Adrien de le Borve comme receveur de Vianne [i.e. Viane, prov. of Flanders] et de Mourbeque [i.e. Morbecque] pour ung an finissant a la Saint Remy l'an mil iiii^c iiii^{xx} et [quattre-] chincq. Pour la court. *Flanders, 1484–85.*

Paper. 22 ff. 29.5 x 22 cm. Ledger notation "VI" in contemp. hand and "n°. 31" in later hand on f.1r. In folder.

Fr. 98°

PROVENCE, Parlement. Collection of 29 items, largely relating to, or emanating from, the Parlement de Provence, partly manuscript, partly printed. The more substantial manuscripts in the volume are: 1. NICOLAS DE NEUFVILLE, seigneur de Villeroy. Premier memoire de M. de Villeroy, pp.1–96. (Copy of memoirs written in 1596).— 2. IDEM. Apologie et discours de Monsieur de Villeroy pour monstrer la peine qu'il a prinse [!] de faire la paix entre le Roy et Monsieur de Mayenne. . . . A Monsieur de Bellieure, pp.99–256. (Copy. Preceding nos.1–2 is a handwritten note, supposedly by Gabriel Peignot, indicating that these items had been printed in A. Petitot, ed., *Collection complète des mémoires relatifs à l'histoire de France*, [ser. I], v. 44. Prel. examination indicates some differences, esp. in no.2.—The same note states "à la suite sont encore plusieurs pièces de Villeroi qui vont jusque à la page 510." Several of the subsequent pieces are of a later date and cannot possibly be attributed to Villeroy).—3. RELATION des affaires de Provence, pp.327–53, ca. 1652–59 (with corrections in a contemp. hand).—4. PIERRE DORTIGUES [?]. Proceedings against the participants in the revolt of Marseilles, notarized and signed, dated April 15, 1659, pp.377–434.—5. DIVERSES MEMOIRES depuis l'année 1631 [jusqu'à 1660], pp.449–501.—6. GASTON, DUC D'ORLÉANS. Memoires de Monsieur . . . contenant ce qui s'est passé de plus considerable en France depuis l'an mil six cent huit jusqu'à l'année 1636, pp.515–674. (With note by G. Peignot [?], with reference to printed editions [cf. also A. Petitot, *op. cit.*, ser. II, v. 22] and the notation: "C'est sans doute ce manuscrit-ci, qui a servi à l'impression de 1684 . . . car la permission du censeur Coudin [*vero* Cousin] est à la fin du manuscrit sous cette date de 1684 . . .").—7. JEAN DE POITIERS. Procès verbal de Monsieur de Sainct Vallier, pp.693–755. (This "procès" seems identical with the trial of 1523, though dated here, erroneously it seems, 1543. Cf. Georges Guiffrey, Procès criminel de Jehan de Poytiers, seigneur de Saint-Vallier, <Paris, 1867>). *France, 16th (?)–17th cent.*

Paper. 756 pp. (last blank). Various sizes, bound in vol. 35.5 x 26 cm. Figurated initials in no. 7. 17th-cent. calf.—Prov.: Gabriel Peignot?

Fr. 99°

TRAITÉ DES DROITS du domaine du roy, et leur origine, comme aussy le prejudice que sa majesté [Louis XV] se fait en surchargeant ses sujets avec des impots. *France, ca. 1755 (cf. p.15, "l'année dernière 1754").*

Paper. 2 ff., 196 pp., 1 f. 23.5 x 16.5 cm. Cloth. A. A. Barbier, *Dict. des ouvrages anonymes*, v.IV (Paris, 1879), lists a number of similar titles under "Traité des droit" and "Traité du droit" (e.g. one attributed to D. Simonel), but not this title.—Same text as Fr. 51.

Fr. 100°

VERZAMELING van Latynsche, Fransche en Nederduytsche Keur-Dichten (title of vol. I) or RECUEIL DE POÉSIES sérieuses, badines et satiriques contenant des élégies, stances, ballades, sonnets, satires, épithalames, madrigaux, virelais, etc. (French title of vol. II). Compiled primarily in two different hands, it also contains a number of pieces in prose. The collection covers the years of Louis XIV's great wars; contemporary events are dealt with in many of the pieces. *Selected contents:* (Vol. I) Comédie faite à l'occasion de plusieurs membres de l'Académie qui vouloient reformer la langue françoise. Aux autheurs de l'Académie qui se meslent de reformer la langue, excepté Gomberville, ff.1–16 (in form of a play).—Pièces curieuses, ff.18–116, incl. Épitaphe de M. [Jean de?] La Fontaine (f.22r); Quadrain by Pierre Corneille (f.27v); La travestie Janneton à sa compagne (f.30r–31r); Épistre au subject du commerce des taxes et autres affaires du temps (f.31v–33v); Sonnet assigned to Constantin Huygens by earlier owner (f.34v); Pourtrait de Mons. [Jean-Baptiste] Colbert (f.35v); Sonnet, Arreste toy. Que veux tu faire, signed Le Clercq [i.e. Michel Le Clerc?] (f.37r); Lettre de Mons. [Isaac de] Benserade . . . à Mons. le Chevalier de Lorraine sur . . . Mlle. de Tienne . . . 1666 (ff.43r–44r); various pieces on the rounding-up of Paris prostitutes (ff.46r–v, 48r–49v); Dialogue d'Acante et de Pegaze, signed [Paul] Pelisson[-Fontaine] (f.51r); poems in Dutch signed [Geeraert?] Brant, [Joannes or Bernard] Vollenhove and J.V.V. (f.53r–v); various poems on the death of Giulio Mazarin (ff.54r–61v); Voorzegging, signed Renselaer (f.64r); Sermon de l'amour humain (ff.66r–69v); Epigramma, signed Corneille (f.70r); Élégie, signed Benserade (ff.71v–72v); Stances au Roy, signed Corneille (f.74r); poems on Colbert (f.71v and 83r); La France à l'Angleterre, and L'Angleterre à la France (f.88r); Stances pour Mlle. Pradel, signed [Jacques de?] Ranchin (ff.90v–92v); Sur la jonction des deux mers, signed Corneille (f.94v); Karel Gustaef, Coning van Zweden (ff.99r–103r); Sur l'embrasement de Londres, 1666, signed Benserade (f.107r); [Adrien Thomas Perdou] De Sublingny "Nobilissimo . . . viro Do. Constantino Hugenio" [C. Huygens] (ff.107r–108v); Épitaphe and other poems on Jean-Baptiste Molière (ff.111v–113v, 114v); Sur le secret des desseins du Roy, signed Pelisson 1673 (ff.113v–114r).—Epigrams on Louis de Bourbon, Prince de Condé, Henri de la Tour d'Auvergne, Vicomte de Turenne, Pieter de Groot, Pietro Aretino, Armand Jean du Plessis, Cardinal Richelieu, and other poems, ff.116v–126v.— Catalogus librorum atque tractatuum proxime prodituorum (imaginary book list), f.130r–v.—Poems on Charles II, king of England, ff.136v–137v.— Voor Renatus Descartes, ff.148r–149r.—L'apothéose de Louis le Grand, roy de France, ff.151v–152v.—Recueil des pièces curieuses (cont.), ff.169r–178v., incl. poem signed Pelisson, (f.169r).—Harangue de Mons. de Bosc au Duc de Montausier . . . à son entrée dans la ville de Caen . . . 1663, ff.186r–187v.—Harangue [etc.] de Mons. de Groot, ff.187v–189v.—Harangue faite au Roy . . . 1668 par le S. du Bosc, 190r–193r. —Proposition touchant l'union de deux religions en France, ff.194v–196r.—Lettre de Mons. Bouchet à Mons. le Mareschal de Crequi [and several similar letters], ff.196v–198v.—Compliment prononcé dans l'Académie françoise à la reception de Mons. [Philippe] Quinault [and other items concerning the Academy], ff.208v–212v.—Lettre de Mons. Pelisson au Roy, f.213r.—Réflexions . . . si l'Espagne doit déclarer la guerre, ff.217r–226r.—Déclaration du Roy d'Angleterre contre les papistes, ff.229r–230r.—Harangue faite au Roy . . . par messrs. les ambassadeurs des Provinces Unies . . . 1679, ff.245v–246v.—(Vol. II) Extrait des registres de la cour souveraine de Parnasse ("collationné Bonsens"), ff.7r–10r.—Plainte des statues du Palais Mazarin au Roy, ff.15r–18r.—Les ombres des müets à la sage Amalthée, ff.27r–29v.— Satire, dialogue [entre] Minos, Pluton, Diogène, Horace, La Pucelle, etc., (name Mr. de Courax on verso of f.58), ff.39r–57v.—Satire contre la science à M. le Marquis d'Hervault, ff.59r–67r.—Épitaphe de Madame par Mr. de Benserade, ff.77r–v.—Aux chevaliers vainqueurs du Rhin, ff.102r–122r.—Mademoiselle de la Vigne à l'ombre de Mr. Descartes, ff.124r–126r.—Amaranthe, ff.128r–133v.—Questions and "Résponses," ff.134r–177v.—La feste d'Erbaud, 1668, ff.203r–221r.— Requeste à nos seigneurs de la cour souveraine de Parnasse (Pierre Gassendi, René Descartes, Jacques Rohault, etc. and Aristotle), ff.241r–246r.—Jouissance imitée d'Ovide, f.269r–v.—Various "lettres," partly in verse and partly in prose, ff.281r–325v.—Songe de Madame de la Baume, ff.330r–337r.—De la nature, des effets et de l'excellence de l'amour, ff.348r–362r. *Low Countries, 1666–1700.*

Paper. 2 vols. (2, 248+ 2; 362 ff., a few ff. blank). 21.5 x 16, 22.5 x 17 cm. Contemp. h/vellum.

Fr. 101°

RECUEIL DE POÉSIE sur le Cardinal Duc de Richelieu et autres personnes de condition. (Polemic against Richelieu mostly in French, some parts in Lat.) *France, ca. 1650.*

Paper. 80 ff. (ff 2, 79-80 blank). 19.5 x 15 cm. Contemp. vellum.

Fr. 102°

ABRÉGÉ de ce qui est traité ce cessione du Sainct Concile de Trente, touchant la refformation [!] des moeurs des Chrestiens. Ou est representé le devoir et privilèges d'un chacun selon sa condition. (With dedication to Cardinal de Plaisance, apostolic legate, i.e. Filippo Sega). Preface signed J. S. M. D. C. *France, late 16th cent.*

Paper. 98 ff. (ff.1, 106-8 blank; numbered 309-406 in a contemp. hand). 17 x 11 cm. Contemp. gilt French morocco, with the arms of Filippo Sega.—Ex libris G. J. Arvanitidi. Bound with printed vol. (ff.1-308) on Council of Trent and classified IC55.T7238.Eh564h.1584.

Fr. 103°

NICOLAS DE GROUCHES, Marquis de CHÉPY. Journal au Marquis de Chépy [Dec. 12] 1740 et [Dec. 29] 1741. Unsigned reports, usually 2 ff. in length, on events in Paris, Versailles, etc., and on political affairs throughout Europe (e.g. the first Silesian war), some with the names of the addressees, the Marquis and Marquise de Chépy. *France, etc., 1740-41.*

Paper. 342 ff. 22 x 17 cm. Contemp. armorial vellum (de Chépy).

Ger. 1

ROBERT FLUDD (De Fluctibus). Ars Geomantica. Tractatus de geomantia in quatuor libros divisa [sic], ff.1-92r (beginning on f.64v the text is in Latin).—TRACTATUS DE NATIVITATE (in German) arranged by months, ff.92v-98. *Germany, second half of 17th cent.*

Paper. 98 ff., folded table. 21 x 16 cm. Contemp. vellum.—J. G. T. Graesse, *Trésor des livres rares* (Dresden, 1861), II 607 lists a *De geomantia* "attribué à Fludd", Verona (i.e. Heidelberg?), 1687, published according to the B. M. Cat. in the *Fasciculus geomanticus*. No comparison of the text of the ms. with the printed text has been attempted.

Ger. 2

ACCOUNTBOOK of unidentified merchant listing income from yearly [payments of] shillings by "Meister" and "Knechte" for the years 1642-1661, as well as expenditures. It is not clear whether this is the account book of a locality, guild or an entrepreneur. *Germany, 1642-1661.*

Paper. 46 ff. (many blank). 36.5 x 10.5 cm. Boards.

Ger. 3

[SUMMA DE VIRTUTIBUS ET VITIIS]. Von allen Rechten der Menschen, und ob dieses oder jenes, Sünde seÿ, oder nicht, *inc.:* Es sprichet ein vil wyʒer man das man die sünde fliehen sol. . . . —*With* RABBI SAMUEL. Epistola contra Judaeorum errores, transl. into Latin by Alphonsus Boni Homines, and into German by unknown person [not Alphonsus von Hispanien as stated in 16th-cent. suprascription]; begins sig.58r. *Germany, 1433.*

Paper. 226 ff.(first blank and f.30 missing; last f.blank), numbered incorrectly. 30 x 21 cm. Contemp. pigskin over wooden boards.

Ger. 4

[KATHERINENLEGENDE], ff.1–22r(958 verses), *inc.:* Eyn keyser hies Maxenciuz/der geboit vnz alsus.—2. VAN DEM SCHOLER VAN PARISZ, ff.22r–24r(108 verses), *inc.:* Wyllet ir horen wasz geschach/van eyme werden studenten eyn sache. (Cf. R. C. Clark, "Two Medieval Scholars," *The German Quarterly*, XXXII[1959], 133–142).—3.[LOB DER HL. KATHERINA], f.24v (55 verses), *inc.:* O Katharina, hochgeborn frucht/Synt dyn junffrauliche zucht.— 4.[LEGENDE DES HL. ALEXIUS], ff.25r–30r(276 verses), *inc.:* Ich wil uch ein gedichte geben/van dem heilligen Lexius leben. (Not identical with any of the versions printed or described in H. F. Massmann, *Sanct Alexius Leben*, [Quedlinburg, 1843]).—5. [ARISTOTELES UND PHYLLIS], ff.30v–47r(854 lines), *inc.:* Horent ir lude uber alle/Wasz dit spiel beduden sal.—6. [DIE KOENIGIN VON FRANKREICH und der ungetreue Marschall], ff.48r–61v(678 verses), *inc.:* Dye schriefft bedudet wasz geschach/Dasz man jn hoen eren siczen sach.—7. MARIANIC SEQUENCE, ff.62r–67r(268 verses), *inc.:* Ave, praeclara maris stella/Got gruse dich, luter sterne glantz.— 8. [DES MOENCHS NOT], f.67v(25 verses), *inc.:* Ir herschaff, nu herent alle/Wie uch diesze mere gefalle.—9. [HYMNE AUF MARIA], ff.68r–69v(86 verses), *inc.:* O Maria, heubt frauwe der cristenheit/Du bist desz sunders hoiste suyssickeit.—10. [VORBEREITUNG AUF DIE BEICHTE], ff.70–79 (in prose), *inc.:* Gelobet vnd geert sie der name vnsres herren. *Lower Rhine (Cologne?), early 15th cent.*

Paper. 79 ff. 21 x 14 cm. Modern full calf.

Ger. 5

ILLUMINEIRR BUCH kunstlich alle Farben zu machen und bereidenn allen Brieffmalern sampt andern solcher kunsten liebhabern nützlich unnd gutt zu wissen. Und wirt getteillt in sieben Bücher. . . . Lutzemburg [partly obliterated], anno domini 1570. *Germany, 1570–1574.*

Paper. 108 ff. (ff.4, 40-41, 49-50 and 73 missing). 20 x 16 cm. Contemp. vellum. Collection of recipes, some in Latin, but mostly in German, for the making and tempering of colors, the coloring of metals, leather and other materials.

Ger. 6

1. SEIFRIT. Alexander, ff.2–160v, written in the year 1400[?], by Hans Schwent.—2. ALBRECHT VON EYB. Grisardis, ff.178r–231v. —3. Pope PIUS II (Aeneas Sylvius). Euriolus and Lucretia, in the transl. of Nicolas von Wyle, ff.233r–288v. *Austria or Southern Germany, 1400(?)—middle of the 15th cent.*

Paper. 8 black ff., ff.1-288; ff.289-357 blank. 20.5 x 15 cm. Early 16th-cent. blind-stamped calf over wooden boards.—Prov.: Widen College Library; Leopold Gruber.—1. Paul Gereke based his publication of the text on cod.2325 in Strasbourg, dated 1566 (cf. *Seifrits Alexander, Deutsche Texte des Mittelalters* [Berlin 1932], v.36). Only one ms. known to Gereke is earlier than this codex, and that is a fragment.—2. One of three mss. known.—3. This text appears to be in the same hand as no.2.

Ger. 7

PASQUILLUS in aulicos colonienses, *inc.:* Der wolgeborne graff Herman zu wiedt/Hat regiert dass stiefft 32 jahr zu guttem friedt . . . *Cologne(?), 1563.*

Paper. 4 ff. 33 x 22 cm. Boards.

Ger. 8

1. EIN GEDICHT von einer stoltzen hofertigen undt prechtigen Jungkfrauenn, *inc.:* Nun hört zu ihr liebenn christen.—2. NEUE ZEITUNG, vndt ein Neues Liedt von dem abgestandenenn, vndt vbellerwölteon Bischoff von Cöllnn. Im Thon, O du armer Judas.—3. DER BISCHOFF ZUE CÖLLEN den Maleuolis vnd bellenden Hundtenn herwieder. *Cologne(?), 16th cent.*

Paper. 4 ff. 32 x 22 cm. Boards.

Ger. 9

EINN SCHÖNN NEU LIEDT vonn dem abgefallnenn unnd ubell erweldenn Bischoff vön Collnn, im Thonn wie mann denn armenn Judas singt. [Same text in ms. Ger. 8[2]]. *Cologne(?), 16th cent. (1583?).*

Paper. 1 leaf. 32 x 21 cm. Boards.—Margin of f.1v: de Archiepiscopo Gebhardo coloniensi c.83.

Ger. 10

TEUTONIC KNIGHTS (Ordo S. Mariae theutonicorum). Regel der Brüder des deutschen Hauses Sant Marie.—Gesetz der Brüder.—Alia Statuta (in German).—[Papal confirmations and benedictions]. *Germany, 15th cent.*

Paper. 22 ff. 27.5 x 20 cm. H/vellum.

Ger. 11

[BANKING] Account book of a money lender, giving entries for the years 1515–1527, (misbound, out of chronological order). (*Rheinhesse?*), *1515–1527.*

Paper. 201 ff. (wrongly numbered 210). 16 x 22.5 cm. 19th-cent. cloth.

Ger. 12

[NÜRNBERG] Juramentbuech, darinnen aller Beambten alsz Burgermäister, Ratsherinn, Stattschreiber, Newen Burger vnd anderer Aide, den sie in Antrettung ihrer Dienst vnd Pflichten publice laisten müessen zu finden. Er begreüfft auch der Officirer als Statt-Cammerer, Bawmäister, Brodtschauer Verrichtung. Gebessert vnd verneüert Anno Christi 1597 denn 11 Avrilis.—Preceding and following the "Juramentbuech" (numbered pp.1–87) are a great variety of "Missiv Brieff" from the latter part of the 16th and earlier part of the 17th cent. *Nürnberg, 1597–1623.*

Paper. 8, 16 ff., 424 pp. (incorrectly numbered in several instances, some pp. missing), in several different hands. 19.5 x 15.5 cm. Contemp. vellum.

Ger. 13

[NÜRNBERG] Hochzeitsordnung vom Jahr 1509. *Nürnberg, 1511–1515.*

Vellum. 20 ff., in a calligraphic hand. 22.5 x 17 cm. Contemp. stamped calf over wooden boards, rebacked.

Ger. 14

PETER SCHMIEHER. Fragment of four folios, containing three poems of which the second can definitely be assigned to Schmieher: 1. Poem (incomplete at beginning?), *inc.:* Der jung sprach ich muss in sehen/ wie mir darvmb mug geschen/. . . .—2. Die Klag vom Wolf am Hage (complete shorter version; cf. C. Wendeler, Studien über Hans Rosenplüt, *Archiv für die Geschichte deutscher Sprache,* I[1874], 97–133, 385–436, esp. 388–408).—3. Poem (incomplete at end?),

inc.: Ich waisz kain besser lust/ wann esen trinken vnd minen/. . . .
Germany, 15th cent.

Paper. 4 ff. (numbered ff.CLXX-CLXXIV by the scribe). 28.5 x 20 cm. Boards.—Prov.: Georg Kloss; Sir Thomas Phillipps (no.11049).

Ger. 16

KESTENHOLTZ (near Strasbourg). "Copialbuch", containing regulations ("Ordnungen"), agreements, taxes on wine, record of elections, etc., dated 1478–1767, the last two leaves used to record taxes on white wines, 1789–1832, in French. *Kestenholtz, 16th-early 19th cent.*

Paper. 154 ff. 31 x 20 cm. 16th-cent. h/pigskin over wooden boards.

Ger. 17

FERDINAND I of Bohemia. Edict of Aug. 1, 1528, against reformers, in 23 chapters. Paragraphus primus (f.2r) begins: Jestlich wellenn wir das nhü hinfurt keiner wider das hochwirdige Sacrament . . . predige. *Expl.*: Finitum est principis mandatum per me fratrem Paulum Göbel lectorem et predicatorem Schwidniczensem anno salutifero incarnationis 2 viii supra M^m et D^m in vigilia nativitatis domini. *Prague(?), 1528.*

Paper. 6 ff. (last f. blank). 21 x 15.5 cm. 19th-cent. boards.

Ger. 18

STAUFFENBURG. Ambts-Stauffenburgisches Geld-, Korn- und Dienst-Register, auch Zehnt-Beschreibung von Trinitatis Anno 1744 bis Trinitatis Anno 1745. *Stauffenburg (Brunswick), 1744–1745.*

Paper. 2 ff., 202 pp., 3 blank ff., 72 pp., 2 blank ff., 19 pp., 1 blank f., 9 pp. 33 x 20 cm. Contemp. vellum.—The name Conrad Viet Reinecke is inscribed on the various title pages.

Ger. 19

VENETIAN WAR, 1515–1519. Welscher Krieg etwas zamengeclaupter neu Zeytt, ff.1–116.—*With* PROPHICEY vor vil Jaren gemacht und awf das 1400 Jar eingeend, ff.120–125.—Des grossen und auch streitparn Sophia [of Persia] Anfanng und Herkomen, ff.129–137. *Southern Germany, after 1519.*

Paper. 137 ff. 20 x 14 cm. Vellum.—[Library of Count Dietrichstein].

Ger. 22

HEINRICH BULLINGER. [Reformationsgeschichte, Teil 2, covering the years 1529–1532], pp.1–793 (numbered [in sections] 1–255; cf. edition by J. J. Hottinger and H. H. Vögeli, [Frauenfeld, 1838–40], 3 v.).—*WITH* appendices: A. Meister Heinrichen Bullingers Testament . . . 1579 [date of copy?; dated at end 1575], pp.795–817 (810–17 blank; cf. the somewhat different text printed in Carl Pestalozzi, *Heinrich Bullinger* [Elberfeld, 1858], pp.618–22).—B. Abgrist [?] des Jamers vnnd niderlag vnnd verlurst [sic] der Cristenn Bij Best vnnd Offenn Im. 1541. Jar, pp.819–26.—C. Abschrift eines Mandats der drizähenn Orten gemeiner Eijdtgnoschafft . . . der Relligion halben . . . 1529, pp.827–30.—D. . . . Warhaffter grundtlicher fürtrag vnd verantwortung . . . Etlicher Beschwärlicher Händlen halb . . . [issued by the mayor of Zürich, 1529], pp.831–41.—E. [Zürich] Anntwurten . . . über ertilich [?] Artigkel . . . 1524, pp.842–63.—F. Ein Sänd Brieff an ein fromme Eijdtgnoschafft Beträffende die kätzerische Disputation Franntz Kolbium . . . vnd Berchtolden Hallers . . . 1528, pp.864–67 (cf. J. Metzler, *Corpus Catholicorum*, 16 (1930), no.64).—G. Ulrichenn Zwingli [addressee, letter by Johann Eck, Dec.15, 1527], pp.867–68 (cf. *ibid.*).—H. [Letter from Johann Eck to Conrad Somen, Dec.31, 1527], printed in the same year, pp.868–69 (cf. *ibid.*, no. 61[1]).—I. Ein schanntlicher Schmach Brief Doctor Eggen . . . wider ein statt Zürich . . . Jan.17, 1532, pp.869–74.—J. Ein kurtzer begriff von der Schlacht zu Meijland . . . 1515, pp.874–79.— K. [Jörg Vögeli] Kurtze aber warhafftte Beschrijbung wie . . . das kriegsuolk K. Caroli des fünfften uff den 6. tag Augusti Im. 1548. Jar die Statt Costanntz überzogen, pp.878–915, (ed. from later ms. by C. Schultheiss, 1846).—L. Was für ernnstliche vnnd Erschrogkennlichee Exemppell . . . innerrthalb sechs iarenn an ettlichenn bsunderbaren perszonen zu Costanntz . . . erzeigt vnd bewesen hatt . . . [in form of letters, 1548], pp.915–25.—M. Ein Christennliche Supplication von den vertribnenn Rotwijleren . . . 1529, pp.925–36.—N. Harnach volgend [Namen der] Burger . . . von Rottwijl . . . vertriben, pp.937–38. *Switzerland, ca. 1579*, written in several hands.

Paper. 938 pp. 30 x 21 cm. H/calf.

Ger. 23*

RATISBON, Schottenabtei St. Jacob. Inventory of the possessions of Abbot Balthasar Dason (?) upon his death, witnessed by the "Stadtschreiber" Johann Epping (?). *Ratisbon, 1566.*

Paper. 23 ff. 31 x 21.5 cm. Unbound.

Ger. 24

GUILD REGULATIONS. Handwergs Büchlein; guild regulation for coppersmiths. *Triptis, 1558.*

Paper. 7 ff. 29.5 x 20 cm. Unbound.

Ger. 25

GUILD REGULATIONS. Des Handberges Büchlein; guild regulation for coppersmiths. *Neustadt a. d. Orla, 1534.*

Paper. 10 ff. 32.5 x 20.5 cm. Unbound.

Ger. 26

MAXIMILIAN II, emperor of Germany, 1527–1576. Form letter, signed. *Prague, March 30, 1570.*

Paper. 2 pp. 31.5 x 21.5 cm. Space for name of addressee left blank. Requests hospitality for his emissary and his entourage, travelling in connection with proceedings against the imperial city Speyer.

Ger. 27

MAXIMILIAN II, emperor of Germany, 1527–1576. Letter, signed. *Vienna, May 8, 1576.*

Paper. 2 pp. 32.5 x 30 cm. With imperial seal. Without name of addressee, but to a relative of Peter Kaiser, approving legal action, but prohibiting action outside the courts.

Ger. 28

GEORG SPALATIN. [Neue Zeitung], June 25 [1524?]. Reports from Venice on concentration of French troops for an attack on Genoa, Florence, etc., also from "Andorff"[same as?, Antwerp, cf. dealer's catalogue] news about plans for a marriage between Charles V and the daughter of Henry VIII. *Würtemberg(?), ca. 1524.*

Paper. 1 f. 32.5 x 21 cm. In folder.

Ger. 29

GEORG SPALATIN. [Neue Zeitung] 1533: 1. Die Erforschung des Glaubens zu Leipzig.—2. Landstand gegen Dresden.—3. Haubitz von Tautha['s] Urteil.—4. Türkischer Friede.—5. Charles V's arrival in Barcelona from Genoa.—6. Dass der König von England ein ander Weib geehelicht. *Saxony(?), 1533.*

Paper. 1 f. 32 x 21 cm. In folder.

Ger. 30

GEORG SPALATIN. Report on visitation, to Heinrich von Einsiedel. *Altenburg(?), Feb. 4, 1544.*

Paper. 1 f. 32.5 x 22 cm. In folder.

Ger. 31

MEISTERBUCH, 1558–1745, of unnamed trade or town. *Southern Germany, 1558–1745.*

Paper. 43 ff. 21 x 17 cm. In folder.

Ger. 32

GERMAN POETRY COLLECTION, with some prose and one text in French interspersed. Among the authors are Gottfried August Bürger, Gottlieb Konrad Pfeffel, Kristian Benjamin Schubert, Gotthold Stäudlin, and Christoph Martin Wieland. *Germany, late 18th cent.*

Paper. 52 ff. and blank ff. 21 x 13.5 cm. Contemp. paper cover, bound in modern vellum.—Prov.: Dr. R. von Viettinghoff.

Ger. 33

BERTRAM REINARTZ. Franckfurter Blumgarten, oder geistliches Gedenckzeichenn, darin underschiedliche Lieb- und tugentriechende Bluhmen seind gepflantzet. Dedicated by the author, "Pfarrer zu Burggrefenrod" to the officials of the city of Frankfurt. Collection of 70 poems. *Burggräfenrode, 1695.* (or possibly slightly earlier).

Paper. 16 ff. (first and last two ff. blank). 15.5 x 9 cm. Pen-and-ink drawings of flowers. Contemp. paper covers.

Ger. 34

[BAVARIA]. Lanndtafel dess Fürstenthumbs Obern und Nidern Bairn. *Bavaria, 1557.*

Paper. 398 pp. 20 x 15.5 cm. Contemp. vellum (sheet from earlier Missal).— Prov.: Jo. Otho(?) à Taufkirchen, 1610; Föring, 1832.

Ger. 35

BAVARIA. Beschreibung dess Lanndtags der auff Absterben . . . des . . . Herrn Hertzog Albrechts in Bayrn . . . von . . . Herrn Hertzog Wilhelmen . . . auf den dritten Tag Decembris geen Minchen ausgeschriben. Was auch daselbs . . . gehandlet und beschlossen worden ist. *Munich, 1579.*

Paper. 178 ff. (first and last blank). 31 x 20 cm. Contemp. blind-stamped pigskin.

Ger. 36

IMMANUEL KANT. Collegium physico geographicum a . . . professore ordinario domino Kant secundum dictata sua pertratum studio vero persecutum ab Joanne Siegismundo Kaehler. Regiomonti per semestre aestinum 1775. (Bound with printed announcement and description of Kant's lecture *Von den verschiedenen Racen der Menschen*, [Königsberg, n.d., but 1775]). *Königsberg, 1775.*

Paper. 530 pp. (preceded by 12 printed pp.) 19.5 x 17 cm. Contemp. h/calf. Ex libris Wilhelm Voss.—These lectures appeared in printed form as pp.125-164 in his *Der Philosoph für die Welt*, (Leipzig, 1777) and again twice in 1783 (cf. A. Warda, *Die Druckschriften Immanuel Kants*, [Wiesbaden, 1919], nos.52-54; the announcement is listed *ibid.*, no.51).

Ger. 37

NICOLAUS AMSDORFF. Ein Gedicht darinn angezaigt wirt wie frum Hertzog Hainrich zu Braunschweig vnnd wie böss die Luterischen sein. (Satire against Duke Heinrich IX, the Younger). *Germany, 1541.*

Paper. 10 ff. (f.1-2 and 10 blank; a1 and b6 pasted into binding). 19 x 14 cm. Boards.—"Abgeschrijben am 25. Tag Augusti anno. . . 1541," (copied from the printed ed. 1541, Goedeke II, 298, no.144). Last f. of text contains 4-line characterization of Duke Heinrich and 4-line "Contrarium" by **Amsdorff.**

Ger. 38

BLARER, JACOB CHRISTIAN. Kurtze Verzeichnus was auf den drittenn Tag Heuwmonats Anno [15]82 zwyschen Herrenn Jacob Christoffel Blaarer Bischoff zu Brundrath unnderthonen der Herrschaft zu Pfeffingen durch die Gesandten der siben Catholischen Orthen der Eydgnossschaft . . . von wegen Religions Sachen fürgenomen unnd verhandlet worden. *Switzerland, 1582.*

Paper. 15 (instead of 16) ff. (last blank). 30.5 x 19.5 cm. Boards.—Prov.: Archiv Schöppi.

Ger. 39

COPIA SCHEDULA, so Henrich Moriz . . . beneben Johann Cyriaxen . . . 1596 . . . bey dem Drückhaus zum Schwan alhie zu Buding . . . gefunden. Und ist das Original in Obmann Heinrichs Cantzley. Poem of 18 lines, *inc.:* Junckher Schadenfro alhie der Schulteis/Für ein Dieb gehalten wurd, wie man weis/. . . . *Germany, 1596.*

Paper. 1 f. 21.5 x 17 cm. Paper cover.

Ger. 40

ARNDT (Professor). Vorlesungen über die Statistik des Churfürstenthums Sachsen und dessen inkorporirten Ländern. Lecture notes, without indication of university, year, or name of student [name cut out at end of vol.2]. *Germany, ca. 1800.*

Paper. 2 vols. 20 x 16.5 cm. Contemp. boards.

Ger. 41

MYSTIC MISCELLANY. 1. Der MOENCH VON HEILSBRONN. Das Buch von den 6 Namen des Fronleichnams, ff.1r–96v, *inc.:* Het ich ein zungen/Geflochten vnd gedrungen/ . . . (with contemp. corrections throughout; text, in different, earlier spelling published by J. F. L. T. Merzdorf, *Der Mönch von Heilsbronn,* [Berlin, 1870] pp.1–68, but with concluding poem which is not found in this ms.).—2. Unidentified prose text, ff.97r–119r, *inc.:* Petre amas me dise wort sprach vnser herr zu sand Peter.—3. Unidentified prose text (by Conradus de Brundelsheim?, who may be identical with the Moench von Heilsbronn), ff.121r–256v, *inc.:* Christus cham zu dem abent essen do man die osterleich speis berait.—4. Beginning of another tract (½ p. only), *inc.:* Drey tugent gehorent an einen geistleichen Menschen. . . . *Southern Germany, ca. 1440.*

Paper, with vellum fly-leaves (inscr. on verso of front leaf: Mein dinst wist vorlieb Johann ich lass dich). 262 ff. (f.120, 258-262 blank). 15 x 11 cm. Contemp. red pigskin over wooden boards, front cover missing.

Ger. 42

[TERMENO, or Tramin, Trentino-Alto Adige]. Wine accounts from the Hapsburg vineyards, 1574–1774. *Southern Tyrol, 1574–1774.*

Paper. 90 pieces. 20.5-32 x 11-16.5 cm. Unbound.

Ger. 43

JOHANN JOACHIM EWALD. 6 autograph "Sinngedichte auf den Briefwechsel des Königs [Friedrich II, king of Prussia] mit Gottsched," *begins:* Der grosse Friedrich sang, und sang auf fremden Saiten. . . . *Germany, ca. 1750.*

Paper. 4 pp. 22 x 17.5 cm. In folder.

Ger. 44

AUGUST, elector of Saxony. Letter signed, without name of addressee, asking for replicas of coins, for his collection. *Saxony, Feb. 10, 1574.*

Paper. 1 f. 31 x 20.5 cm. In folder.

Ger. 45

[COLOGNE, Archdiocese]. 1. REFORMATIO JURISDICTIONIS ecclesiasticae archiepiscopalis curiae coloniensis jussu et authoritate reverendissimi et serenissimi Principis ac Domini D. Ernesti . . . archiepiscopi. . . . Monasterii Westphaliae excudebat Lambertus Raesfelt anno M.D. XCIIII [in Latin, copied July 1695 by E. A. Call <?>, cf.p.91], 4 prel. ff., 92 pp.—2. POLLICEY UNDT LANDTS-ORDTNUNG . . . Getruckt zu Münster in Westpfahlen bey Lamberten Raessfeldt anno M.D. XCVI [ms. copy, undated], 52 pp.—3. RECHTS ORDNUNG dess Maximiliani Henrici, 31 ff.—4. ORDTNUNG des Brüchtenverhör[s] unser Ferdinand von Gottes Gnaden, 5 ff. *Westphalia, 1695–ca. 1700.*

Paper. 112 ff. 29.5 x 18.5 cm. Contemp. vellum.—The second item contains "Constitution oder Mandat wieder [!] die Wiederteuffer," pp. 43–47.

Ger. 46

[BAVARIA]. 1. BESCHREIBUNG des Lanndtags welcher von . . . Wilhelmen Pfaltzgraven bei Rhein, Herzogen in Obern unnd Nidern Bairn auf den 22. Tag Novembris geen Münnchen ausgeschriben . . . anno 1583, 142 ff.—2. GRAVAMINA oder Beschwerung Articl wie dieselben . . . Herzog Wilhelm . . . durch irer etc. gemein Lanndstend von Prelaten, Graven, Herrn Ritterschaft und Adl auch Stett und Märkt . . . übergeben sein . . . 1583, 31 ff.—3. DESS STANDS DER RITTERSCHAFT und Adls Beschwer Articl, wie dieselben . . . Herrn Wilhelmen . . . underthenig fürgebracht . . . 1583, 98 ff.—

4. DESS STANDS DER STETT und Märkt . . . Beschwerden, 154 ff. (last blank). *Bavaria, ca. 1583.*

Paper. 1 blank, 425 ff. 29.5 x 20.5 cm. Contemp. blind-stamped pigskin.—Prov.: "Sum ex libris Eberhardi Adolphi baronis a Muggenthal in Pondorf."

Ger. 48

[PASSAU]. Transcripts of documents dealing primarily with laws, treatises, etc., concerned with the relations between the clergy and the civil authorities (and population) of Passau. 1. WILHELM and LUDWIG, Counts Palatinate and Dukes of Bavaria. Die neuen Sprüch aufgericht 1535, ff.1r-56r.—2. ERNST, bishop of Passau (here acting as "administrator des Stiffts Passau"). Inhalt beeder Partheien Verschreibung auf Volziehung des Vertrags [1535], ff.57r-62r.— 3. ALBRECHT, King of Germany and Duke of Austria. Sprüch . . . ergangen . . . 1290, ff.62v-66r.—4. BERNHARD, bishop of Passau. Brief so aufgericht . . . 1300, ff.66v-74r.—5. ERNST, bishop of Passau. Erleutterung uber Bischof Bernharts Stattbrief . . . 1539, ff.74v-92v.—6. ALBRECHT and LEOPOLD, Dukes of Austria. Vidimus des Anlasbriefs und Hindergangs . . . 1367, ff.93r-96r.—7. IDEM. Sprüch . . . ergangen . . . 1367, ff.79r-101r.—8. IDEM. Sprüch . . . ergangen . . . 1368, ff.101v-115v. *Passau?, ca. 1600.*

Paper. 115 ff. 30 x 20 cm. Boards.

Ger. 49

VIENNA, Criminal Court, 1572–1574. Malefitzsachen veindlicher Bekhanntnusser ingefangen den 30 Maii anno 1572. (Interrogations, testimonies, judgments and at times pardons or records of executions, several signed by Michael Stilzl. Among the trials is that of Elias, or Helias, Gregoritsch [or Gregoritz, Gregorwitz, also called Pribeck] and his followers for organizing and leading a peasant revolt in Croatia, 1572–1573; the beginning of this section is entitled "Crabatischer Paurnkrieg;" cf. ff.104-122; 151-157). *Vienna, 1572–74.*

Paper. 234 ff. (ff.1–2 missing), 7 ff. (copy of petition of Johan Lust to the emperor for promotion, undated, bound upside down, and index of trials on last f.) 30 x 19.5 cm. Contemp. vellum (rebound).—Probably the original minutes of proceedings.

Ger. 50

[COLOGNE]. 1. Von einem erschröcklichen und gewältlichen Uvlauff im Jahr 1513 im Januario, 2 ff.—2. TRANSFIX BRIEFF anno dni. 1513 auffgericht (on the disturbances of Jan. 1513), 10 ff.—3. CONCORTATEN welche zwischen Ertzbischoff Herman, Landtgraff zu Hessen, etc. und dem Thum [i.e. Dom] Capittel an einem, und der Statt Collen am anderen Theil auffgericht. Anno 1506, 9 ff.—4. STATUTA

huius inclitae civitatis coloniensis (in German), 7 ff. (index), 100 ff.—
5. ORDTNUNGH dere Rechts und Stat Richteren, Gerichtschreibern, Procoratoren und gerichtlichen Procesen . . . , 1 f. (index), 1 f. (title in German and Latin title "Reformatio judicialis," dated 1530), 51, 2 ff.—6. RECHT UNND BURGERFREIHEIT, 1, 7 ff.—7. Various legal rulings, 5 ff.—8. VERBUNT BREIFF (=Brief), 11 ff.—9. EDICTUM senatus coloniensis de continuenda in haeredem possessione (in German), 6 ff. (followed on f.6v-7 by another edict). *Cologne, 16th–17th cent.*

Paper. 2, 10, 5 blank, 7, 1 blank, 100, 1, 51 + 2, 1, 7 + 5, 6 blank, 11, 1 blank, 7, 22 blank ff. 28.5 x 19.5 cm. Contemp. vellum.—Various names (earlier owners) in ms., e.g. H. Welckers, Hubertus Westhaus (1808).—Ms. preceded by printed statute, Cologne, 1562, and shelved under fGC55C7143L-562a. Volume used at one time as a "herbarium," with names of plants written on many pages.

Ger. 51

HANNS SCHWARZ (or Schwartz). Miscellany. 1. List of marriages attended, 1585–1598, ff.1r-4v.—2. EXEMPELL BÜCHLEIN (or Exempllum Büchlleinn) über die Species uff der Feder [=introductory arithmetic], anno domini 1565 . . . [date of writing:] 1593, ff.5r-24r.—3. OF HERBS, TREES, etc. (with 10 lines of poetry interspersed, f.26r), ff.25r-33r.—4. Proverbs, religious poetry, moral sayings, etc., altogether 551 lines of VERSE, ff.33v-46v.—5. UEBER DEN BAUERN-

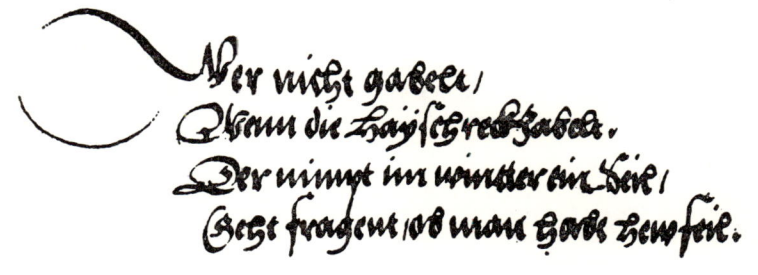

Hanns Schwarz. Example from collection of poems. Ger. 51, f.41r.

KRIEG zu Windsheim und Umgegend (icplt. at beginning), ff.47r-55v.—6. PRAYER "Herz mein Erlöser Jesus Christus," f.56r-v.—7. Die WASSERSNOT in Nürnberg (1504?), 28 lines of verse, f.57r.—8. Der JÜNGSTE TAG, poem of 61 lines, by Hanns Geber (?), dated 1597, ff.57v-58v.—9. ROTTENBURGISCHE CRONICA (697–1582), ff.59r-63r, with addition on the disputation between Luther and Zwingli and the death of Zwingli, f.63v.—10. ANFANG und Ende des verderblichen Baurenkriegs wie er sich allhie zu Rottenburg . . .

zugetragen . . . 1525 [–1526], ff.64r-79v (with list of fugitives).—
11. Ein LIED wie es in dem frenkischen Baurnkrieg ergangen ist, ff.80r-82v.—12. URKUNDE des Diacons Albrecht Renger, Verehelichung des Han[n]s Schwarz, 1582, f.83r.—13. VERZEICHNIS der bei Hochzeit des Hans Schwarz anwesenden Gäste, durch Nicolaus Schmidt . . . Wirt zu Windsheim, ff.83v-84r, followed by 4 entries of business records (f.84r-v). *Rothenburg o.d.T., 1582–1598.*

Paper. 88 ff. (ff.86–87 blank). 21.5 x 16.5 cm. Cloth.—Prov.: August Merz, 1862.

Ger. 52

JOHANN JACOB BREITINGER. Collection of copies or extracts of texts relating to political, social, religious and miscellaneous affairs primarily of Zürich (beginning with a biography of J. J. Breitinger and a list of his published and unpublished writings) and incl. "Fürtrag betreffend den Venedischen und Frantzosischen Ambassadoren" (e.g. pp.155 ff., 194 ff.), "Delineation der Reformation . . . 1622" (pp.218 ff.), "Wyderhollung dess . . . vaterländischen Projects . . . authore Joh. Jac.Brittingero" (pp.235 ff.), "Vom dryten Grad der Bluetsfründtschafft" (p.409 ff.), several sermons, etc. *Zürich, 1670.*

Paper. 690 pp. 19 x 16 cm. Contemp. vellum.—Most of the tracts in this volume are by J. J. Breitinger, acc. to the list of his writing in the early part of the ms.

Ger. 53

PRAYER BOOK, with index. *Germany, 1777.*

Paper. 2 ff., 254 pp., 1 f. 16.5 x 10 cm. Crucifixion and picture of the evangelist Matthew pasted in. Contemp. gilt morocco, with name of original owner "Magdalena Erbsin" and date (1777) embossed on front cover.

Ger. 54

MELCHIOR ADAM PASTORIUS. Autograph volume, in German and Latin, beginning on prel. f. with genealogical entries, followed by Pastorius' "Itinerarium et vitae curriculus, das ist völlige Reis—Beschreibunge und gantzer Lebenslauff," and incl. anagrams and other poetry (cf. lat. poem on William Penn, f.89r): "Familiae Pastoriorum descriptio" (lat., ff.111 ff.); chronology, 1559–1691 (lat., ff.205 ff.) and other historical compilations, among these "Von dem Königreich Engelland"; extensive material on family matters (mostly in germ., e.g. poems at the occasion of Pastorius' fourth marriage, ff.124 ff., death of Dorothea Esther Pastorius, ff.127v ff., etc.) and a detailed name index at end (cf. St. Augustine, St. Brigid, Caesar, Charles V, Huss, Melanchthon, 19 members of the Pastorius family, Tacitus, etc.) *Germany, end of 17th cent.*

Paper. 1 f., 240 numb. ff. (ff.6–7 missing; 2 ff. numb. 22; f. 59 missing; 1 f. inserted between ff.79–80 and another between ff.90–91, 2 ff. numb. 148), 2 ff. 15 x 10 cm. Contemp. [?] leather.—Prov.: J. G. Rosengarten.—The manuscript has been briefly described in M. D. Learned, *The Life of Francis Daniel Pastorius* (Philadelphia, 1908), p. 45, no. 1.

Ger. 55

MELCHIOR ADAM PASTORIUS. Autograph volume, in German and Latin, incl. "Prognosticon sive calendarium perpetuum" (lat., ff.1 ff.); "Colloquium regis Salomonis cum Marcolpho" (lat. ff.6v ff.); calendar pictures with legends (ff.11 ff.); "Dicteria proverbialia rhythmica ab antiquitate mutuata" (lat., ff.32 ff.); "Versus veteres proverbiales" (ff.88 ff.); "Von Aesopi Klugheit" (ff.142 ff.), "Beyhülffe zu denen Teütschen Versen" (ff.187 ff.); "Schatz-Kammer" (ff.226 ff.); "Herbarum appellationes in den Apotheken" (lat. and germ., ff.262 ff.); emblems with text (ff.287 ff.), and index (cf. bibliotheca, educatio, liberum arbitrium, musica, nationum differentia). *Germany, end of 17th cent.*

Paper. 401 numb. ff. (f.232 missing; 2 ff. inserted between ff.255–256; 1 blank f. between ff.276–277; ff.284–286, 292, 294–295, 297–324, 326, 331–333 and 337 missing). 16 x 10 cm. Engr. pasted in on a number of pages, few drawings. Contemp. [?] leather.—Prov.: J. G. Rosengarten.—The manuscript has been briefly described in M. D. Learned, *op. cit.*, p. 46, no. 2.

Ger. 56

CICERO. Ciceros [8] Reden übersetzt von Johann Christian Gottlieb Ernesti. Autograph ms.?, with corrections. *Germany, 1793–97.*

Paper. 206 ff. (ff.23–24, 48, 82, 105–106, 113–114, 158, 160–162 and 204–206 blank). 21.5 x 17 cm. Cloth.

Ger. 57°

WERNIGERODE. Financial agreement between the town of Wernigerode (represented by [cf. *inc.*] "Wir Hinrik Uppelingh, Hintze Muntmeister, Hinrik Aldingh, Hinrik Lume de Eldere, Albrecht Brockenstedes, Oltze Spekhosen, und Oltze Kemeden") and the monastery Unser Lieben Frauen in Halberstadt (represented by "Johan Dekene [i.e. deacon], Hinrik von Suneborn, Canoniken und Ern Bethmann Bruckemann, Schulmester" directed to "alle den de ene seen, horen odd lesen." *Wernigerode, 20. Dec. 1390.*

Vellum. 1 f. 28 x 19 cm. With seals of Wernigerode and Count Cordt of Wernigerode. In envelope.

Ger. 58°

WILHELM, Landgrave of Hessen. Die Einmanüng des Landgraffen zue Hessen den Chürff. zue Sachsen belanget Herrzog Moritzen, Feb. 1552.

—*With* TORGAU LANDTAG. Den Wilhelm Landgraff zue Hessen, missive sent by "die vonn der Landschaft zue Torgaw," March 4, 1552. *Germany, ca. 1552.*

Paper. 6 ff. 18.5 x 14 cm. Bound in boards, with P. Melanchthon's Bedencken auffs Interim, 1548.

Ger. 59°

JOHANN MAXIMILIAN, Freiherr von PREYSING. Urbarium, Stifft und Saalbuech (concerning his properties in Upper Bavaria, "Hofmarck Altenpreising, genant Cronwinckhel, im Churfürstl. Lanndtgericht Erding," listing individual assessments and assignments, e.g. "ist schuldig in die Schweinhaz zu gehen"). Durch Johann Baptisten Leidl, beider Rechten Doctorn, with signatures, seals and notarial signet. *Landshut?, 1661.*

Paper. 3 ff. (ff.1–2 blank), 120 ff., 1 blank f., ff.120–53, 1 blank f., ff.153–66, 1 blank f. (=174 ff.) 30 x 20 cm. Contemp. blind-stamped pigskin.—Prov.: Von Preysing.

Ger. 60°

SIEGISMUND JUSTUS EHRHARDT. Historische Abhandlung von einigen Gottes Gelehrten, welche vorher Rechts Gelehrte gewezen sind. (Dedicated to Friedrich Wilhelm Kreidenmann. Among persons discussed are Tertullian, Prudentius, Arator, Pope Gregory I, Photius, Thomas Aquinas, Luther, Oecolampadius and Del Rio). With corrections in a contemp. hand. *Jena?, 1754.*

Paper. 152 pp. 20.5 x 17 cm. Boards.—Prov: Prince Liechtenstein.

Ital. 1

BRAGADIN FAMILY. Records of agreements between members of the family regarding property and obligations, largely in Italian; incl. list and valuation of real estate properties. *Venetian territory, 1540–1565.*

Vellum. 42 ff. (ff.31–37 blank). 23 x 16 cm. Various notarial signets (Hieronymus Canalis, Joannes Sanini?, Paulus Leoncinus, etc.). Contemp. vellum.—Estate of Dr. Morris Jastrow.

Ital. 2

RELIGIOUS TRACTS: 1. SAINT CATHERINE OF BOLOGNA. Le sette armi spirituali (incomplete), ff.1r–56v.—2. ISAAC OF SYRIA. Libro della contemplazione del mondo (incomplete), ff.57r–94r.—3. Nine sermons in Italian, ff.94v–158r.—4. LEGGENDA DI S. BONAVENTURA, ff.158v–159v.—5. SAINT BONAVENTURE. Delle sei ale dei serafini (incomplete), ff.160v–166r. *Italy, late 16th cent.*

Paper and vellum. 166 ff. 22 x 16 cm. 17th-cent. pigskin.—Prov.: Francis Campbell Macauley.

Ital. 3

LA VITA DI SANTA DOMITILLA, ff.1–6v (fragment, last f. only of first signature present).—*With* LAUDE DI SANTA DOMITILLA, ff.6v–10v, *inc.*: Una stella ea parita/ Vergine di grande honore. . . . —DI SANTA EUFRASINA, della sua natività et come essendo maritata . . . , ff.10v–21v.—DI SANTA MARIA VERGINE, ff.21v–24v, *inc.*: Uno huomo secolare & imanendo. . . .—LA VITA E LEGENDA DELLA BEATA EUGENIA, ff.24v–30 (one or more ff. at end missing), *inc.*: Quomodo imperadore nel septimo anno del suo imperio. . . . *Italy, 15th cent.*

Paper. 30 ff. 22 x 18 cm. Paper boards.—Prov.: Francis Campbell Macauley.

Ital. 4

ARISTOTLE. A Summary of the Ethica Nicomachea, *inc.*: Qui comenza lo libro chiamato Leticha. . . . *Italy, ca. 1500.*

Paper. 33 ff. (last f. wanting). 28 x 20 cm. Decorated initials throughout. H/vellum.—Prov.: Dr. Charles W. Burr.—Cf. L. W. Riley, *op.cit.*, no. M4.

Ital. 5

PIETRO ARETINO. Il genesi, a poetical paraphrase. *Italy, first half 16th cent.*

Paper. 109 ff. 21 x 14 cm. Contemp. vellum.—Prov.: Vicentius Marini (bookplate).

Ital. 6

HIERONIMO DIVIACO. Informatione di Bergamo & del suo territorio all' illustrissimo Signore Giorgio Cornaro, suo podestà, MDXCVII. *Bergamo (?), ca. 1600.*

Paper. 144 ff. (several blank) and folded table "In statutis Philippi Mariae vicicomitis, que iugebant ante felicissima adeptione Veneta . . .". 20 x 15 cm. Contemp. vellum.

Ital. 7

GUILIO QUINZIANO, called Tonello. Rime di Tonello (a paraphrase of Petrarch?, in the dialects of Bergamo and Brescia). *Italy, late 16th or early 17th cent.*

Paper. 130 ff. (1 unnumb. f. between ff. 24 and 25). 27 x 21 cm. Contemp. gilt red morocco.—Prov.: Walther Sneyd.—Gabriele Rosa in his *Dialetti, costumi e tradizione delle province di Bergamo e di Brescia* says that there is a similar ms. in the library of Bergamo.

Ital. 8

VITERBO. Statutorum Viterbii Liber (3–6 only) de extraordinariis, de potestate et arbitrio D. D. Priorum circa extraordinaria. *Italy, 17th cent.*

Paper. 226 ff. 26 x 19 cm. Contemp. h/vellum.—Prov.: V. Drichiarelli(?).

Ital. 9

CARMINE ALLA BEATA VERGINE MARIA, 236 (and 4½ deleted) six-line stanzas, *inc.:* O gloriosa vergene Maria/ Regina dellu celu et de omne gente/ Prestame gratia nella mente mea/ Che io te pocza ludare cigniamente/. . . . *Southern (?) Italy, 15th cent.*

Paper. 7 ff. (criginally folded). 26.5 x 20.5 cm. Vellum.

Ital. 10

GIOVAN THESEO NARDEO GALATHEO. Il tempio di castitade [and other poems]. Alla valorosa & inclita signora . . . Margherita d'Austria. . . . With dedications to Pietro Lippo and Hettore Piscicello. *Rome (?), 1553.*

Vellum. 30 ff., in two different hands. 21 x 14 cm. Illum. crest and coat of arms on title page. Vellum.

Ital. 11

ARISTOTLE. Portion of the Ethica Nicomachea in a Venetian dialect by Gabriello Paradixo, ff.1r–50r.—*With* (2) SERMONES, ff.51r–55v. —SONETTO DIZE EL LIBRO, f.55v.—INDULGENCES (in lat.), ff.56r–67v. *Italy, the tr. of the Ethica dated 17 June 1456 (f.50r).*

Paper. 67 ff. 20.5 x 14 cm. Boards.—Cf. L. W. Riley, *op.cit.,* no. M5.

Ital. 12

GIOVANNI BOCCACCIO. Teseide. *Italy, late 14th cent.(?)*

Paper. 69 ff. (3 first ff. wanting), written in two hands. 29.5 x 22 cm. Morocco (R. R. Donnelley).—Prov.: Francis Campbell Macauley.—This ms. lacks the first 20 verses and ends with verse 83 of book xii, followed by a somewhat later inscription indicating ownership of "Bartolomeo & Tomaso Cholnj(?) Chessetto (or Chessello)" and an inscription on the verso of the last leaf. Contemporary ms. corrections throughout. Text belongs to B group of mss., with variant readings (cf. the critical edition, edited by Salvatore Battaglia, <Florence, 1938>, and publ. by the Accademia della Crusca).

Ital. 13

ITALIAN MISCELLANY: 1. LA VITA DE JOACHIM del Tribu di Juda, ff.1r (and 2; the beginning on f.1, incomplete, repeated on f.2) –24r, *inc.:* In quello tempo iera uno homo.—2. LA PASSIONE DEL NOSTRO SIGNOR, ff.24r–44r, *inc.:* E proximando lo tempo.—3. LIBRO DELLA RESURRECTIONE, ff.44r–54v, *inc.:* E quando vene.—4. LI MIRACOLI de la vergine Maria, ff.54v–65r, *inc.:* Dixe sancto Epifanio.—5. PIANTO de la vergene Maria (in verse), ff.65r–76r, *inc.:* Ave regina vergine glorioxa/ Che de dio. . . . —6. A LAUDE E GLORIA . . . de lo omnipotente dio e de la glorioxa vergine Maria e de madonna sancta Theodoxina, ff.75r–81v.—7.

THOMAS DE AQUINO. [Selections], ff.84r–94r. *Lombardy, 1464, 1473 ff.*

Vellum. 94 ff. (ff.82–83 blank). 28.5 x 20 cm. Decorated initials. Contemp. blind-stamped calf over wooden boards.—Prov.: Monastery of the Holy Spirit, Verona (f.94v).

Ital. 14

[VENICE]. Manual of a Venetian consigliere, written for Giovanni Francesco Basadona, signed Marc Antonio Padavia. *Venice, ca. 1560.*

Vellum. 60 ff. (ff.58–60 blank). 22.8 x 15.5 cm. Colored full-page miniature of St. Francis and St. John (the patron saints of Basadona) on f.1r. Contemp. red velvet.—Prov.: "Comes Hercules Silva" (f.57v).

Ital. 15

COLLECTION OF POEMS by unnamed author, one identified as an imitation of Tasso (f.12r), one addressed to a friend (of the author?) Marolino Giorgini (f.17v), another to Ranucci Farnese (f.29r), etc. Amorous as well as spiritual poems; madrigals interspersed toward the end. *Italy, ca. 1680.*

Paper. 99 ff. 20 x 13 cm. Vellum.

Ital. 16

GIANNOZZO SALVIATI. 1. Amatory correspondence between the author and Lucrezia [de Medici?], pp.1–80.—2. Una pistola . . . a Lucrezia, pp.82–84.—3. Poem, in terza rima, concerning "Il magnifico Lorenzo de Medici" and "Fra Mariano dal ordine d[ominicantorum]," pp.84–91.—4. Fasta e chommada . . . fatta alla cicilia di Fiesole (in terza rima), pp.92–102.—5. Bernardo Giambullari a Giannozzo Salviati, pp.137–139, letter dedicating Giambullari's *Sonetti rusticani* (known in only one copy of a printed edition, 1515, and lacking this dedication; cf. C. Arlia, *Sonetti rusticani*, <Città di Castello, 1902>). *Florence, 1488, 1515, and 1522.*

Paper. 140 pp. (pp.103–136 blank). 18.5 x 13.4 cm. H/leather.—Prov.: Giannozzo Salviati and other members of the family (p.140); G. Melzi; De Marinis.

Ital. 17

POETICAL MISCELLANY. From the collection of Henry Chandon de Briailles. *Italy, ca. 1600.*

Paper. 86 ff. (last blank). 21.5 x 15.6 cm. Contemp. Italian gilt morocco.

Ital. 18

VITA JESU CHRISTI. Questo libro tracta de la vita e de la conversione del nostro segniore Jhesu Christo. *Italy, 15th cent.*

Vellum. 60 ff. 24.5 x 17 cm. Contemp. h/leather over wooden boards.

Ital. 19

[VENICE]. Cronica di tutti li dogi di Venetia sino a quello che hora vive, con le armi loro; aggiontovi l'indice e origine delle casate, con quelle che sono estinte. *Venice, compiled in or shortly after 1556, ending on p.48 with the name of Laurentio Prioli (1556–1559); continued in different hands in the 17th cent. down to 8 April 1658.*

Paper. 4, 57, 1, 5 (blank) ff. 20.5 x 15 cm. Title within decorated border, with colored coats of arms. H/vellum.—Prov.: Earl of Guildford; Essington Library (no.139).

Ital. 20

NICCOLÒ ROSSI. Inventario della raccolta di libri ritrovata nell'eredità della Ch. M. del Signore Abbate Niccola Rossi, che con le stime di ciascuno volume si presenta agli illustrissimi signori provveditori, residenti del Magistrato dei Pupilli di Firenze, dai Ferdinando Giovannucci e Francesco Saverio Lucchesi. *Rome, 1785.*

Paper. 2 vols. (vol.I: 291 ff.; vol.II: 159 ff.). 21 x 31 cm. and 19.5 x 27 cm. Contemp. vellum.—Contains the carefully compiled catalogues of 7,782 (falso 7,722) volumes of post-1500 printed books (ff.1–241 of vol.I), with individual prices for all items and a total value of "scudi romani" 7,975.05; 1,307 incunable volumes (ff.242–290 of vol.I), valued at sc. rom. 4,501.40; 415 manuscript codices, valued at sc. rom. 1,212.10. Each volume is notarized at end.—The library of Rossi was actually sold during his lifetime to Bartolomeo Corsini and later became part of the Biblioteca Corsiniana in Rome.

Ital. 21

LORENZO GUALTIERI. Il publico di Lorenzo Spirito Perugino nel quale si contiene il Lamento di Perugia essendo sogiogata, *inc.:* Lume del ciel che l'universo vedi/ notando sempre lo svellato chiostro/. . . . *Italy, second half 16th cent.*

Paper. 80 ff. (ff.76–80 blank). Signed by scribe Carlo Lippi (f.75v). 13 x 19 cm. Contemp. vellum.

Ital. 22

[LUCCA]. Fondatione della città di Lucca et altre memorie sino al anno 1370; part II, from p.242 on, continues the chronicle from 1370 into the 16th cent. The last folio contains a few additions from the 18th cent. *Lucca(?), 17th cent.*

Paper. 1 f., pp.2–399, 1 f. 15 x 21 cm. (part II, 15.5 x 22 cm.). Blind-stamped leather.

Ital. 23

[SAVOY]. War of 1691 between Savoy and France. Copies of letters and documents from the years 1690–1692 in various hands, dated for the most part in Turin or Milan. Bound with 2 printed texts: *Relatione di quanto è successo nell'assedio della città di Cuneo* (Milan, 1691) and *Lettera di Monsu il Marchese di Louvoi* (Turin, 1691). *Savoy, ca. 1690–1692.*

Paper. 124 pp., and 1 loose f. at end. Various sizes, partly folded, in 1 vol. (21 x 16 cm.) Contemp. paper over boards.

Ital. 24

LEGHORN (Livorno). Riforma della Dogana di Livorno. Statutes and trade regulations. *Leghorn, 1565–1649.*

Vellum. 2 vols. (vol.I: 4 unnumb., 105 ff.; vol.II: 103 ff.) 19.5 x 26.5 cm. and 21 x 30 cm. Illum. initials in vol.I. Contemp. stamped leather over wooden boards.—Prov.: Walter Ashburner, Florence.

Ital. 25

VITA DI LADISLAO, Re di Napoli e di Giovanna II, Reina di Napoli. *Italy, ca. 1700.*

Paper. 153 pp., 6 blank ff. 22 x 15 cm. Contemp. vellum.—"Ex libris Marchionis Salsae" and bookplate with device "Comme je fus."

Ital. 26

ANTONIO MILLEDONI. Dell'historia del Sacro Concilio di Trento, scritta da Antonio Milledoni, segretario del Consiglio de x di Venetia, in detto Concilio. Libri due. *Venice, early 17th cent.*

Paper. 119 ff., and loose quire of 4 ff. with index. 27 x 20 cm. Contemp. vellum.

Ital. 27

MIRABELLA. Capitula Mirabellae, in Italian and a few in Latin, incl. "gravamina" of the "universitas et homines terrae Mirabellae" against Fabritio Giundatio, baron of Mirabella, 1548–1551, and other legal documents, of later date. *Naples and Mirabella, 1551, with additions down into 18th cent.*

Vellum and paper. 4 prel. ff. with table of contents, 62, 3 ff. 28 x 21 cm. H/morocco, front cover of 17th-cent armorial binding bound in.

Ital. 28

LIBRO DI SANTO JUSTO PALADINO. Il Cantare, *inc.:* [S]ignori e done azoche per fortuna/ Nisuno de nui se meta a desperare/. . . . *Italy, 15th cent.*

Paper. 60 ff. (last 3 blank). 19 x 14.5 cm. Boards.—The printed edition, produced from the Venice, 1490 edition (E. Lommatzsch, *Beiträge zur älteren italienischen Volksdichtung*, <Berlin, 1950–1951>) differs considerably from this ms.

Ital. 29

ITALIAN RELIGIOUS MISCELLANY: 1. FR. JACOMO [da Todi?]. Meditatione de la vita de Cristo, ff.1r–85v, *inc.*: Qui comenza lo prologo de la meditatione d[e la vita] de Cristo conposto per frate Iacomo de lo ordine [de frati mi]nuri traslatato de gramatica in latin[o]. [C?]iasche una persona de quisto mondo . . . , followed by La Vendecta de Cristo, *expl.*: Isto libro finiendo/ Gratias Christo referendo/ Deprecor ut qui legitis/ Dicta suprascripta/ Relinquatis omnia delicta/. Expletus fuit liber iste per me Iohannes Benedicti Pauli de Nursia die quarta mensis martii 1457.—2. RELIGIOUS POEM of 7 lines, f.87r, *inc.*: Splendore superdo [sic] domini summo favore.—3. Fragment of a visionary work, ff.93r–98r.—4. MEDITATIONE della vita de sancto Johanni Baptista, ff.100v–162v, *inc.*: Ad laude de dio et della gloriosa vergine Maria. . . .—5. LA VITA DE SANCTO HONOFRIO confessore, ff.164r–180v, *inc.*: Panuntiu humile servo della vostra santita a tucti li servi . . . . *Italy, 1457, and mid-15th cent.*

Paper. 180 ff. (incl. several blank). 22 x 14.5 cm. Contemp. vellum.—Inscription on inside cover: "Questo libro e de Santa Eucharistia de la gla (gloria?)."

Ital. 30

ST. ANTONINUS FLORENTINUS. Confessionale, Omnis mortalium cura, ital.: Specchio de coscienza, in the form ending "la dicta età" (Cf. *Gesamtkatalog*, nos.2158–2169, in this ms. ending spelled "alla detta eta"). Stagnone (Stagno Lombardo near Cremona?), *21 April 1466, written by Andreas, son of Bartolus de Lunigiana* (f.81v).

Paper. 81 ff. (beginning incomplete). 21 x 14.5 cm. Contemp. h/leather over wooden boards, front missing.—Inscription on fly leaf at end: "Iste liber est meus presbiter Domenico de Mairis." Cf. Ital. 39.

Ital. 31

ARISTOTLE. Ethica, in the epitomized version of Brunetto Latini, tr. into Italian by [?] Bono Giamboni, *inc.*: Comincia il libro primo dell etica Aristotile nel quale tratta della felicitade. Ogne arte et ogne doctrina. . . . *Italy (Florence?), 14th cent. (before 1356?)*

Vellum. 69 ff. (last 3 blank, first f. replaced ca. 1450). 21 x 15 cm. Decorated initials, red and blue capitals. Contemp. stamped calf over wooden boards.—Cf. L. W. Riley, *op.cit.*, no. M2A.

Ital. 32

ALESSANDRO DA SASSOFERRATO. Sermone, *inc.*: Incomença uno sermone overo predicatione. Sermon delivered at the monastery on the Mount of Olives on October 3, 1462 (f.1). *Italy, 15th cent. (post 1462).*

Vellum. 10 ff. 20 x 13 cm. Vellum.

Ital. 33

ACCADEMIA DEGLI ALTERATI: 1. POEMS (in a calligraphic hand, title, 2 ff. dedication signed "Accademico Innominato," 109 ff., 3 blank ff.), incl.: Sopra gl'occhi della sua donna, L'ra del S. Andrea Salvatori di Dorindo ad Eurilla, Riposta d'Eurilla, Scherzo per cantar in musica, Lettera di Tirsi à Eurilla, A Clori, In lode di Papa Urbano VIII, several poems addressed to Cardinal Antonio Barberini, etc. With [author's?] corrections.—2. POEMS (in a second, more cursive hand, 95 ff.) addressed to Maria Medici, Ferdinando di Toscana, Cosimo II, In morte del re Filippo, Ferdinando Gonzaga, Pope Leo XI, etc.—3. CANZONETTI (in a later hand, 42 ff.) *Italy (Florence?), first half 17th cent.*

Paper. 255 ff. 22 x 16 cm. Boards.—The first item dedicated to Cardinal Antonio Barberini. The first (and possibly the other parts) were written by an unidentified member (or members) of the Academia degli Alterati.

Ital. 34

MATTEO VALLI. Dell'origine et governo della republica di San Marino. Breve relazione. Copied (?) contemporaneously from printed book: *Padua, G. Crivellari, 1633.*

Paper. 30 ff. 19 x 13.5 cm. Paper boards.—Ex libris Leo Valli.—With dedicatory introd. by the editor Gabriel Naudé.

Ital. 35

FRANCESCO CESIS—SAVELLI. Il Goffredo, opera drammatica heroica (performed in Cotrone, June 1653). *Italy, 1653(?).*

Paper. 115 ff. 20 x 14.5 cm. Drawing of Hercules (f.3), and the siege of a fort (f.14). Vellum.—Inscription "Bartolo Macherani(?) 1644 [sic!]" on f.3r.

Ital. 36

[VENICE]. Cronica de tutte le casade della nobel città de Venetia cioe delli zentilhomeni che sono venuti ad habitar in quella . . . con le arme de tutti li zentilhomeni. . . . *Venice, first quarter 17th cent.*

Paper. 888 pp. 30 x 20 cm. Colored decorative title pages; colored coats of arms throughout; beheading of the Doge Marino Falieri (pp.376 and 777); hanging of Marco Donado dalla Madale (p.321); beheading of Francesco Carmignola (p.233); strangulation of Francesco da Carrara in 1405 and beheading of Marsilio da Carrara (p.228). Contemp. gilt levant morocco.—Prince Liechtenstein Library.

Ital. 37

CRESTOMAZIA di poeti italiani del Cinquecento. Contains 9 sonnets, 1 canzone and "motti" by Pietro Bembo, poems by G. Guidiccioni, B. Capello, Molza, B. Daniello, U. Martegli, C. Tolomei, Della Casa, and several anonymous poems. *Italy, ca. 1550.*

Paper. 1–15, 15–59 pp. 20.5 x 14.5 cm. H/leather.

> Motti del Bembo.
>
> Pur, che di lui pensier ui stringa il core;
> Ogni cosa da uoi gl'è dolce honore.
> Non impedir l'altrui fatal cammino
> & sappi, che lo muoue alto destino.

Ital. 38

L'AMBASCIATA DEL CIELO fatta da San Pietro a cardinali nel conclave dell'anno 1626 [in the form of a play], *inc.:* Christo Redentore parla à S. Pietro Se queste humane spoglie già glorificate. . . . *Italy, 17th cent.*

Paper. 16 ff. (last 3 blank). 32.5 x 20.5 cm. Boards.

Ital. 39

ST. ANTONINUS FLORENTINUS. Confessionale, "Omnis mortalium cura," i.e. Specchio di coscienza. *Italy, second half 15th cent.*

Paper. 110 ff. (ff.103v–105v, with additions dated 1557; ff.106–110r blank; poem of owner on f.110v). 21 x 14 cm. H/leather.—Prov.: "1557, Est mei Joanes Pauli Civitella;" Libreria F. Strozzi. Cf. Ital. 30.

Ital. 40

S. MARIA DI LORETO, Rome. Trattato della bolla della fondazione della chiesa di S. Maria di Loreto di Roma.—Statuti della venerabile Compagnia di Santa Maria di Loreto. *Italy, 17th cent.*

Paper. 104 pp. 21 x 15 cm. Contemp. gilt morocco.

Ital. 41

LETTERE scritte da donna di senno e di spirito per ammaestramento del suo amante. *Italy, early 17th cent.*

Paper. 107 ff. (last 4 blank). 26.5 x 19 cm. 18th-cent. gilt morocco.

Ital. 42

GISBERTO ORLANDI and GIUSEPPE ORLANDI. Memoranda book, incl.: accounts, e.g. money given to Antonio Orlandi, studying at Perugia. *Tuscany, 1554–1613.*

Paper. 43 pp. (and 2 ff. laid in). 22 x 16 cm. Wrapped in contemp. vellum document, apparently from an account book (back cover missing).

Ital. 43

POESIE VARIE. Begins with sonnets, with name "Michele Brugueres" added in a different hand, and is followed by unassigned sonnets including "All' Italia nell'1690" (p.17), "Per l'elettione dell'Duca di Sassonia alla corona di Polonia" (p.22), "Nella sorpresa della gran fortezza di Buda rivolta à Turchi . . ." (p. 24), several poems relating to Louis XIV, king of France, and Prince Eugene, Philip V, king of Spain, Pope Clement XI, etc. *Italy, first half 18th cent.*

Paper. 1 blank f., 73 pp., 8 blank ff. 19 x 13 cm. Contemp. vellum.

Ital. 44

DIPLOMATIC RELATIONS: 1. CONTARINI. Relatione della corte di Roma nell' anno 1648 descritta dal Cavaliere Contarini, ambasciatore della Republica di Venetia et avvertimenti politici da osservarsi dà chi vol servire in corte, ff.2–25.—2. RELATIONE DI ROMA, ff.27–72, *inc.*: Io sono à pagar il tributo dovuto.—3. BATTISTA NANI. Relatione della Germania del Cavalier Battista Nani ritornatovi dalla sua ambascieria appresso la Maestà di Leopoldo Primo per la serenissima Republica di Venetia, ff.72–100.—4. RELATIONE delle potenze e forze delli principi d'Italia, ff.104–123.— 5. RAGGIONI state presentate ad instanza del Re di Portogallo alla Santità di nostro signore Alessandro VII circa il ricevimento del suo ambasciatore nella corte di Roma, ff.128–145.—6. MEMORIALE presentato dal Duca di Terra Nuova ambasciatore cattolice à nome di quella Maestà alla Santità d'Alessandro Settimo contro le pretentioni del Duca di Braganza preteso Rè di Portogallo del 1656, ff.149–161. *Italy, 17th cent.*

Paper. 161 ff. 26 x 19.5 cm. Contemp. vellum.

Ital. 45

ISTORIA DEL SACCO DI ROMA, e sua origine, scritta da' persona presente all'ora in Roma, ff.1–45.—*With* VITA, PROFEZIE, MIRACOLI, e morte del Ven. Bartolomeo Carosi, eremita Senese cognominato Brandano, e dal volgo detto il Pazzo di Cristo ò il contadino di Petroio, il tutto fedelmente raccolto da quello che di lui si trova scritto nell'Archivio della Città di Siena, ff.49–98.—DISCORSO dell'ambasciatore dello Stato Ecclesiastico al conclave per la sede vacante di Clemente XII, ff.100–142. *Italy, 18th cent.*

Paper. 142 ff. 26 x 19 cm. Contemp. vellum.

Ad. Ital. 44, no. 1: Cf. F. Antonibon, *Le relazioni a stampa di ambasciatori Veneti* (Padua, 1939), p. 103.—No. 3: Cf. *ibid.*, p. 71.—Parts 1, 3–7 = Ital. 184.

Ital. 46

EUGENE IV, CLEMENT VIII and PAUL V. Papal diplomatic instructions and other correspondence from 1570 to 1670 (vol. IV only of a set; see spine "Tom. iiii"), incl.: instructions to Spain (1591); Hungary (1594–1596); Transylvania (1594–1595); Poland (1595); Republic of Venice (1607); Kingdom of Naples (1620); several relating to the war against the Turks (1570); negotiations with the King of Spain (1594–1595); a letter of Cardinal Orsini about negotiations in France, etc. *Italy, (Rome?), 17th cent. (after 1620).*

Paper. 282 ff. 33 x 23 cm. Contemp. vellum.—Library stamp "L. Santacroce."

Ital. 47

HISTORIA de Papa Alexandro [III] et Phridrico Barbarossa, *inc.*: Hec sunt iurisditiones et regalie. . . . No possando messer lo Papa trovar. . . . Supposedly a copy of the original (found in the Venetian chancellery archives by a secretary and presented to the Doge Francesco Dona), made at the request of Pietro Morro. *Venice, mid-16th cent.*

Paper. 10 ff. (first and last 5 ff. blank). 20 x 14 cm. Contemp. vellum.

Ital. 48

THEBAID LEGION. La legenda di sanctissimi Thebey soto Dioclitiano et Maximiano imperatori, ff.1v–7v, *inc.*: Dioclitiano essendo doppo Numeriano imperatore electo principo.—*With* Un ALTRO MIRACULO che adopo idio per questi sancti martiri, f.7r–7v, *inc.*: Anchora non voglio lassare. *Italy (Florence?), 15th cent.*

Vellum. 8 ff. (last blank). 19 x 14 cm. Boards.

Ital. 49

FLORENCE, Priorista. Chronicle and records, 1201–1509. *Florence, late 15th–early 16th cent.*

Paper (2 vellum ff. at beginning, 1 at end). 4 unnumb., 249 numb., 4 blank ff. 29 x 22 cm. 18th-cent. vellum.—"Questo libro e di Lionardo d. Paolo Adimari."

Ital. 51

RIME di Timante Frascerepnico [pseud.?] in vita, e in morte di Elisa, *inc.*: Chi vuol saper la mia amorosa vita/ Scorra per poco queste brevi carte/. . . . *Italy, 17th cent.*

Paper. 1 f., 120 pp., 1 f. (index). 24 x 18 cm. Contemp. vellum.

Ital. 52

JOANNES ANTONIO de COLIS. De logica sive summole, *inc.*: Intellectus, sive ratio, a quo homo dicitur animal rationale. . . . *Italy, 17th cent.*

Paper. 92 ff. 19.5 x 13.5 cm. Contemp. boards.

Ital. 53

TRATTATO come si coltivino li giardini, *inc.:* Risposta di lettera ad un amico. Mi ricerchi con gran premura la descrittione del mio giardinetto. . . . *Italy, late 17th cent.*

Paper. 34 ff. (last 4 blank). 20 x 14 cm. Boards.

Ital. 54

TRENT, Council. Canons, down to the 14th session, ff.2r–149v.—*With* TRACT ON ORDINATION, ff.175r–197r.—LITANY OF THE VIRGIN in ottava rima, ff.197v–202v, continued on f.173v–174v. *Italy, 17th cent.*

Paper. 202 ff. (numb. ff.1–123, and 123–202; ff.150–172 blank). 20 x 13 cm. Contemp. vellum.—Purchase note obliterated, dated Rome, Feb. 1, 1752; Antonius Albani.

Ital. 55

[MATHEMATICS]: 1. DE TRIANGOLI, ff.1–34.—2. [EUCLID]. Di alcune premissioni necessarie alla introdutione e dichiaratione del.5. libro di Euclide, ff.38–57.—3. [IDEM]. In primam propositionem libri primi Euclidis, ff.58–59.—4. SUPER DATA RECTA LINEA terminata in angulum equilatenem constituere propositio; ad datum punctum date recte linea equalem rectam lineam ducere; various other short geometrical propositions, ff.61–88.—5. Part 1–4 of the ms. are followed by several short tracts, from f.61 to the end, all dealing with problems of geometry. *Italy, 17th cent.*

Paper. 176 ff. 31 x 21 cm. Unbound.

Ital. 56

ACCADEMIA DEGLI INNOMINATI. Fasti della Accademia . . . dalla sua instituzione, secolo secondo (from Dec. 10, 1789, to June 2, 1847), all signed for, or by, the secretaries of the Academy. *Siena, 1789–1847.*

Paper. 154 ff. 30 x 20 cm. 19th-cent. gilt calf.—Owner's stamp of **Luigi Lazzeri,** Siena (f.1).—Cf. M. Maylender, *Storia delle accademie d'Italia,* (Bologna, 1929), vol.III, p.298; "Accademia degli Innominati—Seconda—Siena."

Ital. 57

MADRIGALE e CANZONI, music with text. *Italy, late 16th cent.*

Paper. 28 ff. 23.5 x 17 cm. Contemp. vellum.—Partial list of incipits: **Donna per acquetar vostro desire.**—Lagrime mie messi dolenti.—Pace non trovo.—Pargoletta vezzosa e ridente.—Ma qual hora vezzosetta.—Se non hai di ferro il cuore.—Cruda Amarilli che col nom ancora.—Amarilli crudel e ria.—Ecco Lidia mia bella.

Ital. 58

CAVALLI family. Notarial instruments, incl. accounts, concerning the Cavalli family of Venice, covering the years 1597 to 1613, largely written by one scribe; with notarial signatures and signets. *Venice, early 17th cent.*

Vellum. 41 ff. 30 x 22.5 cm. Boards.—From the Morbio Library.

Ital. 59

DESIDERIUS ERASMUS. Moriae encomium, ital., tr. by Rafaello Pastore, with ms. corrections in the hand of the translator; attested as "ms. originale dell'autore Rafaello Pastore" by G. C. Bellomo (f.79). *Italy, late 18th cent.*

Paper. 81 ff. (ff.1, 80–81 blank). 14 x 9 cm. Contemp. paper.

Ital. 60

VENICE. Officii e magistrati. List of offices of the Republic of Venice, with salaries. *Venice, early 17th cent.*

Paper. 107 ff. (ff.103–107 blank). 11 x 7.5 cm. Contemp. vellum.

Ital. 61

CLAUDIUS CLAUDIANUS. De la rapina di Proserpina [tradotta] di Livio Sanuto, with dedication "Al reverendis et illustrissimo signor il card. di Trento." *Lombardy(?), before 1546.*

Vellum. 73 ff. (ff.1–2 and 70–73 blank). 21 x 14 cm. 18th-cent. gilt leather.—Inscription at end: "19 ienno [januario?] 1546 A[lexandro?] Fascoli[?]." Accordingly this ms. precedes the first printing of the text, in 1551, by at least 5 years. Bookplate of J. J. Middleton; left to Henry Middleton of South Carolina in 1849.

Ital. 62

PATRITIO DE ROSSI. Il sacco di Roma.—IDEM. Compendio delli casi più degni e memorandi occorsi nelli pontificati da Gregorio XIII sino ad Innocenzo X. *Italy, 17th cent.*

Paper. 1131, 41 pp. 26.5 x 19 cm. Contemp. gilt calf.—Prov.: Francesco Casado y Velas Chesa (17th cent.); E. Silvestri (1908).

Ital. 63

CALISTO MAZZOLLA (or Mazzuola). Filofistea: nella quale, in un'essamerone di sei giornate, si va altamente discorrendo, et pratticando, come con amor naturale, et divino, tutte le creature . . . si sforzino, et attender debbano all'ordine . . . dal suo creatore, with dedication "All'illustrissimo et reverendissimo cardinal Colonna." *Rome, 1561.*

Paper. 425 ff. 28 x 18 cm. Contemp. morocco with Cardinal Colonna's arms, and his name on f.2.

Ital. 64

VENICE, Deputazione all'Agricoltura del Magistrato delli Beni Inculti. Copies of letters, mostly sent to Spalato, by the Deputazione and related bodies, concerned with Dalmatia and Albania, 1788–1807, the last few documents issued under the heading "Regno d'Italia." *Venice(?), 1788–1807.*

Paper. 39 ff. of text and numerous blank ff. 22 x 31 cm. Contemp. vellum.

Ital. 65

GIUSEPPE CASTALDO. Notte sacra. Drama in 5 acts, with ms. corrections. *Naples, 24 June 1645;* written by Domenico Caravita.

Paper. 111 ff. 15 x 10.5 cm. Contemp. vellum.—The author is not listed in N. F. Haym, *Biblioteca italiana* (who lists a Giulio Cesare Castaldo) or in B. Gamba, *Serie dei testi*.

Ital. 66

GREGORY XV, Pope. Instruttioni data per ordine di N. S. Papa Gregorio XV a Mong. Carafa Vescovo d'Aversa destinato Nuntio alla [corte] dell'Imperatore a di 12 de Aprile 1621; a note regarding the bull of Boniface VIII granting indulgences in Germany is prefixed on f.1. *Italy, 17th cent.*

Paper. 40 ff. (originally numb. pp.52–132). 27 x 20 cm. Boards.

Ital. 67

GUIDO BENTIVOGLIO. Registro di lettere scritte da Monsig. Guido Bentivogli sopra la fuga di Francia del Prencipe di Condé, sino alla morte del Ré Enrico IV, ff.1–90.—IDEM. Registro di lettere che contengono l'elettione d'un ré de Romani . . . scritte da Monsig. Guido Bentivogli, nuntio in Flandra (1609–1611), ff.95–112.—IDEM. Lettere scritte in materia dell'elettione d'un nuovo imperatore (1612), ff.113–140.—IDEM. Lettere sopra le cose d'Alemagna dell'anno MDCXIII(–MDCXIV), ff.141–159.—IDEM. Lettere scritte in materia del convento de i prencipi austriaci in Praga (1609–1610), ff.160–165.—IDEM. Lettere scritte sopra le cose di Germania, et in particolare sopra i motivi . . . dalla soldatesca (1611), ff.166–183.—IDEM. Registro di varie lettere scritte da Monsig. Guido Bentivogli a diversi ministri a Roma sopra varie materie spettanti la sua nuntiatura di Flandra (1608–1615), ff.193–306. *Rome(?), ca. 1625.*

Paper. 1 blank, 315 ff. (ff.307–315 blank). 30 x 21 cm. Contemp. vellum.—Phillipps ms. 5642.

Ital. 68

LETTERA DI UNA MONACA a sua nipote nella quale dipinge la vita monastica, ed esorta la medesima a volerla abbracciare se le pare ai suoi desideri conveniente, ff.3–25, Finestra prima (–decima), Pelegrino e monaca, etc. *Italy, 18th cent.*

Paper. 88 ff. (first and last blank). 23 x 18.5 cm. Boards.

Ital. 69

LIBRO DELLA DISCIPLINA delli spirituali (in 3 parts), *inc.:* Quanto a dio displacia lo peccato dela tepidita; the second and third parts are entitled Libro de la paciencia loquale si chiama medicina del core (f.124v). Chapter XII of the second part (cf. f.46r) was omitted and placed at the end of the codex by the scribe. The actual end of the "Libro dela paciencia" are the verses on ff.125r–127r. *Italy, 15th cent.*

Vellum. 130 ff. (index on f.1 incomplete, i.e. one prel. f. missing; one more f. <131> cut out at end). 21 x 15 cm. Contemp. blind-stamped calf over wooden boards.

Ital. 70

DEL NASCIMENTO DELLA VERGINE MARIA et del nascimento del nostro signore yhesu christo salvatore et molti miracoli di nostra donna et la inventione della cintola, ff.1–48, *inc.:* La beata vergine maria la quale fu madre di Christo . . . (dated Sept. 22, 1473).—*With* PASSIONE E RESURREZIONE di Christo, (2,208 lines of verse = 278 eight-line stanzas), ff.51–97, *inc.:* O increata maesta di dio/ o infinita eterna potenza/ . . . (dated Sept. 30, 1473).—LA RESURREXIONE di Christo (a continuation of the previous; 1,976 lines of verse = 83 eight-line stanzas), ff.101–142, *inc.:* Volendo della resurexion santa/ parlare chiamo yhesu che re del cielo/ . . . (dated Dec. 6, 1473). *Italy (Florence?), 1473.*

Paper. 142 ff. (ff.2, 49–50, 98–100 blank). 21 x 14 cm. Vellum.—Prov.: Hermann Suchier.

Ital. 71

THEOLOGICAL MISCELLANY: 1. LUCIDARIUS super biblia (lat.), ff.1r–11v.—2. ST. JEROME. Regula (ital.) Tr. of his letter to Paula and Eustachius, ff.12r–13v.—3. History of Apollonius, (without beginning), ff.14r–22v.—4. ISTORIA de Santa Euphrosia, ff.23r–28r, *inc.:* In Anthiochia era uno devoto homo giamato Panutio.—5. DE SANTO JOANNE HEREMITA, ff.28r–31r, *inc.:* Era uno monacho heremito sancto.—6. Qualiter humiliatus fuit quidam rex superbus, ff.31r and v, *inc.:* Se leze che fu uno re superbo e potente.—7. VITA AMELII, ff.32r–38v, *inc.:* Nel tempo de Pinino re de Franza. *Italy, 15th cent.*

Paper. 38 ff., numb. 2–12, 2 unnumb. ff., 21–45. 15 x 10.5 cm. Boards.—Ex libris Hermann Suchier.

Ital. 72

GIOVANNI BATTISTA DELLA TORRE. Qualità di ogni sorte di moneta d'oro e argento. Treatise on coinage and exchange rates, also on bills of exchange and other financial matters, with alphabetical thumb index, ff.1–65.—*With* FILIPPO GONDI. Del modo di fare gli arbitrii. Treatise on the method of making arbitrage on bills of exchange and ascertaining commissions (dated June 17, 1648), ff.66–81.—Catalogue of 140 books, presumably of F. Gondi's library, ff.101v–103r. *Naples(?), 1632 and Florence, 1648.*

Paper. 104 ff. (some few blank), incl. conversion tables. 32 x 22 cm. Contemp. vellum.—Prov.: Filippo Gondi (inscr. on fly leaf).

Ital. 73

RELIGIOUS VERSE (and prose) MISCELLANY: 1. VISIONE CONTEMPLATIVA, (21 eight-line stanzas), ff.2r–6r, *inc.*: Questa si chiama una visione contemplativa la quale visione fu mostrata a uno grande procettore et cosi co lui che cosi vidde la ricopio poi in rima.— 2. Untitled poem (a continuation of the previous?, in a different hand; 35 lines), ff.6v–7r, *inc.*: Pero tipito che tumiri spondi/. . . .—3. ORATIONE, f.8r–v, *inc.*: Qui addomanda la gratia de la quale tu ai desiderio davere, Per la quale oratione te singularmente prego come certa cosa. . . .—4. ORATIONE DELLA VERGINE MARIA, ff.8v–9v, *inc.*: Ad voi signor mio Yesu Christo. . . .—5. [Fragment? of] 2 seven-line verses.—6. LA LAUDE del corpo di Christo (1 two-line and 11 six-line stanzas), ff.12r–13v, *inc.*: Ogniuno adori in questo pan sagrato. . . .—7. LA LAUDE di Santa Caterina da Siena (1 four-line and 7 five-line stanzas), ff.13v–14v, *inc.*: Qual vergine a dio sia tanto acietta. . . .—8. LA LAUDE del uenardi santo, (8 eight-line stanzas), followed by another untitled poem (1 two-line and 9 six-line stanzas), ff.14v–17r.—9. LAUDE del uano parlare, ff.17r–18v.—10. LAUDE di Santo Ansano martire, ff.18v–19v.—11. LAUDE (pestilence in Siena), ff.19v–22v.—12. Prayers, ff.32r–33v.—13. 30 three-line poems, ff.34r–36r, *inc.*: Ave pastor al sommo grado dengnio. . . .—14. FRANCESCO PETRARCA. Oratione optima a nostra dona di misere (Canz. 366), ff.37r–40r.—15. Prayer in Latin, f.41r–v.—16. 2 ff. of historical data, 1186–1327, concerning Florence, in a later hand. *Italy (Siena?), 15th and 16th cent.*

Paper. 54 ff. (ff.1, 10–11, 23–31, 42, 45–54 blank). 22 x 14 cm. Boards.

Ital. 74*

SAPONARA (Kingdom of Sicily), Nunnery of S. Croce (O.S.B.). Inventarium omnium et singulorum bonorum, iurisdictionum, et reddituum spettantium ad venerabilem monasterium Sante **Crucis** terre Saponarie (not identified in L. H. Cottineau, *Répertoire* . . . *des abbayes et prieurés*, < Macon, 1939>). Italy (?), *1654*, with later additions.

Vellum. 20 ff. 30 x 23 cm. Contemp. blind-stamped calf.—According to later inscription, inside front cover, this is the 9th vol. of "fascicolo primo."

Ital. 75

THEOLOGICAL MISCELLANY: 1. LEGGENDE DI S. DOMITILLA, ff.1–49, *inc.*: Volendo dare alchuna chosa e laude e chastitade della verginitade togliamo por a sempro la groriosa [sic] vergine Domitilla.—2. DODICI ARTHICHOLI della fede, followed by the seven works of mercy, the seven sacraments and short prayers, ff.50r–51r.—3. IL SAVIO ROMANO, (79 four-line stanzas), ff.51v–56v, *inc.*: Al nome di dio et di buono inchominciate/ Tutte le chose che l'uomo viene affare/. . . .—4. On confession, ff.57r–76v, *inc.*: Omanda la santa chiesa acia scheduno christiano maschio e femina. . . .—5. LEGGENDA DI SANTA ORSINA, ff.76v–84r.—6. I FIORETTI tracti della storia della beatissima Lisabetta, ff.84r–95r.—7. Four short prayers, ff.95r–95v.—8. ST. BERNARDUS. Orazio ad Jhesum Christum, and other short items, ff.95v–98v.—9. JOHN XXII, pope. Orazione, ff.98v–99r.—10. LEGGENDA DI CHRISTOFANO (Christophorus) [title cropped and unreadable] ff.99v–103v.—11. Short poem; De santo Jacopo; short poem, ff.103v–105v.—12. PERCITIO DELL' ANIMA, ff.107r–129r.—13. SEQUENCES AND LECTIONES, ff. 130r–228v, *inc.*: In cominciano l'epistole e letioni et i santi vangelii i quali si leghone in tuto l'anno nelle sancte masse . . . , numb. 1–43, unfinished by scribe. *Tuscany*(?), *15th cent.*

Paper. 236 ff. (229 to end blank). 21 x 14.5 cm. Early 16th-cent. calf over wooden boards.

Ital. 76

SEVEN DEADLY SINS. Lacks first signature, i.e. part of Superbia, *expl.*: . . . Mapuo bene in alcuno caso temperare lo rigore della guistitia a non punire il peccatore come a meritato. The "Peccati mortali" are followed, without paragraphing, f.58v, line 9 by I boti [voti], *inc.*: Circha i boti nota che boto secondo Sancto Thomaso, e una promessa fatta. . . . *Tuscany*(?), *1455*: Scritto per me Brunetto d'Aldobrandino et finito questo di XXIIII° d'aprile MCCCCLV. a riverencia et honore diddio, et per sua gratia amen.

Vellum. 61 ff. 23 x 16.5 cm. Leather.—Prov.: "Di Bartolomeo di Larione Martelli" (f.1r. name of owner, or possibly author?).

Ital. 77

BENEDETTO MARTINOZZI. Gli amori di Tibullo e Glicera, ff.1v–12r preceded by dedication: Nobilissime puelle Francisce Scotte

... Benedictus Martinozzus ... Salutem plurimam dicit (f.1r–1v). —IDEM. Opusculum ... in amorem, quo ratio ac apetitus loquentes inducuntur (400 lines of verse), ff.12v–20v., *inc.:* Per allentar lo immaginato exilio/ Che amor contanto sforzo tiene elcore/ Nel tempestoso mar senza navilio .... *Italy, early 16th cent.*

Vellum. 20 ff. 26.5 x 18 cm. Illum. initials. 18th-cent. vellum.—Bookplate: "Gualteri Sneyd."

Ital. 78

PHALARIS. Le epistole, tr. from Greek into Italian by Francesco Aretino, and from Latin into Italian by an unnamed translator (Giovanni Andrea Ferabos, or Bartholomeo Phontio [or Fontio]?, cf. the early printed Italian translations—1471, 1488, etc.—listed by S.F.G. Hoffmann, *Lexicon bibliographicum*, III, pp.214–215). With the dedication of Francesco Aretino to Novello Malatesta. *Tuscany(?), second half 15th cent.*

Vellum. 67 ff. (first leaf, blank or with dedication of this ms.?, missing). 18.5 x 12 cm. Vellum.—Macauley Collection.

Ital. 79

PIETRO METASTASIO. Il conclave; dramma per musica da recitarsi nell'Teatro delle Damme nell carnevale del 1775; about the conclave of cardinals selecting a successor to Pope Clement XIV. Followed by "Nell'iminente sopressione de Gesuiti; sonetto" (f.37) and "Scusa dell'Abbate Serto, ritenuto in carcere, come creduto autore del dramma, Il conclave; al sommo Pontefice Pio Sesto" (ff.38–41). *Rome, 1775.*

Paper. 42 ff. (last blank). 30 x 20 cm. Contemp. paper.—Prov.: Giuseppano Fumagalli (f.); from the Morbio Library.

Ital. 80

[TURKISH WARS]. Letter asking military support from the great powers for the war against the infidels. *Italy(?), second half 17th cent.*

Paper. 15 ff. (numb. 186 [187]–200 [201] in a contemp. hand; part VII of a larger ms.) 27 x 21 cm. Boards.

Ital. 81

SIENA. Schedule of tariffs on goods entering the city of Siena, or passing through the city or "contado" of Siena, with appropriate statutes, drawn up by nine citizens (named on f.4) in 1470, *inc.:* In questo libro sonno scritte e specificate tutte le quantita denari che pagare si dieno per nome di cabella al camarlengo ... (f.4r, 2nd para.). Two vellum ff. from 14th-cent. theological tract used as fly leaves. *Siena, 1470.*

Paper. 40 ff. (ff.38–40 blank). 33 x 23 cm. Contemp. vellum with leather bands.

Ital. 82

PETRUS CANISIUS. Due historie christiane . . . , la prima dell' Apostolo S. Beato . . . , la 2.ª del famoso Abbate S. Fridolino . . . composte per il Padre Pietro Canisio . . . anno 1590. Nella stampa di Friburgo in Vehtlandia d'Abraamo Gemperlin . . . in lingua tedesca, e la prima . . . tradotta in italiano. *Italy, early 17th cent.*

Paper. 66 ff. 27 x 18 cm. Boards.—Baker-Sommervogel, *op.cit.*, II, 679, lists this ms. from the Morbio collection as the only Italian translation of the legend of St. Beatus.

Ital. 83

[CARLO GONZAGA]. Amori, vita e morte di Carlo Gonzaga, duca di Mantova, etc., *inc.:* Gli errori di principi. . . . *Italy, 17th cent.*

Paper. 122 ff. 29 x 18 cm. Boards.—Library of Gust. C. Galletti, Florence.—Cf. *Amori di Carlo Gonzaga* . . . , *pubbl. da* B. Biondelli (Milan, Bernardoni, 1861).

Ital. 84

[DICTIONARY]. Historical and philosophical dictionary, with miscellaneous interpolations and additions, *inc.:* [in lat.] f.2r, "ANIMA. Anima est actus primus corporis." The articles vary greatly in length; they seem to be written by the same hand, but at different times. At the end of each letter of the alphabet are blank pages. The contents reflect particular interest in philosophy, classical persons and objects, historical figures, and the Turks. Among the inserts and additions are: Relatione del illustrissimo signore Federico Badoer [Badoaro, Venetian family] riturnato da Carlo V. imperatore, l'anno 1558 (ff.22–33); Novella di Ricardo e Cattilla(?), poems, and short stories, (ff.248–254); beginning on f.324 are largely madrigals, sonnets, canzoni, sayings, epitaphs, proverbs and conclusions; ff. 398–399 contain a cipher, and the verso of f.400 (i.e. the last leaf) a recipe for making wine. *Venice(?), second half 16th cent.*

Paper. 400 ff. (ff.203–210 and 373 missing). 34 x 23 cm. Contemp. vellum.—Macauley Collection.

Ital. 85

ASCANIO SAVORGNANO. Discrittione delle cose di Cipro con le ragioni in favore ò contra diverse openioni, et delle provissioni, che erano necessarie per quel Regno. Fatta per lo Sigr. Ascanio Sauorgnan . . . che fu eletto dall' Illma. Sigria. di Venetia . . . e mandato nel Regno di Cipro per haver la sottoscritta informatione, innanti la guerra di esso Regno. Dedicated by the scribe Francesco Marcaldi "Al Molto illre. Sigre. Giovan' Battista Pio . . .", Ferrara, April 20, 1573. *Ferrara, 1573.*

Paper. 60 ff. (first blank). 18 x 13.5 cm. Contemp. gilt red morocco.

Ital. 86

[ASTROLOGY]. Discorsi dell'astrologia, *inc.:* Molte volte io son andato ricercando nell'animo mio. *Italy, 17th–18th cent.*

Paper. 57 ff. 20 x 13.5 cm. Contemp. vellum.—From the Albani and Boncompagni libraries.

Ital. 87

[BENEDICTINE ORDER]. Declaratorio sopra la regola del padre nostro Sancto Benedeto, ff.1–26, incl. Ordo ad recipiendam novitiam ad professionem, ff.26–30. *Italy, 16th cent.*

Paper. 30 ff. 21 x 15.5 cm. Boards.

Ital. 88

NATALE DELLA LASTE. LXXXII Sonetti. *Venice, 18th cent.*

Paper. 48 ff. (ff.1, 46–48 blank). 23 x 17.5 cm. Contemp. boards.—On inside cover a note, supposedly by Tessier: "Sonetti . . . autografo."

Ital. 89

TEODORO MAUROMATTI. Trassunto ò sia superficiale idea di tutte quelle mattematiche cognizioni, nella quale istruito esser doverebe un officialle, diviso in discorsi sei . . . il tutto estratto dalle massime di diversi celebri autori, antichi e moderni, dal'Capitan Teodoro Mauromatti, e consacrato al merito sempre grande di S. Ezzelenza il Sig. M. Antonio Diedo. Handbook on fortifications, artillery and mathematical information necessary to army officers. *Corfu, 1749.*

Paper. 16 ff. 28 x 21 cm. Mathematical figures and drawings of fortifications. Contemp. vellum.—Phillipps ms. 2654.

Ital. 90

CORONA DOMINI, ff.2r–17r, *inc.:* Incommensa la regula overo ordine sopra la corona del signore . . .—*With* CORONA BEATAE MARIAE VERGINIS, ff.17r–34v, *inc.:* Incommensa la corona dominicale dela madonna. . . .—EXPOSITIONE de lo patre nostro, ff.37r–42v, *inc.:* [P]ater:Noster: Carissimi sogliano. . . . *Italy, late 15th cent.*

Paper. 44 ff. (1, 35–36, 43–44 blank). 14.5 x 11 cm. Vellum.

Ital. 91

PRATICA deli devoti, *inc.:* Incomenza la pratica deli devoti overo devotioni de menare la mente ad Yesu Cristo secundo le visioni dela beata Mechtilde. *Italy, late 15th cent.*

Paper. 40 ff. (first and last blank). 14.5 x 11 cm. Vellum.

Ital. 92

VINCENZO MARIA BORGHINI (pseud.: Il Boschereccio). [Sonetti] Il Boschereccio contra F. Giovan' Maria Tarsia (Alv).—Il Boscherecci, "Quanto la ragion . . .", Agli scultor da il cuore (inserted f. between D2 and D3 of *Oratione o vero discorso di M. Giovan Maria Tarsia*, <Florence, 1564>).—Il Boschereccio contra alle lasche (f. inserted between D4 and D5).—Il Boschereccio loda questi (f. inserted between D5 and D6).—Il Boschereccio contro la Tarsia, Il Boschereccio, "Nesun puo dar iuditio . . ." (2 ff. bound in at end of Tarsia's *Oratione*). *Florence*(?), *ca. 1564.*

Paper. 10 pp. 18.5 x 13.5 cm. H/leather.

Ital. 93

ROMENA, Compagnia della Gloriosa Vergine Maria et di Santo Egidio. Capitoli . . . nuovamente fatti et ordinati per . . . Francesco di San Giovanni, priore, Bidoro d'Antonio, carmalingo [etc.] . . . composti per Sig. Nicholo di Jacopo, rettore dello Oratorio di Sancta Maria a Romena . . . M.D.XXXIX, ff.1–9v, followed by official approval by Marianus Tuccius (in lat.) and signed by notary Bernardinus (?, written "Brnus"; f.10), with later additions on ff.10v–15r, 54 (mention of earthquake), and 73–76. 1 f. vellum and 1 f. paper at beginning and 1 f. vellum at end, contain poems in honor of the Virgin Mary and Saint Egidius. *Castello di Romena, 1539–1717.*

Paper. 1, 76 ff.(ff.16–53, 55–72 blank), 2 ff. vellum. 21 x 14.5 cm. 16th-cent. leather.

Ital. 94

LA MARCHESA CASTRACANI. Comedia rappresentata in Napoli . . . anno 1754. *Naples, 1754.*

Paper. 110 ff. (ff.1, 109–110 blank). 20 x 11 cm. Contemp. boards.

Ital. 95

MARCO FOSCARINI. Relazione dell'ambaschiatore Marco Foscarini fatta al Smo. Senato di Venezia nel ritorno della sua solemne ambaschiata dalla Real Corte di Torino. L'anno 1743. *Venice, after March 1743.*

Paper. 106 ff. 23 x 17.5 cm. Contemp. vellum.

Ital. 96

HENRY II of Lorraine, Duke of Guise. Memorie nelle quali si contengono tutti gli accidenti più notabili arrivati in Napoli pendente le ultime sollevationi, e tutti gli intrighi piu segreti di questo principe con la nobiltà, e de gli Spagnuoli col popolo, tirate dal francese nell' idioma italiano da D. Pietro Guzzotti. 1647. e 1648. *Italy, 17th cent.*

Paper. Title, 257 ff. 26 x 20 cm. Contemp. calf.

Ad. Ital. 95: Cf. Antonibon, *op. cit.*, p. 114.

Ital. 97

PASSIONE. Passion of Christ and apocryphal stories (incl. tr. from the Nicodemus Gospel), *inc.*: Aprosimando la festa de la pasqua. *Lombardy, second half 15th cent.*

Paper. 69 ff. (blank f. at beginning and several ff. at end missing). 29 x 21 cm. H/vellum.—G. Martini collection.

Ital. 98

[NAPLES]. Li diornali del'historie del Regno di Napoli [1266–1478] che si conservano per li signori duchi di Monteleone. Da Ettore Capece Latro Napolitano (probably the person who commissioned this ms.) *Naples, first half 17th cent.*

Paper. Title, 177 ff. 24 x 19 cm. Boards.

Ital. 99

GIOVANNI DOLFINI. Relatione nel suo ritorno [a Venezia] dall ambascieria di Roma [corte di Clemente VIII]. *Venice, ca. 1598.*

Paper. 70 ff. 27 x 20 cm. Contemp. boards.

Ital. 100

NICOLÒ MOROSINI. Relatione della corte di Francia fatta dall' Eccmo. Sigr. Nicolò Morosini, ambasciatore della serma. Republica di Venetia appresso Sua Maestà . . . l'anno 1655. *Venice, 1655.*

Paper. 92 ff. (last blank). 26 x 20 cm. Contemp. vellum.—"Ex m.s. Caes. Card.[inale] Rasponi."

Ital. 101

[PISA]. Compendio delle istorie di Pisa [1498–1512]. *Pisa(?), 1512.*

Paper. 100 ff. (ff.1–2, 87–100 blank). 28.5 x 21 cm. Contemp. vellum.

Ital. 102

NAFISSA. La Nafissa, o vero lo sforzo poetico deli abbate D. G. P. tra gli Academici indiavolati detto S. Invelenito. *Italy, 17th cent.*

Paper. 10 ff. (last blank). 20 x 18 cm. Paper.

Ital. 103

IL CAPITOLO FRATESCO. 14 (instead of 15?) canti, written in at least three different hands, *inc.*: Canto primo./ Argomento./ Al luogo del capitolo assegnato/ arrivano i vocali à schieve à schieve/ si grida, e romoreggia in ogni lato/. . . . *Italy, 17th cent.*

Paper. 226 ff. and blank ff. 29.5 x 19 cm. Boards.

Ad. Ital. 100: Not in Antonibon, *op. cit.*

Ital. 104

[PORTOLANO]. Maps of Mediterranean ports. Not all maps entered; mostly executed in colors, several unfinished and in various stages. *Italy, ca. 1700.*

Paper. Title, 1, 147 ff. 36 x 24 cm. Title page signed: "D. Rocco invento, per il Sigr: Cap: Tore." and "R. Cornico pinxit." Contemp. calf.

Ital. 105

GIOVANNI BOCCACCIO. Alcune novelle [Giorn, V, nov. 1–2, 5; Giorn. X, nov. 3, 10] . . . tradotte in verso sciolto per Riccardo Petroni da Siena; dedicated to Giovanni Battista Alberti. With contemporary [author's?] corrections. *Siena(?), 1731.*

Paper. 146 ff. (ff.38–39, 72–73, 86, 109 and 146 blank), in two different hands. 26 x 15 cm. H/leather.—G. Martini collection.

Ital. 106

MIRACOLI e LEGGENDE. 1. MIRACULO come l'usura e gravissimo pecchato . . . , ff.1r–2v, *inc.:* Un grande husuraio.—2. Uno molto bello assenpro . . . , 2v–3v, *inc.:* Una donna della citta di Chartagine.—3. MIRACHOLO d'una reina, ff.3v–5v, *inc.:* Fue una reina sterile.—4. MIRACHOLO chome una santa donna . . . chanpoe suo marito da morte, ff.5v–7r.—5. MIRACHOLO di nostra donna . . . , ff.7v–9r, *inc.:* Fue in Roma un chavaliere.—6–18. Various MIRACOLI, ff.9v–25v.—19. LEGGIENDA di messere Santo Gilio, ff.25v–27r.—20. MIRACHOLO . . . della vergine Mara di dua donzegli cherano chonpagni, ff.27r–28r.—21. DEL PECCHATO del parlare disonesto, ff.28r–30v.—22–24. DEL PECCHATO de vani e disoluti, and similar short sections, ff.30v–37r.—25. MIRACHOLO et assenpro d'una gentile donna et d'un santo monacho, ff.37r–39v, *inc.:* Una bella donna e molta nobile.—26. MIRACHOLO che facie la vergine . . . , ff.39v–41r, *inc.:* Nella citta di Vinegia.—27. MIRACHOLO et assenpro d'uno gran chavaliere, ff.41v–43r.—28. LEGGIENDA di Santo Alesso, ff.43r–44v.—29. STORIA di Santo Sebasstiano, f.44v.—30. [STORIA d'un romito del contado di Venezia], ff.50v–52r.—31. [Leggenda di Susanna], ff.52r–53v.—32. Ff.53 to end follow a few more short sections. *Tuscany(?), second quarter 15th cent.*

Paper. 61 ff. (a few at end missing). 29 x 19.5 cm. Boards.—Prov.: H. Suchier; G. Martini.

Ital. 107

CESARE RESSANO (HORATIO and GIOV. PAOLO RESSANO). 48 istromenti di quittanze, ed altri contratti; notarized documents bound together in chronological order. *Pinerolo, 1568–1632.*

Paper. 216 ff. Various sizes bound in 1 vol. (29.5 x 21 cm.) H/cloth.

Ital. 108

PIETRO MAGNO. L'introduttione . . . nell'antica republica romana, dedicated to Cardinal di Gambara. *Italy, early 16th cent.*

Paper. 120 ff. (first blank). 27 x 20 cm. Contemp. morocco.—An edition of this work was published in Rome in 1606.

Ital. 109

DEMOSTHENES. Contra Leptinem. *Italy, mid-16th cent.*

Paper. 22 ff. (first blank). 33 x 23 cm. Contemp. vellum.

Ital. 110*

GIOVANNI CORNER (in ms. Correr, corrected to Corner). Relatione di Savoia . . . al tempo del Duca Emanuel Filiberto. (Cf. F. Antonibon, *Le relazioni a stampa di ambasciatori Veneti* <Padua, 1939>, p. 110, here attributed to Andrea Boldù.) *Venice (?), second half 16th cent.*

Paper. Title, 90 ff. (last blank). 26.5 x 19 cm. Contemp. vellum.

Ital. 111

VIRIDARIUM consolationis (not identical with the Viridarium of William of Auvergne), ff.1r–25v, *inc.:* Si chome la misericordia ella verita.—*With* On virtues and vices, ff.25v–52v, *inc.:* Chonsiderando una stagione. *Italy, 15th cent.*

Paper. 52 ff. 29.5 x 22.5 cm. H/leather.—Prov.: Hermann Suchier.

Ital. 112

BERNARDINO CENCI. Comedie (Il trionfo della belleza; L'Alceste; L'amante occulto; Dall'odio, l'amore; Le gare dell'amicitia). *Perugia or Pistoia, ca. 1695.*

Paper. 4 ff., 390 pp. 26.5 x 19 cm. Contemp. vellum.—Prov.: Giuseppe Martini.

Ital. 113

[ROVIGO]. Collection of 14 documents relating to real estate, wills and investitures of the town and territory of Rovigo. *Rovigo, 1276, 1428–1474.*

Vellum. 14 ff. Various sizes. Unbound.

Ital. 114

CANZONI SICILIANE raccolte da diversi autori [followed by] Domnos Iosephos Amarchios anno a partu virginis 1653 [name of compiler?, in Greek letters, i consistently spelled η]. *Sicily, 1653.*

Paper. Title, 175 ff. 13.5 x 9.5 cm. Vellum.—Prov.: Walther Sneyd; Arthur John Butler; Giuseppe Martini.—Anthology of almost 700 stanzas in ottava rima.

Ital. 115

SICILIAN RELIGIOUS POETRY. 60 poems in ottava rima, in Sicilian dialect. *Sicily, early 17th cent.*

Paper. 148 ff. 9 x 14 cm. Contemp. vellum.—Prov.: Giuseppe Martini.

Ital. 116

[VENICE]. La zucchetta onde si contiene tutte le rettorie di questo serenissimo dominio . . . con il cognome di tutte la casade nobili. *Venice, early 18th cent.*

Paper. 85 ff. 16.5 x 11 cm. Title within decorative border. Contemp. paper.—Prov.: Giuseppe Martini.

Ital. 117

ST. JOHANNES CHRYSOSTOMUS. De reparatione lapsi hominis, ital., *inc.* (title): Questo e el libro de San Zuanne . . . scripto a Demetrio . . . (text) Chi dara laqua al mio chavo. *Vicenza, Nov. 29, 1456* (?, cf. colophon f.69r: "fo compida questa translacione").

Vellum. 69 ff. 16 x 11 cm. Contemp. stamped calf over wooden boards (rebacked).—Donation plate from Georges d'Aubusson de la Feuillade to the Jesuit College of Metz, 1693; ms. inscription of same college (f.1r); Giuseppe Martini.

Ital. 118

SAPPHO. La Faoniade; inni ed odi di Saffo . . . traduzione dal Greco. *Italy, 18th cent.*

Paper. 3 ff. (first and second blank), XXIII pp., 33 ff. (last five blank). 22 x 16 cm. Contemp. calf.

Ital. 119

[BRESCIA]. Libro di crediti; accounts of an agricultural estate (of Jacobus Sanonus?). *Brescia, 1476–1503.*

Paper. 142 ff. 14 x 10 cm. Contemp. vellum.

Ital. 120

TRIUMPHO DE LA MORTE contra li magni & valenti homeni de Italia: cum le additione de li capitani moderni novamente composte & correcta la prima hystoria. 91 eight-line stanzas. *Italy, first half 16th cent.*

Paper. 24 ff. 22 x 15 cm. H/vellum.—Prov.: Giuseppe Martini.—Named in the poems are Sforza, Galeazo, Contarini, Gonzaga, Malatesta, Spinola, Brandolini, etc.

Ital. 121

[TREVISO]. Breve descrittione dell'origine della città di Trivigi [al anno 1319], (cover-title: Storia trivisana); initials L.D.O.M. at beginning. *Treviso, 17th–18th cent.*

Paper. 2 blank, 100, 12 ff. 17 x 11 cm. Contemp. boards.

Ital. 122

AURELIO RICCI. Teatro di casa Carrafa, dove succintamente si vedono le dignità, titoli, honori, e grandezze . . . di ella casa . . . con le gloriose attioni, et ossequii alle serenissime corone d'Aragone, et . . . d'Austria, dedicated to Decio Carrafa and with 2 introd. verses by Giulio Cesare Cortese. *Naples(?), 17th cent.*

Paper. 36 ff. (last blank). 19 x 12.5 cm. Arms of Cardinal Carrafa, printed in red and black, pasted on title. Vellum.

Ital. 123

[COLOGNE, Congress]. Discorso del congresso e la pace in Colonia [1673?]. Apparently a confidential report made to the Pope. *Cologne(?), 17th cent.(?).*

Paper. 6 ff., last blank (numb. pp.133–143 in contemp. hand). 27 x 20 cm. Paper.

Ital. 124

PESCARA PAPERS. Collection of documents, letters, etc., mostly in Italian. *Various places, 1512–late 19th cent.*

Paper. 2 boxes. Various sizes.

Ital. 125

SETTE SALMI PENITENZIALI, in terza rima, ff.1r–8v, *inc.*: Signor nel tuo furor non mi riprehendere.—*With* MARIOTTO DAVANZATI, Trattato dell'amicizia, in terza rima, ff.9r–14r, *inc.*: Quel divo ingiegno qual per voi sinfuse.—GIOVANNI BOCCACCIO. Lettera consolitaria a Pino de Rossi, ff.14v–36r. *Tuscany(?), ca. 1460.*

Vellum. 2 blank, 36, 4 blank ff. 16.5 x 10.5 cm. Illum. figurated initial "S" and decorated border (f.1r), illum. initials. Velvet.

Ital. 126

ALBERO del ben e del male. [Title begins:] Opera nova astronomica intitolata Albero. *Italy, 17th cent.(?)*

Paper. 25 ff. (numb. in contemp. hand 87–111, and 1–25). 19 x 13 cm. Boards.

Ital. 127

ARCISATE. Minutes of March 1729 "sub J. C. D. pre[fet]tore Viglunii [?]" (cf. spine). *Arcisate* (territory of Milan), *1729*.

Paper. 74 ff., 24 blank, all stamped "$\overline{\text{F I}}$." 29 x 19.5 cm. Contemp. boards.

Ital. 128

GALILEO GALILEI. Lettera a Madama Cristina di Lorena, Granduchessa di Toscana [1615], *inc.:* Alla serenissima madama la Gran Duchessa (cf. his *Opera*, v. 5 <Florence, 1895>, pp.307–348). In defense of the Copernican system. *Italy, 17th cent.*

Paper. 58 ff. (ff. 1, 57–58 blank, 1 f. inserted between ff. 1 and 2). 21.5 x 15.5 cm. Engraved portrait of Galilei (Piroli sc.) inserted as frontispiece. H/vellum. —Macauley Collection.

Ital. 129

JOSEPHUS SANFELICIUS (or Sanfelice). Collection of papers concerned with the mission of Josephus as nuntius to Cologne.—1. Viaggio d'Italia a Colonia (in the autograph of Josephus?).—2. Official copies of 21 Latin letters of recommendations from Pope Innocent X to various dignitaries for "Joseph Maria," all but one signed F. Pistorien. —3. Two unsigned Latin papal memoranda.—4. Report, in Italian, on religious conditions in Germany, signature undeciphered, addressed to Antonio Abbondanti(?). *Various places, 1652.*

Paper. 168 pp. (numb. 186–352 in a contemp. hand; several ff. blank). Various sizes, bound in 1 vol. (30 x 22 cm). Boards.

Ital. 130

DOMENICO GUAGNI. I pastori al presepio; dramma rustico pastorale . . . dedicato al merito impareggiabile dell'Illmo. Sigr. Marchese Iacopo Nerli. Preface signed Domenico Emiliano Guagni. *Italy, 1728.*

Paper. 58 ff. (ff.1–2, 58 blank). 21.5 x 16.5 cm. Cloth.

Ital. 131

GIASONE DI NORES. Sphera di Jason Denores raccolta da nobilissimi scrittori, e con novo ordine sommamente facilitata agl'illustrissimi signori accademici innominati di Parma . . . *With* TRIPHON GABRIELLE. Spheretta. *Padua(?), 1589* (date of dedication).

Paper. 108 ff. (last 3 blank). 21.5 x 16.5 cm. H/leather. An edition of this work was printed in the same year, 1589.

Ital. 132

ITALIAN HISTORICAL MISCELLANY: 1. HISTORIA dei re di Portugallo raccolta in breve compendio, ff.1r–16r, *inc.:* Lasciando da parte l'antichissima historia dei re et signori di Portugallo.—2. RELA-

TIONE di tutta la Provincia di Dalmatia, ff.17r–57v, *inc.:* Fra l'altre bonissime leggi di questa bene instituta republica.—3. JULIUS III, Pope. Instruttioni e memoriali 1551, several signed Julius Cananus, ff.59r–105r.—4. PIUS IV, Pope. Copia della lettera che scrisse . . . al ser^{mo} doge di Venetia (Sept. 23, 1560) with Reposta della ser^{ma} Signoria di Venetia (Oct. 3, 1560), ff.109r–111v.—5. INSTRUTTIONI E MEMORIALI, 1553–1554 (à Honofrio Camaiano per li SS^i duca et duchessa di Fiorenza; per Giovanni Andrea Vimercato; per Achille de Grassi; per Giuliano Cesaria; à Antonio Augustino), ff.113r–134r.— 6. DISCORSO sopra la riforma, ff.135r–146r.—7. ANTONIO DORIA. Discorso sopre le cose turchesche, ff.147r–151v.—8. INFORMATIONE del successo di queste armate, ff.152r–155v.—9. GIOVANNI ANDREA DORIA. Scrittura (signed by G. A. Doria; autograph?), ff.162r–169r.—11. DISCORSO sopra le scritture, che si sono vedute intorno al disparer nato tra il Sig. Marc Antonio Colonna et il Sig. Giovanni Andrea Doria, ff.170r–180r.—12–14. Three minor tracts (Summario; Copia di una lettera; Modus in visitatione), ff.182r–195v. *Italy, second half 16th cent.,* written in a variety of hands, on different papers.

Paper. 195 ff. (ff.58, 106–108, 112, 161, 181, 190 and 195 blank). 27.5 x 20.5 cm. Contemp. vellum.

Ital. 133

DESCRIZZIONE della Germania. Anonymous autograph ms. with corrections and annotations throughout. *Italy(?), ca. 1800.*

Paper. 128 ff. (top of f.1, with title, torn off, but supplied in slightly later hand). 30.5 x 21 cm. Contemp. vellum.—Prov.: Lord Guilford; Phillipps ms. 5170.

Ital. 134

CESARE CORTE (or Curtius). Poesie [Italian and some Latin]; idilli; orazioni nella sua laurea; elogio e poesie in lode del fù vescovo di Bergamo; avvertimenti sopra Tacito; poesie de mascherati sanesi; versi nel Cardinal [Julio] Roma; lettere, etc., all or most in the autograph of Corte and with his corrections. Bound in the same volume are various writings addressed to Cesare Corte and pieces (mostly poetry) by Traiano Boccalini, Sigismundo Boldoni, Guido Lanzi, Carlo Orchi, Lorenzo Girardelli, Giulio da Brisighella and Girolamo Ghilini. A summary of the contents by Carlo Morbio on f.3r. *Northern Italy, 1605–1628.*

Paper. 120 ff. (ff.1–2, 118–120 and a few ff. within the vol. blank). Various sizes (many ff. had originally been folded) in 1 vol. of 31 x 22.5 cm. H/morocco. Morbio Library.

Ital. 135

GIOVANNI DE FRANCHI (Banking house, Genoa). Ledger, 1638–1648. *Genoa, 1638–1648.*

Paper. 117 (followed by 72 blank) ff. 35 x 24.5 cm. Contemp. blind-stamped leather with gilt coat of arms and date, 1638.

Ital. 137

STORIA dell'impero d'occidente [742–1273], preceded by Serie degli'imperatori d'occidente [814–1792]. *Italy, end of 18th cent.*

Paper. lii, 561 pp. 30 x 20 cm. Contemp. h/calf. Title on spine: Imperador. Par. II. Tom. II. Fragment of a larger work.—Not identical with ms. Ital. 138.

Ital. 138

STORIA dell'impero d'occidente [1047–1272]. *Italy, 18th cent.*

Paper. 1 f., 437 pp. 30 x 20 cm. Contemp. h/vellum. Title on spine: Storia dell'Imp. d'Occide. Tom. III.—Preliminary comparison indicates that this text is not identical with ms. Ital. 137.

Ital. 139

RIFLESSI E DISCORSI politici. 1. RIFLESSIONI politiche sopra Tacito, ff.1-43 (icplt.)—2. DE SUPREMO REGNO . . . dissertatio (lat.; icplt.), *inc.*: Authoris animus et intentio. . . . Quaestionem examinationi inpraesens admoveo, ff.45-56.—3. DISCORSO POLITICO sopra la forza del denaro, ff.57-68.—4. DEL GABINETO de prencipi (Papa Alessandro e il Card. Pallavicino; L'imperatore e il Principe Portia, and other "discorsi" or "concerti"), ff.69-177.—5. IL MERCURIO, dialogista fra Polimede, cavalliere del campo turchese, e Filomaco, cavalliere di Vienna, ff.179-220. *Italy, 17th cent.,* written in several hands.

Paper. 220 ff. 30 x 21 cm. H/leather.

Ital. 140

J. DU FRESNE FRANCHEVILLE. Lo spion Turco a Francfort nel tempo della dieta e dell'incoronamento dell'imperadore nell'anno 1741. Tradotto dal francese dal Michele Giambattista Spreti l'anno 1744. [Originally printed in French] a Londra appresso i librai associati. MDCCXLI, ff.2-142.—*With* GIOAN BATTISTA COMAZZI [GIAMBATTISTA COMMAZZI in ms.]. Tradizioni diverse dall'italiano in francese della Morale di principi . . . dal Michele Giambattista Spreti l'anno 1742, ff.143-178.—FREDERICK II, King of Prussia. Il Contro Machiavello ovvero saggio di critica sopra il Principe di Machiavello publicato da Monsieur de Voltaire. Nuova edizione dove sonosi aggiunte le variazioni di quella di Londra. Tradduzione di Giovanni Battista Spreti, fatta in tempo dalla villegiatura l'anno 1741 [dated at end "25 giugno 1743"], 352 pp. *Italy?, 1741–44.*

Paper. 179 ff. (first and last blank), 352 pp. 29.5 x 21 cm. Contemp. h/leather.—Ms. written by Michele Giovanni Battista Spreti? With contemp. corrections throughout, especially in the second and third parts.

Ital. 141

[PAPACY]. Istruzioni, memoriali, lettere, ricordi, 1534–1596. *Italy, 17th cent.*

Paper. 6,298 ff. (last blank). 33.5 x 23 cm. Contemp. vellum. Title on spine: Tomus VI.—Prov.: L. Santacroce [Florence?].—Ff.1–157 consist largely of copies of instructions to legates in the Holy Roman Empire under Popes Paul III, Julius III and Pius IV; this part ends with instructions by Carlo Borromeo to Carlo Visconti for the Council of Trent, dated 1563.—Ff.157v–186v are mostly copies of letters concerned with Germany, 1537–1560.—Ff.187r–250 are instructions 1592–1596, returning on f.251 to 1556, followed by miscellaneous copies and concluding with a "Discorso sopra l'unione et ubbidienza delle chiese Alessandrina e Constantina con la sede apostolica" (f.285r *et seq.*) and "Regem Romanorum et archiducem Austriae . . . esse regem Hungariae triplici titulo . . ." (ff.290v to end).

Ital. 142

BROSINOPIANO (Brusiniplanum, Brusinpiano, district of Arcisate). Vicecomitium in causa detentionis Oratii Molinarii nuncupatus il Suizzeretto. (Interrogation in the trial of Oratio Molinari, accused of having rendered pregnant Johanna Lombardina, daughter of Antonio Lombardini.) *District of Como, 1740–41.*

Paper. 95 ff., 4 ff. (two individual documents laid in). 29.5 x 20.5 cm. Contemp. boards. Each f. stamped FI.

Ital. 143

VINCENZO FIDELE. Relatione di Messer Vincenzo Fidele ritornato ambasciatore per la serenissima signoria di Venetia dal Signor Duca di Fiorenza, del Conte Filippo Maria Anguissola [1561], ff.1-101.—*With* RELATIONE dell'institutione, privilegi, et obligi della religione dei cavalieri di Rodi, hoggi di Malta, in forma di dialogo (Mons. Giustiniano, Com. Cambiano, Mons. Girolamo Quirini), ff.102-213.—RELATIONE et sommario della forma et modo de negotiare con Swizzeri et Grisoni, ff.214-240. *Italy, late 16th cent.*

Paper. 240 ff. 25.5 x 19 cm. Contemp. vellum.

Ital. 144

CARLO CARAFA. Instruttioni e lettere dell illust. et reverend. signore D. Carlo Cardinale Carafa, nipote di Papa Paolo IV, concernenti le controversie e li dispareri con la corona di Spagna cioè Filippo II e

Ad. Ital. 143, no. 1: Cf. Antonibon, *op. cit.*, p. 44.—Line 1: FIDELE *read* FEDELI.

Carlo V con il sudetto pontifice massimo. (71 instructions, dispatches and letters, Aug.1555-March 1563). *Italy, first half 17th cent.*

Paper. 1 blank, 137, 1 blank ff. 25.5 x 18.5 cm. Contemp. vellum.—Prov.: Card. Antonio Saverio Gentili.

Ital. 145

[PIACENZA]. Legal register, primarily from July 1582 to Feb. 1582 [i.e.1583], but with entries up to 1587. (Cover title: "Quartus Inte. N. T. 1582"). *Piacenza, 1582–87.*

Paper. 347 ff. 30 x 20.5 cm. Contemp. vellum.—Name of contemp. owner: Trajano Dordoni (on front cover).

Ital. 146

FEDERIGO BADUARI. Relatione istorica de costumi, forze, e governo civile della Germania, e dell'Italia . . . incominciato sull'anno 1527.— *With* LORENZO CANTARINI. Relatione di N.N., ambasciatore Veneto appresso Ferdinando, Re de Romani. *Italy, 17th cent.*

Paper. 155 ff. 27.5 x 20 cm. H/vellum.—Prov.: Sir Thomas Phillipps (no. 5176).—These texts were printed in E. Alberi, *Relazioni degli ambasciatori veneti*, (Florence, 1839–63), ser.1, I, 371 *et seq.* and III, 175 *et seq.*

Ital. 147

ANTONIO SABINI. Giudizio pronunciato d'ordine publico dal signor . . . Antonio Sabini da Capodista, jurisconsulto della republica di Venezia sopra [J. B. Dubos'] l'Istoria della Lega di Cambrai [fr.: *Histoire de la ligue faite à Cambray*, Paris, 1709]. *Venice?, 1709.*

Paper. 22 ff. 16.5 x 10.5 cm. Contemp. vellum.—Bound with J. B. Dubos (cf. *supra*) and shelved as FC7.D8528.709h.—Prov.: Biblioteca Giuliari.

Ital. 148

[CURIA ROMANA]. Sommaria relatione et breve avviso della gran corte di Roma solo per istruttione di nuovo cardinale (ends f.85v).— *With* RACCOLTA d'alcuni avvertimenti politici di Monsignore [Marsilio?] Landriani [legate to France, 1591?]. *Italy, early 17th cent.*, the two parts by different scribes.

Paper. 4 ff. (introd., index, and poem "In lode della SS. Trinità"), ff.1–70, 72–85 (f.71 omitted without loss of text, unnumb. f. between 85 and 86 missing), ff.86–153 (ff.151–2 missing, but text of Raccolta complete). 26.5 x 19.5 cm. Contemp. vellum.—Prov.: Antonio Ubaldini.—The "relatione" probably deals with the court of Sixtus V.

Ad. Ital. 146: Cf. Antonibon, *op. cit.*, pp. 65 and 61.—Line 1: BADUARI *read* BADOER. Line 2: *vero* 1557.

Ital. 149

DEL REGNO DI FRANCIA. (Title on spine: La Francia). Autograph of anonymous author or translator?, with corrections throughout. *Italy, late 17th cent.*

Paper. 78, 2 blank ff. 21 x 13.5 cm. Contemp. vellum.

Ital. 150

CONCLAVE fatto per la sede vacante di Papa Alessandro VIII, nel quale fu assunto al pontificato il Cardinal Antonio Pignatelli napolitano, che prese il nome d'Innocento XII°. *Rome, ca. 1691.*

Paper. 34 ff. (ff.30–34 blank; old foliation 110–138). 25 x 19 cm. Boards.

Ital. 151

[BOOKLIST]. Enumeration of 26 books (among them Ariosto, Grisone, Petrarca, Bembo, Sansovino), supposedly a bill, but possibly a bookseller's inventory. No place or name. *Italy, second half 16th cent. (after 1567).*

Paper. 1 f. 32.5 x 22 cm. In folder.

Ital. 152

PACHOLO FALCONIERI. Newsletter addressed to "spectabili viro Giovanni di Filippo Arrighini, hon. consolo di mare a Pisa," August 19, 1467, reporting on the campaign between the ligue of Milan, Florence and Naples against Bartolomeo Colleoni and Venice, the armistice talks in Florence, Francesco Sforza and Ferrante of Aragon. *Florence, 1467.*

Paper. 1 f. (14 lines). 22 x 15 cm. In folder.

Ital. 153

LUDOVICO MARIA SFORZA. Copy of sales contract of property "vendita fatta dalli . . . signori Antonio de Landrini . . . e Gualterio di Basilicapietra . . . come procuratori di Ludovico Maria Sforza . . . al . . . Sig. Antonio Zanardo [?] de Lando" of Piacenza, 21 Nov. 1496. *Milan?, 17th cent.*

Paper. 2 ff. (f.2 blank). 30 x 19 cm. In folder.—Prov.: Duke of Parma; Thomas H. Montgomery (acc. to pencilled note on f.2r). Once filed as "cassetta H, vol. V, No. I."

Ital. 154

[POLAND]. Risposta quale l'eletto maresciallo de stati di Polonia nella presente dieta in Varsavia diede alle regie propositioni versa la m[ajestà] regia in nome di tutti li stati, li 26. decembre [?] del passato 1688. *Poland or Italy, 1689.*

Paper. 8 ff. 27 x 20.5 cm. Boards. Autograph?, with corrections.

Ital. 155

ALESSANDRO TASSONI. Alla infante [?] Anna Caterina cantatrice sonetto, *inc.*: Trasmigrato d'Orfeo d'alto tenore.—*With* untitled sonnet to the same, *inc.*: O qual di saggio dar, Anna gentile. Autograph? *Modena?, ca. 1600.*

Paper. 2 ff. (old foliation 653, 418). 27.5 x 20 cm. In folder.—Prov.: Casa Altoviti.

Ital. 156

ALESSANDRO TASSONI. Due sonetti. (1) *inc.*: Vana belta piu non m'aletti . . . , (2) Hor che' n piu vaga, e piu leggiadra. . . . Autograph? *Modena?, ca. 1600.*

Paper. 2 ff. (old foliation 654, 655). 24.5 x 20 cm. In folder.—Prov.: Casa Altoviti.

Ital. 157

[TUSCANY]. Narratione [or Relazione] delle cose piu importanti del Gran Duca di Toscana, nella quale si tratta dei luochi, stati, fortezze, et città e quello possiede. . . . *Florence?, ca. 1598.*

Paper. 6 ff. 25 x 19 cm. Boards.

Ital. 158

ANTONIO ANTONELLI. Spechio di direcione delli pesi, valute, prezii, e pagamente dell'armate da mar, e terre del serenissimo dominio, Veneto, et altre particularità. *Venice, 1727.*

Paper. 271 ff. (ff.2–3, 271 and a few others blank). 18 x 13.5 cm. Engraved title border. H/vellum. Title on spine: Prontuario per le paghe e l'armamento delle milizie venete.

Ital. 159

TRAJANO BOCCALINI. Consideratione . . . sopra la vita di Giulio Agricola, scritta da Caio Cornelio Tacito. *Italy, June 1698.*

Paper. 244 ff. (f.1 with bibliogr. note in a later hand; ff.2–3, 241–244 blank). 21 x 15 cm. Contemp. boards.

Ital. 160

ANTONIO CASTALDI. Rumori di Napoli in tempo del governo del vicere di Pietro di Toledo (ff.1-77). . . . Premessovi un RAGIONAMENTO di quanto successe a i baroni (20 prel.ff.). *Italy, late 16th or early 17th cent.*

Paper. 98 ff. (last blank). 19 x 13 cm. Contemp. vellum.—Text differs from edition printed in 1769 in vol. 6 of G. Gravier's *Raccolta.*

Ital. 161

PASSIONE del nostro signore cio e del venerdi sancto, *inc.*: . . . Facciam conseglio de quel mal factore/ propheta et qual conmone multa gente/. . . . (Passion play in verse.) *Italy, ca. 1500.*

Paper. 58 ff. (last blank). 14 x 10.5 cm. Boards.

Ital. 162

SCELTA DI CANZONI siciliani (di Antonio Veneziano, Cesare Gravina, "Liuni Russelli" [=Leone Rosselli?], Michele Moraschino, Giuseppe Durazzo, Gabriele Cicero, Giuseppe Moretto, Vincenzo Giuffre [=Gioffre?], Antonio Carvuni [or Carvoni, Carvini?], Giuseppe Galeano, Andrea Rizzo, Gilormu La Ma'na [=Girolamo Lamanna?], Franciso Gaita [Gaeta, Gaito?], "diversi autori" e "autori incerti"). Ca. 800 poems; alphabetical index of beginnings of verses on 21 ff. at end of vol. *Sicily, second half 17th cent.*

Paper. 317 ff. (of which 34 ff. blank). 20.5 x 15 cm. Contemp. gilt morocco.

Ital. 163

TRACTATO breve della via della salute: Cum natus esset Jesus . . . , ff.1r-40r.—*With* SERMONE sopra la beatitudine dell'nostro salvator, vide Jesus turbas ascendit . . . , f.40r-68r.—TRACTATO breve della perfectione della vita spirituale, *inc.*: Ogni chosa creata secondo la sua natura, ff.68r-98v. *Italy, 16th cent.*

Paper. 102 ff. (ff.99–102 blank). 21.5 x 14 cm. Contemp. vellum.

Ital. 164

F.T.C. [initials of unidentified author]. LA MONARCHIA SPAGNOLA (with chapters on the relations with foreign countries, incl. Poland, Russia, Turkey, the Western Hemisphere, and a chapter on navigation). *Italy, 17th cent.* (before 1690, a date added in a later hand).

Paper. 141 ff. 16.5 x 12.5 cm. Title border and initials decorated in pen-and-ink. Contemp. vellum.—Prov.: J. C. Jacobi, parodii Papiae.

Ital. 165

BRUNETTO LATINI. Pataffio . . . cavato da un manoscritto del signore D. Anton Maria Salvini con alcune annotazioni de medesimo. *Italy, first half 18th cent.*

Paper. 3 prel. ff. (with notes by earlier owners), 105 pp. 18.5 x 12.5 cm. 19th-cent. leather.—Prov.: Rev. Thomas Crofts (1722–81); H. J. T. (Rev. Henry J. Todd who acquired the book in 1802 and added a note on provenience on f.3v); R. W. (Roger Wilbraham, with notes in his hand on ff.1v, 2r, and the entry "a present from my respected friend the Rev. H. J. Todd" on p.1); bookplates of George Wilbraham and Richard C. Jackson (ms.date 1898).—The ms.

contains apparently only those passages of the Pataffio which relate to A. M. Salvini's commentary. On text and two other mss. see (besides the notes on ff.1v–2r) Antonio Padula, *Brunetto Latini e il Pataffio*, (Milan, 1921).

Ital. 166

[MACCIOCHI FAMILY]. Wills, contracts and other entries, relating to members of the family, in several hands. *Italy, 1665–1834.*

Paper. 182 pp. 16 x 11 cm. A few entries with notarial seals. 17th-cent. vellum.

Ital. 167

GIULIO GAULLI. Lettere d'avvisi ed altro dell'agente [Giulio] Gaullo de Roma (al Sig. Giovanni Vincenzo Ventura, segretario della serenissima repubblica di Genova, Jan.3-Dec.27, 1711). *Rome, 1711.*

Paper. 58 documents, of varying length (1–6 ff.) Ca. 26.5 x 19.5 cm., all folded in archival fashion. Within contemp. boards, front cover with title "Avvisi da Roma, Gaulli, 1711."—Incl. printed broadside, *Editto. Gio. Battista Spinola* . . . , *inc.:* Conoscendosi per esperienza . . . [on devalued foreign gold and silver coins], Rome, Camera apost., 1711.

Ital. 168

GIOVANNI TOMASI DI FIORE [author or scribe?]. Racconto della sollevazione di Napoli accaduta nell 1647, distribuito per giornali sino al tempo, che furono reintrodotti li Spagnoli. Cominciando dalli 7. di luglio 1647, giorno di domenica, e finisce à 6. di aprile 1648, giorno di lunedì [and continued to 1655]. Nel quale anco si tratta dell'inconveniente seguito trà il Cardinale Filomarino, e la città con li motivi ancora di detta sollevazione. *Naples, ca. 1655.*

Paper. 1, 311 ff. 25 x 18.5 cm. H/morocco.—Prov.: Property stamp, unidentified, on title (which also bears designation: manoscritto 15); J. Auld, jr. (?); William Stirling.

Ital. 169

GIUSEPPE CAMPANILE. Memorie appartenenti alle rivoluzioni populari accadute in Napoli negli anni 1647, e 1648 . . . colle annotazioni di Innocenzio Fuidoro. Trascritte da D. G. R. L. in Napoli in questo anno MDCCXXXI. *Naples, 1731.*

Paper. 107 ff. 18.5 x 14 cm. 19th-cent. leather.—Prov.: William Stirling.

Ital. 170

GAETANO STEFANI. Historia della revolutione di Napoli seguita nel tempo di Masaniello . . . 1646. *Naples, late 17th cent.*

Paper. 75 ff. 20.5 x 15 cm. Engr. portrait of Masaniello used as frontispiece, pen-and-ink portrait of the same on f.2. Contemp. vellum.—Prov.: John Auld, jr. (?); William Stirling.

Portrait of Masaniello. Ital. 170, f.2r.

Ital. 171

GIUSEPPE DONZELLI. Partenope liberata. Rivoluzione di Napoli con pienissimo raguaglio d'ogni successo, e trattati segreti, e palesi nell'anno 1647. *Naples, second half 17th cent.*, in three different hands.

Paper. 109, 204, 64 ff. (incl. a few blank). 21 x 15.5 cm. H/morocco.—Prov.: William Stirling, with his brief notes at the beginning and end of each part. According to W. Stirling parts 1–2 were printed in 1647, but most copies destroyed; part 3 had not been printed (cf. f.[63] at end).

Ital. 172

RACCONTO della sollevatione di Napoli, accaduta nell'anno 1647. (Corrected title in a later hand: Raconto della origine et prencipii della sollevatione . . .), *inc.*: Dovendo far racconti. . . . *Naples, ca. 1647–48.*

Paper. 125 pp. (p.72 omitted in contemp. numbering). 33 x 23 cm. H/morocco.—Prov.: John Auld, jr. (?); William Stirling.—Day-by-day account of the Masaniello revolt, incl. copies of official documents.

Ital. 173

ALESSANDRO FARNESE. Letter "al molto reverendo signor monsignor il governatore di Roma," reporting the capture of two priests, to be brought to Rome for questioning; signed by Cardinal Farnese, and dated Sept. 10, 1539. *Nepi, 1539.*

Paper. 2 ff. (text on f.1r). 29 x 21.5 cm. (folded to 21.5 x 14.5). In folder.

Ital. 174

ACCADEMIA DEI RAVVIVATI, Siena. Raccolta delle compositioni recitate da gli accademici ravvivati alla presenza delle serenissime AA. Vittoria della Rovere, Anna Maria Luisa e Francesco Maria di Toscana, governatore di Siena, protettore della medesima accademia il di 13. giugno 1683. (Contains an introd. by Giulio Bandinelli, lecture by Tomaso Maria Squarci, a dialogue between Silvio Gori and Lodovico Sergardi <the founder of the academy>, and poems by Agusto Gori, Ottavio Bandinelli, Muzio Urgurgieri, Scipione Savini, Adriano Ballati, Lodovico Sergardi, Antonio Piccolomini, Pandolfo Spanocchi, Agostino Chigi, Francesco Piccolomini and Filippo Segardi. *Siena, 1683.*

Paper. 34 ff. (last blank). 19.5 x 13 cm. Pen-and-ink drawing of emblem of the academy with their motto: Un raggio di beltà gli spirti avviva.—Cf. M. Maylender, *Storia delle accademie d'Italia*, (Bologna, 1929), V, 375–6.

Ital. 175

[DANTE]. Lettura di Dante. (Lecture notes on the Divine Comedy.) *Italy, ca. 1800.*

Paper. 3 parts in 1 vol. Oblong, 15 x 11 cm. Cloth.—Prov.: Francis Campbell Macauley.

Ad. Ital. 171: Cf. Lozzi, *Biblioteca istorica*, no. 3013.

Ital. 176

DIOPHANTUS. Le quistioni aritmetiche di Diofanto generalmente risolute; with solutions and commentary from Jacques Billy's *Diophantus Geometra promotus*, (Paris, 1606, cf. A. de Backer and C. Sommervogel, *op.cit.*, III, col.1478, no.7). *Italy, 18th cent.*

Paper. 238 ff. (first and last blank). 29.5 x 20.5 cm. Contemp. vellum.

Ital. 177

FRANCESCO BARBERINI. 8 messages in cipher, 2 letters (1 with insert) and 1 "nota," from Card. Barberini to Mons. Verospi, Governor of Umbria and Perugia, 1623–1626. Attached to these are the instruction sheets for deciphering the code (addressed from Barberini to Verospi), one dated 1623, another "rinovata" 1626. *Rome, etc., 1623–26.*

Paper. 30 ff. (some blank). Various sizes, in folder (31.5 x 24 cm.)

Ital. 178

GIULIO SACCHETTI. Viaggio in Spagna (ff.2r-30v); Alcune note de negotii per Spagna (ff.31r-37v); Ristretto di quanto a bocca mi e stato accennare da Mons. Magalotti per conto di Spagna (ff.38r-46r); Ristretto contenuto nella consulta in Spagna (ff.47r-54v); Note cavate (ff.55r-63r); Ristretto della capitolatione [per la Valtellina] (ff.64r-66r).—*With* Pope URBAN VIII. Brevi (in Latin), ff.67v-152r.—PHILIP IV, King of Spain. Lettere del re e ministri (in Spanish) and Altre materie diverse (also in Spanish), ff.153r-275v. *Italy, 17th cent.*

Paper. 279 ff. (ff.276-279 blank). 26.5 x 19 cm. Contemp. vellum.—Prov.: Francis Campbell Macauley.

Ital. 179

[CARAFA FAMILY]. Copia tradotta da latin in volgare d'una scrittur'antiqua de Conte de Ruvo, hora Duca d'Andri[a] de la famiglia Carrafa. History of the Carafa from the beginning to the late 16th cent., with extensive alphabetical index of members of the family (ff. 47-59). *Italy, ca. 1700.*

Paper. 2, 59 ff. (first f. blank). 26 x 19 cm. H/leather.

Ital. 180

LA VIRTU TRIONFANTE; opera scenica dedicata al'altezza di madama serenissima Margarita Medici Farnese, duchessa di Parma (61 ff., f. 1 <blank?> wanting, ff. 60-61 blank).—*With* GIORGIO IPPOLITO GIORGI. Peripecie del merito (1, 69 ff., ff. 64-69 blank). —[Opera scenica, without title, among main figures are Alcante, King of Catalonia; Ferrante, Count of Sessa and Amelinda] (60 ff., last blank).—[Idem, among the main figures are Ermangard, Queen of

Italy; Berengar, Anscar, etc.] (65 ff., ff. 62–65 blank). *Italy, ca. 1700*, written in four different hands.

Paper. 1 vol. Ca. 27.5 x 20 cm. Contemp. boards. With contemporary corrections. The Virtu trionfante has the appearance of a prompt book.

Ital. 181

RIME BURLESCHE. Anthology of satirical poems by Francesco Berni, Andrea Lori, Francesco Maria Molza, and others unidentified, some attributed to Mauro Mattei of Florence (cf. pencilled note on flyleaf), altogether 32 poems. *Italy, 2nd half 16th cent.*

Paper. 4, 185 ff. (ff. 183–86 blank; one f. between ff.62–3 and unnumbered blank f. between ff.51–2 and 106–7) = 188 ff. 17.5 x 13 cm. H/vellum. Title on spine: Poesie libere. Prov.: "All'illustre signore" [rest undeciphered] in more or less contemp. hand, and later notation "No. 405 La" on f.1r.; Giuseppe Martini.

Ital. 182

LORENZO GIACOMINO DE TEBALDUCCI MALESPINI. Ragionamento d'amore . . . fatto nel' Ac[c]ademia fiorentina. Autograph ms.? *Florence, last quarter 16th cent.*

Paper. 44 ff., last blank. 33.5 x 22.5 cm. Contemp. vellum.—Prov.: Gozzini sale, 1925, no. 1045. This speech seems to have remained unpublished.

Ital. 183°

SALMISTA DI DAVID secondo la Bibia con le virtù dei detti Salmi. . . . *Italy, early 18th cent.*

Paper. 80 ff. (ff.1, 78–80 blank). 15 x 10 cm. Boards.—Prov.: Biblioteca S. Francesco (f.1r).

Ital. 184°

[DIPLOMATIC RELATIONS]. 1. CONTARINI, ALVISO DI NICCOLÒ. Relatione della corte di Roma nell'anno 1648 . . . , ff.2–12.—2. AVERTIMENTI politici da osservarsi per chi vol servire in corte, ff.16–23.—3. RELATIONE DI ROMA, ff.25–65.—4. BATTISTA NANNI. Relatione della Germania . . . dalla sua ambascieria appresso la Maestà di Leopoldo Primo per la . . . Republica di Venetia, ff.66–86.—5. RELATIONE delle potenze e forze delli principi d'Italia, ff.89–105.—6. RAGGIONI state presentate ad instanza del Re di Portogallo alla Santità . . . Alessandro VII . . . , ff.108–23.—7. MEMORIALE presentato dal Duca di Terra Nuova, amb. catt. à nome di quella Maestà alla Santità di Alesandro Settimo contro le pretentioni del Duca di Braganza, preteso Rè di Portugallo del'1656, ff.125–36. *Italy, 17th cent.*

Paper. 136 ff. (a few blank). 25.5 x 20.5 cm. Contemp. vellum. Parts 1, 3–7 are the same as Ms. Ital. 44, parts 1–6.

Ital. 185°

MANUALE d'aritmetica commerciale. *Italy, 18th cent.*

Paper. 220 pp. 22.5 x 16 cm. Contemp. boards.

Ital. 186°

Count LOUIS of NASSAU. Lettera del conte Lodovico di Nassau ai popoli del Contado di Ennau [sic?] li XXII di maggio 1572. (Somewhat later copy?) *Italy?, ca. 1600?*

Paper. 2 ff. 27.5 x 20.5 cm. Boards.

Ital. 187°

FRANCESCO MICHIEL. Relatione di Francia. (Report on embassy to Louis XIV, King of France, 1671). With signature at end, and autograph corrections. *France or Italy, 1671.*

Paper. 44 ff. 30 x 21 cm. Contemp. vellum.—Cf. Antonibon, *op. cit.*, p. 58.

Ital. 188°

POEMA sopra le guerre dall'anno 1733 a tutto 1746. Nuovamente stato, corretto et accresciuto, ff.1–18, 25.—*With* SERVIO SENNA. [Pompi?] funerali del Re di Prussia [Friedrich Wilhelm I, 1740?] ideati dalla fantasia di Servio Senna, ff.19–23.—Illustrissimo . . . Comiti Donato de Silva . . . Epistola [in verse], 2 ff. folded and tipped in between ff.25–6.—BELLI ITALICI et praeclariorum eius gestorum compendiosa descriptio. Argumentum [in verse; Lat.], f.27, 19 pp., 1 f., pp.20–67, 38 ff. *Italy?, middle 18th cent.*

Paper. 104 ff. (last blank). 18.5 x 14 cm. Contemp. calf.

Ital. 189°

COMPENDIO di sfera, e di geografia nel quale si contengono li costumi, governi, religgioni, e proprietà di tutti i paesi dell' mondo. . . . *Italy, 18th cent.*

Paper. 2, 251, 9 ff. (second f., and ff.5–7 at end, blank). 21 x 17 cm. Astron. drawings. Contemp. calf. This is v. 1 (of a 2-v. set) only, incl. the "De sfera" and physical geography; the title lists a tract on changes brought about by the Treaty of Utrecht, not mentioned in the contents to either volume, bound at the end of ms.

Ital. 190°

SAVERIO DE COLLA. Passi istorici e morali che possono servire d'instruzione a principi, a loro ministri, e generali. *Italy, 18th cent.*

Paper. 40 ff. (ff.38–40 blank), 140 pp., pp.142–524. 23.5 x 17 cm. Contemp. vellum.

Ital. 191°

[FAENZA]. Cronaca, e leggende inedite Faentine. With ms. corrections, additions, deletions and editorial notations. *Italy, 18th cent.*

Paper. 150 ff. (3 ff. at beginning removed). 30 x 20.5 cm. H/leather.

Ital. 192°

CAPITULATIONI of "il Landrichter, capitani e consiglio" della Lega grigia, addressed to the "Duca di Feria, per S.M. Cattolica governatore dello stato di Milano e capitano generale in Italia." *Italy, 1621.*

Paper. 2 ff. 31 x 20 cm. In folder.

Ital. 193°

GIOVANNI DELFINO. La Lucrezia; tragedia, ff.1–86.—*With* IDEM. La Cleopatra, ff.89–174.—IDEM. Il Medoro, ff.177–237.—IDEM. Il Creso, ff.241–346. *Italy, 18th cent.*

Paper. 2 blank, 346, 2 blank ff. 27 x 20 cm. Contemp. boards.

Ital. 194°

SEBASTIANO CHIESA. Capitolo de frati; distinta raguaglio de loro usi, maneggi e costumi. Opera del patre N. N. Agostiniano. (A. de Backer and C. Sommervogel, *op. cit.*, II, 1124–5, C, describe a ms. of the same text under title "Il capitolo fratesco; poema di Tisabesano Sechia," with reference to mss. in London, Paris and Forli.—Satirizes the monks of the Franciscan order). *Italy, 1754.*

Paper. 2 v. (1 blank, 137; 1 blank, 139; 1 blank ff.; this ms. contains 8 of 16 canti). 16.5 x 12.5 cm. Contemp. boards.

Ital. 195°

GIOVANNI FRANCESCO CACCIANI. Tragico avvenimento di Rosana, reina de' Romani rappresentato parte in Roma, & parte in Cesarea di Filippo, e dedicato alla M. Ill.re Sig.ra Co: S. Chiara Maria Albana. *Bergamo, 1615* (date of dedication).

Paper. 3 ff., 75 pp. 18 x 14 cm. Coat of arms "Clarior his ipsa" (f.2v). Contemp. vellum.

Ital. 196°

ANTONIO DA SANGALLO. [Scritture sul'istoria di Genoa:] La genealogia di casa Feltra et Rovere legata; Capitoli della pace conclusa fra i fuori usciti Genovesi et il reggimento di quella città . . . 1575; Lettera de deputati della nobiltà vecchia di Genova l'anno 1575 alla signoria de detta città; Lettera de Ser.º Don Francisco de Medici . . . al S. Gio. Andrea Doria; Riposta del S.re Gio. Andrea Doria. (Ff.1–2 autograph, dedication to Ferdinand II of Tuscany signed). *Italy, ca. 1575.*

Paper. 37 ff. (f.20 and last f. blank). 28.5 x 21 cm. Geneal. tables (ff.3–4). In folder.

Ital. 197°

CARLO ARCHINTO. Relazione della Corte Cesarea, genaro 1665, fatta del Sen.re Conte Carlo Archinti al Ecc.mo Sig.e il Sig.e Don Luiggi Ponze de Leon, governatore di Milano. *Italy, 2nd half 17th cent.*

Paper. 104 (and 10 blank) ff.—Originally folded; archival copy? 32 x 22 cm. Paper cover.

Ital. 198°

[GIUSEPPE POZZABONELLI, card. of Milan]. Poem in Milanese dialect in celebration of the elevation of G. Pozzabonelli to the archbishopric, dedicated to Giuseppe's brother, Marchese Girolamo Pozzabonelli, *inc.:* Nobellissem sur marches/Don Ironem Posbonell/. . . . *Milan, 1743.*

Paper. 48 ff. 20 x 14.5 cm. Contemp. boards.

Ital. 199°

LA NENCIOTTA, 12 8-line poems, with 9 poems forming the Riposta della Nenciotta. *Italy, 17th cent.*

Paper. 8 ff. (first and last blank). 19.5 x 13 cm. Bound in contemp. calf with F. Bracciolini, La Croce racquistata, Venice, 1611 (IC6/B7217/605c/1611).

Ital. 200°

ERNEA. Dramma [in three acts]. *Italy, 17th cent.*

Paper. 28 ff., (last blank, numb. 297–324 in a contemp. hand). 18 x 13 cm. Boards.

Ital. 201°

OTTAVIO FALCES. Supplica alla maestà del re, nostro signore (King of the Two Sicilies; against the establishment of a Jesuit college at Brindisi). *Brindisi?, ca. 1760.*

Paper. 90 ff. 30.5 x 22 cm. Contemp. boards.—Cf. A. de Backer and C. Sommervogel, *op. cit.*, XI, col. 1104.

Ital. 202°

BENEDETTO MENZINI. Satire. *Italy, early 18th cent.*

Paper. 74 ff. (ff.72–4 blank). 20 x 14 cm. Engr. portrait of author, J. D. Ferrotti del., C. Megalli sc. Contemp. boards.—Written before the printed ed. (1718)?

Ital. 203°
DISCORSI FAMILIARI da diversi a confratelli per la dottrina christiana. *Italy, 17th cent.*

Paper. 50 ff. (f.1 blank). 28 x 20.5 cm. Contemp. vellum, with label on front cover and inscr.: Al molto Rev. Dr. G. Battista Zandonella . . . di Meduna.

Ital. 204°
LETTERE INEDITE del secolo XVI–XVII, con note mss. Collection of 200 letters, in Italian and Latin, the largest number addressed to Luigi (also called Aloysius) Lollino, Venetian patrician and bp. of Belluno from 1596 until his death in 1625, all letters in clear 18th-century copies, with careful annotations about the writers of the letters, location of the originals, persons and books mentioned, etc. Another group of letters is addressed to Wilhelm Schickard, professor of oriental languages in Tübingen. Other recipients are Lodovico Celio Ricchieri, ecclesiastic authorities in Belluno, etc. Among the writers (listed, with biogr. notes in a separate index) are: Gaspare Barleo, Pietro Bembo, Scipione Chiaramonte (mathematician), Enrico Davila, Daniel Einsius (of the Univ. of Leiden), Jacopo Golio (mathematician and orientalist), Angelo Grillo, Domenico Lampsonio (poet and painter), Wilhelm Meursius, Andrea and Donato Morosini, Fulvio Orsino, Antonio Possevino, Card. Richelieu, Martino Sandelli, Paolo Sarpi, Pierio Valeriano (=Giampietro Bolzanio, secretary to Pope Clement VII), etc. The compiler is unknown; most letters concern in some way the town and district of Belluno. *Italy, post 1766.*

Paper. 475 ff. (ff.443–end blank), 16 ff. index laid in. 21.5 x 15 cm. 19th-cent. cloth.

Ital. 205°
FRANCESCO VECELLI. Problemi di geometria pratica, copiati [per Leonarducci] da manoscrito del R. P. Francesco Vecelli, Veneziano, nel Liceo vescovile di Treviso, 1767. *Treviso, 1767.*

Paper. 244 ff. (ff.1–2, 243–4 blank). 24 x 18 cm. With figures and drawings. Contemp. boards.

Ital. 206°
TRATTATO DELL' ASTROLOGIA giudiciaria, preceded by chapter "Della sustanza, et movimento del cielo" and with a "Compendio dell' aritmetica," (ff.150–5). *Italy, 17th cent.*

Paper. 2 blank, 172 ff. (ff.156–9, 172 blank). With tables. Contemp. armorial vellum.—Prov.: Boncampagni Library; Marzucchi sale, Florence, 1827.

Ital. 207°
ESTRATTO delle historie dell' Impero Ottomano sino al 1640. *Italy, 17th cent.*

Paper. 96 ff. 20.5 x 15 cm. H/cloth.—Prov.: Count Paolo Vimercati-Sozzi.

Ital. 208°
FERRANTE PALLAVICINO. Il corriere svaligiato. (50 satirical discourses). *Italy, 17th cent.*

Paper. 146 ff. 19.5 x 14.5 cm. Contemp. boards.—No attempt has been made to collate the text of the ms. with the edition printed in 1646.

Ital. 209°
JACOBUS DE VORAGINE. Legenda aurea, ital., *inc.:* Questi sono i sermoni dell' avento di Christo e poi drie segue le legende di sancti de la corte di Roma. . . . [Text:] Tutto il tempo della vita presente. . . . *Italy, April 19, 1459 (f.154v).*

Paper. 154 ff. (ff.3-4, following "tavola," blank). 23 x 15.5 cm. H/calf.— Prov.: S. Maria Angelorum, Ferrara; Giuseppe Martini. Different from transl. used in early printed eds. Descr. of G. Martini calls it "volgarizzamento del sec. XIV."

Ital. 210°
GIUSEPPE VALLETTA. Discorso della filosofia. ("Testimonianza al mondo dell' empietà della filosofia aristotelica, e dell' innocenza di quest' altra, che chiaman moderna," dealing with classical, mediaeval and contemporary writers, mentioning frequently among many others Descartes, Helmont, Kepler, Gassendi, Boyle, Galilei, Malebranche, etc.) *Naples, 3 May, 1700.*

Paper. 10 ff. (ff.2-10 blank), 212 pp. 21.5 x 15.5 cm. Contemp. vellum. Cf. also Mss. Lea 167, 169-70, 187.

Port. 1°
PORTUGUESE FORTUNE BOOK. *Portugal, 18th cent.*

Paper. 36 ff. 16.5 x 11 cm. Contemp. vellum.—Prov.: Henry Seybert.

Rhaeto-Roman 1
ST. GALL. Statuts criminaeles d'ün hundro comoen da Brawuoing, vertiens dalg linguaigh Tudaish in Romannsh . . . da me Peidar p. Jovalta . . . 1717, 2 ff., pp.1-23.—*With* IDEM. Ledschas et schantameints . . . scritts tra's commissiun . . . dalg Nob.ᵐ et Ill.ᵐ Sigr. Wicari, Sigr. Hans Heinrich Plan . . . 1680, pp.41-86, (with additions to 1724).—COPIA vaira, et expressa dels vairs, et sigillos originâls della chiarta della lia, fatta à Vicarol . . . translata . . . da me Peidar p. Jovalta . . . 1712, pp.1-7 (second count).—REGISTER

dellas ledschas et schantameints, pp.9–12.—DAVARD ils Gôds, cioe Giardauna, et ilg Tex da Latsch, ff.15–16. Cover title: Statuta criminalia et civilia Communitatis Burgunniensis. *St. Gall, 1712–1724.*

Paper. 4 ff. (ff.1–2 blank), 108, 21 pp. (pp.17–21 blank), 2 blank ff. 19.5 x 12.5 cm. Contemp. h/vellum.

Rhaeto-Roman 2

SERMONS. Anonymous sermons, all but one (German) in Rhaeto-Roman. *Switzerland, 18th cent.*

Paper. 1 f., 570 pp., 2 ff. 21 x 17.5 cm. Contemp. calf.—Prov.: Hermann Suchier.

Span. 1

DIEGO HURTADO DE MENDOZA. Poesias y obras. *Spain, ca. 1600.*

Paper. 219 ff. 20 x 14.5 cm. Contemp. vellum.—Macauley Library.

Span. 2

PHILIP II, King of Spain. Carta executoria for Alonso de Montalvan. *Spain, 1588–1589.*

Vellum. 58 ff. 31 x 21 cm. 3 ff. of illuminations; illum. initials. Contemp. gilt morocco over wooden boards.

Span. 3

LOPE DE VEGA CARPIO. Carlos V. en Francia. Toledo, 20 November, 1604, [signed] M. Lope de Vega Carpio (f.61v). Holograph ms. *Toledo, 1604.*

Paper. 68 ff. 21 x 15 cm. Brown gilt morocco binding in slip case.—Prov.: Duke of Sessa (Lope's employer and patron); Salustiano de Olózaga (1805–1873); John Hobart Caradoc, second Lord Howden (1799–1873); Robert Hoe; Mr. and Mrs. John B. Stetson, Jr.—Cf. Arnold G. Reichenberger, *The Library Chronicle*, XXIII (1957), pp.82–83.

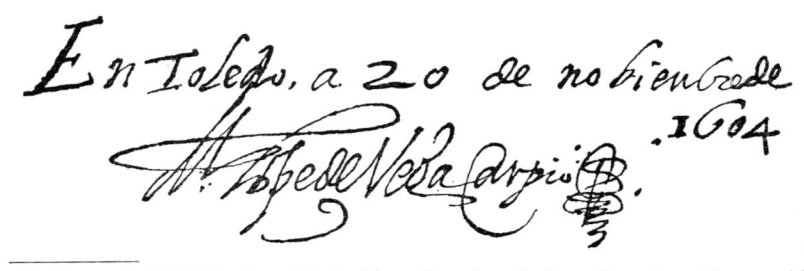

Ad. Span. 3: Published as *Carlos V en Francia, ed. from the autograph ms. with introduction and notes by Arnold G. Reichenberger* (Philadelphia, 1963).

Span. 4

GABRIEL FONTOLI. El Masaniello [Tommaso Aniello]; o discursos narrativos de la sublevacion de Napoles [July 7, 1647], originally written by G. Fontoli, tr. from Italian into Castilian by Padre Alonso de Flores, S.J., at the command of his excellency The Duke of Arcos. With (translator's?) corrections throughout. *Spain, ca. 1650.*

Paper. 60 ff. 22 x 14.5 cm. Boards.

Span. 5

GAUBERTE FABRICIO VAGAD ("Fray Gamberto"). Linea de los reyes de Aragon, autor. fray Ganberto [continued in later hand] Fabricio de Bagad Cisterciense acia el año 1490, 96 ten-line verses, *inc.*: Quando fuel cruel castigo/ Julian conde malbado/. . . . *Spain, mid-16th cent.*

Paper. 7 ff. 29 x 20 cm. Cloth.

Span. 6

[TERVEL]. Letra missa per Dominicum Caberico(?) per quendam nuncium . . . Carta publica, notarized on f.7r. *Tervel (Aragon), August 1387.*

Paper. 8 ff. (last blank). 22.5 x 15 cm. In folder.

Span. 7

[CERVERA]. [Carta] Executoria comforma a pedimiento de Don Alonso Albarez [Alvarex] de Toledo con el fiscal de su magestad y concejo y vezinos de Cerbera [Cervera] sobre el casa de la dicha villa. *Cervera(?), 1610.*

Paper. 22 ff. 30 x 21 cm. Contemp. vellum.

Span. 8

[DIEGO DE ANAYA (Enriques de Funto)]. Inventario de los bienes, Nov. 21 and Dec. 21, 1540, in the presence of Pedro Garabito. *Salamanca, 1540.*

Paper. 8, 10 ff. 29.5 x 21.5 cm. In folder.

Span. 9

FERNANDO V, King of Spain, and ISABEL I, Queen of Spain. Permission to Pedro de Anaya to erect a house, provided it is not to be fortified. *Spain, 2 October 1498.*

Paper. 2 ff. and half a sheet with description in later hand. 30.5 x 22 cm. In folder.

Span. 10

FERNANDO V, King of Spain, and ISABEL I, Queen of Spain. [Commission to Fernando de Quesada to inspect houses capable of defense]. With attached summary in a later hand. *Granada(?), 23 March 1501.*

Paper. 1 prel. (later), 14 ff. 30 x 22 cm. Unbound.

Span. 11

GONZALO PERES DE CARTAGENA. Establishment of memorial masses "en el monesterio de Señor Ssancto Agostin . . . de Burgos," by Gonzalo and his wife, 1517, ff.1–9 (f.10, blank?, missing).—IDEM. Testament, executed in Arroya, 1518, ff.11–26 (f.12 missing).—IDEM. Codicils, 1519, ff.27–30 (last blank). All documents are notarized. *Arroya, 1517–1519.*

Vellum. 30 ff. (ff.10, 12 missing, f.30 blank). 31.5 x 21 cm. Unbound.

Span. 12

SUMMA de las coronicas de Viscaya y algunos otros linages de aquel señorio, la qual yo Castilla rey de armas del susodicho emperador y rey nostro señor halle escritas en un quaderno, escrito ano M.CCCC.iiij ([corrected in later hand to] fortè anno MCCCCC.III.). *Spain, 16th cent.*

Paper. 13 ff. (numb. pp.180–190, <1 unnumb. p.>, pp.191–203). 31.5 x 21.5 cm. Unbound.

Span. 13

[MARIA DE URRIA]. Deed of a dowry of 250,000 ducats to Maria de Urria, "fija del Sr. . . . Juan de Urria . . . dela ciudad de Salamanca, muger . . . de Juan Serrano, maestre sala dela reyna." *Salamanca, ca. 1500.*

Paper. 18 ff. (ff.11–12, 16–18 blank). 22 x 15.5 cm. In 17th cent. archival paper cover (no.26), and unbound.

Span. 14*

[ÉCIJA, Andalusia]. Repartimientto de las tierras de Écija quando segano de los moros (title in later hand on prel. f.). 1. List of property holders divided by villages, ff.1–11.—2. Notarial addition dated 1289 stating that this copy was made from a charter of Alfonso X given at Seville 2 May, 1282, f.12r.—3. Another list of property holders, ff.14–7. (Apparently a version of that of 1263, cited by Manuel Varela y Escobar, *Bosquejo histórico de la ciudad de Écija* < Écija, 1892>, pp. 60–1). *Écija, late 13th cent.*

Paper. 17 ff. (f.13 blank). 29 x 20 cm. 17th-cent. vellum.

Span. 15

PHILIP II, King of Spain. Carta executoria for Juan Ximenez de Angulo, vezino de la ciudad de Sancto Domingo de la Calcada. *Spain, 1564.*

Vellum. 32 ff. (f.1 blank). 30 x 23.5 cm. Illum. coats of arms on f.2v, illum. initials. Contemp. gilt morocco.

Span. 16

FERDINAND V, King of Spain. Draft of a dispatch to Ramon de Cordova, Viceroy of Sicily, stipulating policies in Italy, 1507. With corrections. *Spain, 1507.*

Paper. 4 ff. 29.5 x 22 cm. Unbound.

Span. 17

DEFENSA DE ESPAÑA contra las calumnitates de Francia, dedicated to Pope Urban VIII, signed D. I. P. D. T. (f.5v). *"En Venecia, Año . . . 1635"* (dedication: Madrid, 28 oct. 1635).

Paper. 142 ff. 20 x 14.5 cm. Calf.—"Soy de dn. Antonio Manuel Paxiente, medico . . . . "

Span. 18

NAXAMENT del Niño Jesus. Christmas pageant in Castilian, with stage directions in Catalan, *inc.:* Copia per representar lo acte del naxament del Niño Jesus y altrament anomenat los Pastoreillos y se representa de la forma sequent. . . . With dramatis personae (f.130r), list of exits, etc. *Spain, 17th cent.(?)*

Paper. 1,129, 10 ff. 15 x 10.5 cm. Boards (with ms. title: Pastoreillos).—Gillet Collection.

Span. 19

ANTONIO DA FONSECA SOARES, das Chagas. La Filis; obra heroica tragica. Text in Spanish, introduction and notes in Portuguese. *Ca. 1800.*

Paper. 147 ff. 20 x 14 cm. Contemp. calf.—Prov.: Southey, 1801. "Autograph of Robert Southey," later penciled note on fly leaf; Gillet Collection.

Span. 20

COMEDIA DELS PASTORETS, Nativity play divided into three "jornadas," the birth of Our Lord and the Life of Our Lady (with some stage directions), *inc.:* Le, Le, Le, Le/ de decirlo acabare/. . . . *Spain, 18th cent.(?)*

Paper. 114 ff. (ff. 105-114 blank). 22 x 16 cm. Cloth.—Gillet Collection (his ms. title notation: Los pastoreillos). Not identified in Madrid, Bibl. nac., *Catalogo de las piecas de teatro* (Madrid, 1934).

Span. 21

COMEDIA EL MAS FELÍZ CAUTIVERO y los sueños de Josef, with stage directions. *Spain, before 1791(?)*.

Paper. 70 ff. 20.5 x 15 cm. Contemp. boards.—Gillet Collection. Cf. Madrid, Bibl. nac., *op.cit.*, I, no. 2253 describing a similar ms. of the same comedy; it was printed in 1791. The date "24. de Agosto de MVCCCXX[1820]" on front cover may be that of a performance.

Span. 22

VARIOS PAPELES de poesias a diferentes asumptos compuestos por diversos ingenios, written in a great variety of hands and on different paper. It begins with Decimas (3 ten-line verses, f.1v) and Pintura de una dama (ff.2r–6r, numbered ff.1–5 in a contemp. hand). Included are Pregunta fabio à Menandro; Ignazio de Salazar, Poema eroico; Obras satiricas de Dn. Juan de Faz[?], conde de Villamediana; De Lope de Vega Carpio Decima; etc., etc. *Spain, 17th–18th cent.*

Paper. 1 unnumb., 133, 33 unnumb., 98 ff., and 2 ff. numb. 87–88. 20.5 x 15 cm. 18th-cent. calf.—Unidentified stamp with date 1722 on 15th of the 33 unnumb. ff.; Gillet Collection. Several ff. had at one time been folded, one has the address of a Gomez de Medina. The name Gutierrez appears on the margins of several poems. Title on spine "Papeles varios."

Span. 23°

[VALDENOCEDA, prov. of Burgos]. Notarial document: Sentenzia contra el Almeriens [?]. *Valdenoceda, 1447.*

Vellum. 8 ff. 28 x 19 cm. Notarial signets. Contemp. vellum.

Span. 24°

[VALDENOCEDA, prov. of Burgos]. Notarial document: Sentenzia arbitraria . . . sobre el monte de Axzaedo y otras cosas ano 1459 ante Juan Alfonso de Bene . . . [? undeciphered]. *Valdenoceda, 1459.*

Vellum. 5 ff. 27 x 19.5 cm. Notarial signets. Outer side of document used as vellum cover.

Span. 25°

[VALDENOCEDA, prov. of Burgos]. Notarial document: Sentenzia arbitraria . . . [por] los conzejos de Quintana [?] y Valdenozeda y Lapuente. *Valdenoceda?, ca. 1450.*

Vellum. 6 ff. 25 x 17.5 cm. Notarial signets. Contemp. vellum.

Span. 26°

[URGEL, Canons Regular]. Agreement pertaining to the rents and privileges of the Canons Regular of Urgel (prov. of Lerida), prologue in Latin, text in Catalan, drawn up and written by the notary and rector

Petrus Bertrandus, ending "Bernardus [of Bescaran] consulis vocatur qui scripsit a domino benedicatur (f.11v). *Urgel, 2 September 1415.*

Vellum. 12 ff. (last blank). 22.5 x 15 cm. Two figurated initials on f.4v. Vellum.

Span. 27°

CHARLES V, Emperor of the Holy Roman Empire. Letter to the Duke of Arcos, signed, dated Feb. 20, 1529, stating his desires for peace. Being threatened by the blockade of the Kingdom of Naples and attacks against Sicily, he has decided to aid them and the King of Hungary against the infidel. He orders the duke to make preparations for a campaign. *Toledo, 1529.*

Paper. 2 ff. (63 lines of text on f.1r–v). 30 x 21.5 cm. (folded to 21.5 x 16). In folder.

Span. 28°

ANTONIO DE SOLIS [y Ribadeneira]. Obras liricas. *Spain, second half 17th cent.*

Paper. 1, 88 ff. 20 x 15 cm. Contemp. vellum.—Prov.: Macauley Library.

Span. 29°

LUPERCIO LEONARDO Y ARGENSOLA. Codigo [Poesias varias]. *Spain, 17th cent.*

Paper. 130 ff. (and blank ff. at beginning and end). 20 x 14 cm. Contemp. h/calf.—Bibliotheca Mayansiana, sold in London, 1840; P. de G.

Span. 30°

JUAN DE TARSIS, Conde de Villamediana. Obras satiricas, poesias varias del Conde de Villamediana, non impresas. (Incl. "Decimas contra Villamediana," ff.21v–22v, and Villamediana's "Respuesta," ff.22v–23v; several poems on King Philipp III and King Philipp IV; "Dialogo entre dos pastores Rivato y Pasqual," ff.138–142; "Sermon en titulos," "Comedias," ff.164–204). *Spain, ca. 1700.*

Paper. 206 ff. (ff.1–3, 162–163, 204–206 blank). 24 x 17 cm. Contemp. calf.— Prov.: Valentin de Carder D. de Monte (1849); R. M. Baralt; Hugo Albert Rennert.

Span. 31°

LUPERCIO and BARTOLOME LEONARDO Y ARGENSOLA. Libro de todas las obras que se han podido recoger de los dos hermanos Lupercio y Bartolome Leonardo. (Lupercio Leonardo y Argensola's "sonetos, canciones, decimas, liras, tercetes y otros diversos versos," ff.1–111.—"Obras de Bartolome Leonardo," incl. "Dialogo de Luziano," "Democrito," "Menipo litigante," and "Advertimientos a los diputados del Reyno de Aragon," ff.112–369.—"Aforismos de cartas españolas [y latinas] de A. P.," ff.371–387). *Spain, 17th cent.*

Paper. 12 ff. (ff.1, 11 blank), 392 ff. (ff.278–322, 370, 388–399 blank). 20 x 15 cm. H/calf.—Prov.: Biblioteca de Salva (front cover); bookplate with interwoven DRAH.

Span. 32°

PEDRO CALDERON DE LA BARCA. Autos sacramentales: 1. La redemcion de captivos, ff.1–20.—2. A Maria el corazon, ff.22–45.—3. El valle de la Zarzuela, ff.49–78.—4. El segundo blasson del Austria, ff.79–106.—5. El endulto general, ff.107–128.—6. El jardin de Falerina, ff.129–193.—7. Llamados yescojidos, ff.157–177.—8. El arbol de mejor fruto, ff.181–223.—9. No ay mas fortuna que dios, ff.229–255.—10. El cordero d'Yssaias, ff.258–310. Nos, 4, 8 and 9 "sub correctione S.R.E." *Spain, 18th cent.*

Paper. 1, 311 ff. (last blank). 21 x 15 cm. Illus. initial "S" on f.1r. Contemp. vellum.—Prov.: Convent "A Franca"; Hugo Albert Rennert.

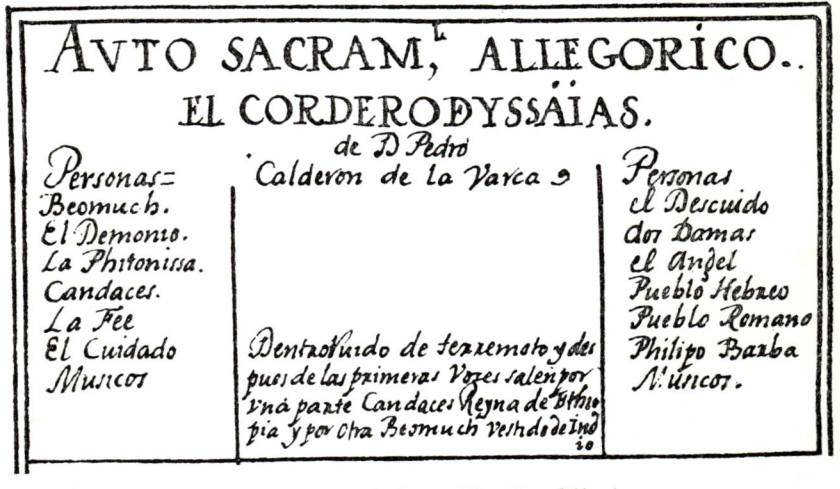

Pedro Calderon de la Barca. El cordero d'Yssaias.
Span. 32, f.258r (detail).

Span. 33°

PEDRO CALDERON DE LA BARCA. Loa para el auto, intitulado La serpiente de metal, ff.1–50.—*With* IDEM. Auto sacramental alegorico: A dios por varon de estado, ff.51–81.—IDEM. Auto sacramental alegorico intitulado: Atu proximo como ati mismo, ff.82–122. *Spain, 17th cent.*

Paper. 122 ff. 22 x 15.5 cm. Contemp. vellum.—Prov.: Hugo Albert Rennert.

Span. 34°

JOHN II, King of Castile. "Carta" on payments of 800, 960 and 1030 maravedi for armaments and a naval force of 40 ships, prepared to aid Charles VI, King of France in 1419; it is addressed to his "contador" Martin Lopez de Cordova, who had been charged with the procurement. *Inc.:* Sepan quantos esta carta vieren como yo Don Juan . . . Rey de Castilla, de Leon . . . et conosco que recebi de vos Martin Lopes de Cordova . . . [stating amount] que vos recebistes por mi mandado. . . . *Ocaña, 20 July 1433 [?]*.

Vellum. 1 f. (113 lines). Ca. 74 x 49 cm., folded to ca. 30.5 x 25 cm. Various signatures on verso. In folder.

Span. 35°

JOSEPH DE CAÑIZARES. Comedias: 1. De los echizos de amor.—2. De comedia nosetrate [h]allaba ese disparate.—3. El domino Lucas. *Spain, 18th cent.*, written in two different hands.

Paper. 192 ff. 20.5 x 15 cm.—Prov.: Hugo Rennert.—Contains only these 3 plays out of 10 listed on f.1r.

Span. 36°

CHARLES V, emperor. Letter to Francesco Maria Sforza, Duke of Milan, on the conditions in Italy. Signed "Carolus." *Madrid, 26 Oct. 1533.*

Paper. 1 f. (6 lines of text on recto, address on verso, seal removed). 20 x 13 cm. In folder.

Span. 37°

LOUIS DE GONGORA Y ARGOTE. Poesias, beginning with 37 ff. "Indice de las poësias, que en este quaderno se contienen . . . ," followed by Sonettos heroicos, amorosos, satyricos, burlescos, funebres, sacros; Canciones, etc. With contemp. marginalia, incl. names. *Spain, first half 17th cent.*

Paper. 37 ff., 452 pp. (title, pp.60–70, 77–8, 135–6, 149–50, 227–30, 275–8, 299–302, 367–70, 453–68 <end of Soledad segunda> missing; the "Indice" also lists the Panegyrico <p. 469> and 3 comedias <p. 489, p. 551, p. 595> which may have been in this or a second volume; since the binding has been repaired and rebacked, the original extent of the volume cannot be ascertained). 21 x 14.5 cm. Contemp. gilt calf.—Prov.: Bateman; Hugo A. Rennert.

Span. 38°

BARCELONA, Universidad. Remonstrance concerning an ordinance of Philip IV, King of Spain, requesting "listas o memorias distintas de los sujetos que siguen los opiniones tomista e non tomista." Copy. *Barcelona, 1682?*

Paper. 6 ff. (ff.5–6 blank). 29 x 21 cm. In folder. See also Ms. Lat. 190.

Span. 39°

SEVILLA, Universidad. Copy of a mandate of Philip V, King of Spain, sent by Lorenzo Angulo, Abbot of Vivanco, to the cathedral church of Urgel granting to the Colegio mayor of the University of Seville the same treatment as to the colleges of Salamanca, Alcala and Valladolid. *Spain, 1730.*

Paper. 4 ff. 30 x 21 cm. In folder.

Span. 40°

[SPANISH UNIVERSITIES]. Representation concerning "becas vacantes" (vacant fellowships?) of the "seis colegios mayores de Salamanca, Valladolid, y Alcalà" to Charles III, King of Spain. *Spain, 1771.*

Paper. 6 ff. 31 x 21 cm. In folder.

Span. 41°

MALAGA, Colegio Jesuita. Autos en razon dela entrega del depositto del dinero que se custodiava en el Colegio dela Compania perttenesiente al espolio del Y. S. Obispo Don Juan de Eulatte, avertura delas escuelas de primeras letras y establecimiento deellas y delas catedras de latinidad y retorica al oposicion conlo demas correspondientte dette asunto. *Malaga, 1768-78.*

Paper. 45 ff. Ca. 30 x 21 cm. Several docs. with stamp "Para despachos de oficio quatro" of Charles III. In folder.

Span. 42°

[SPANISH UNIVERSITIES]. Petition to Charles III, King of Spain, of the "seis colegios mayores de Salamanca, Valladolid y Alcala," in 62 points, Madrid, 11 May 1771.—*With* Royal address to "el rector del colegio del arzobispo de la Universidad de Salamanca," 3 March 1774. *Spain, ca. 1771.*

Paper. 25 ff. (last blank). 30 x 21 cm. Remains of seal on f.1. In folder.

Span. 43°

SALAMANCA, Universidad. Informacio[n] del P. Poveda Domistico, inquisidor, addressed to "Exmo S[or]" [Charles IV?], an "Apologia de la Suma de Santo Tomas." *Salamanca, 1793.*

Paper. 14 ff. (f. 13 blank). 29.5 x 20 cm. In folder.

Span. 44°

JUAN DE LUCAS Y LOPEZ. Estado de la Universidad de Alcalà desde sus màs remotos principios que manifiesta sus fundadores, agregadores, reformadores, sus cathedras y colegios, sus dependientes, y ministros, su jurisdiccion, y potestad, sus bienes, y rentes, su manejo, y distribucion. Signed by author (f.7). *Alcala, 1798.*

Paper. 4, 74 ff., (ff.1–2, 72–7 blank), 1 folded table (chronology). 31 x 21 cm. Contemp. calf.

Span. 45°

ALCALA DE HENARES, Colegio mayor. Alegata, *inc.:* Joseph de la Camera Martinez en nombre del rector, and signed at end: Dr. Dr. Antonio Villanueva, Pacheco. *Alcala, late 18th cent.*

Paper. 2, 164, 1 ff. (first and last blank). 31 x 21 cm. Contemp. boards.

Span. 46°

SALAMANCA, Universidad. Memorandum on the state of universities in Spain, caused by the disturbances at the University of Salamanca, which had been investigated by Don Juan Pablo Forner. *Salamanca?, late 18th cent.*

Paper. 24 ff. 30 x 21 cm. In folder.

Span. 48°

SPANISH UNIVERSITIES. Miscellaneous documents. (Alcala, 1672; Barcelona, 1624; ibidem, 1854; Cervera, 1729; ibidem, 1792; ibidem, 1826; Salamanca, 1729; ibidem, 1779; Sevilla, 1730; Valladolid, 1715; Zaragoza, 1779; ibidem, 1790). *Spain, 1672–1854.*

Paper and vellum. 12 ff. Various sizes; partly printed. In folder.

Span. 49°

BERNARDO PABLO DE ESTRADA Y NABA [NAVA]. Compendio geografico y breve descricion del mundo, dase noticia de las partes, que le componen, de sus principales reynos, y probincias, con algunes noticias historicas, y un resumen del descubrimiento y conquistas de America. *Spain, 1784.*

Paper. 140 ff. (ff.1, 139–40 blank). 20.5 x 15 cm. Contemp. vellum. In form of questions and answers. The author was "comisario ordenador de los reales exercitos, intendente de la Probincia de Valladolid, y corregidor de su capital." He does not appear in Palau y Dulcet.

Span. 50°

LOPE DE VEGA CARPIO. Los Benavides. Madrid, 15 de Junio de 1600. Holograph ms., signed. *Madrid, 1600.*

Paper. 57 ff. (2 blank). 21 x 15.5 cm. Portfolio.—Prov.: Duke of Sessa; Karl Geigy-Hagenbach.—Cf. A. G. Reichenberger, "The Autograph Manuscript of Lope de Vega's Play *Los Benavides*," *The Library Chronicle*, XXVIII (1962): 106–8.

Henry C. Lea Library Manuscripts

Ms. Lea 1 (Lat.)

ST. AUGUSTINE. De spiritu et anima, ff.1r-56v.—*With* IDEM. Soliloquia animae, ff.56v.-143v. *Italy, September 13, 1463*, by a scribe "Gaspar" (ff.56v. and 143v.).

Vellum. 144 ff. (last blank). 16 x 10.5 cm. Two illuminated initials (ff.1 and 58). Contemp. blind-stamped calf over wooden boards, rebacked.—Prov.: Rev. Henry Drury.

Ms. Lea 2 (Fr.)

BROUSSES, Seignory. Livre des cens et rentes, *inc.:* Ceci est le livre des cens et rentes dehus a noble home mossier It[h]ier Bonea, chevalier seignor des Brousses [i.e. Brosses], tant en ble que en deniers. Et autres chousses es porroisses qui sansuyvent fait lan mil iii, iiii, et quatre.$\overset{c\ xx}{}$ (Among properties mentioned are De la Barde, Lezignac, Chirac, Chabaneys [i.e. Chabanais], Lobers, etc.). *Charante?, 1384*, with some later insertions.

Vellum. 83 ff. (ff.9,19,29,39,49,59,68-9,81-3 blank; ff.19 and 81-2 are later inserts). 22 x 14 cm. H/morocco.

Ms. Lea 3 (Lat.)

[ARTES DICTAMINIS]. 1. THOMAS DE CAPUA. Summa dictaminis, seu ars scribendi quascumque epistolas, instrumenta, libellos, ff. 1-86v.—2. JOHANNES BONDI DE AQUILEGIA. Theorica, sive ars dictaminis, ff.87r-89v.—3. IDEM. Pratica sive usus dictaminis, ff.90v.-99r.—4. IDEM. Tractatus exordiendi, ff.99v.-105v.—5. IDEM. De quibusdam usurpantibus alienum officium, ff.106r-v.—6. IDEM. Libellus de epythetis, ff.107r-111r.—7. IDEM. Collectio florum super arte et usu dictaminis, ff.111v-125v.—8. IDEM. Exordia super diversis materiis applicanda, ff.127r-134v.—9. IDEM. Proverbia sive latina cursulata super diversis materiis applicanda, ff.134v-136v.—10. IDEM. Exordia sive proverbia cursulata per alphabetum collecta, ff.137r-140r. —11. IDEM. De proverbiis Salomonis, ff.140v-142r.—12. IDEM. Exordia curialia in diversis negociis applicanda, ff.142r-v.—13. IDEM. Lucerna dictaminis, ff.143r-155v.—14. IDEM. Quare exornationes colores rethorici nominantur, ff.155v-159v.—15. IDEM. Varietates exordiorum quibus a summo pontifice audientia postulatur, ff.159v.— 16. IDEM. Arengae a diversis doctoribus compillate, ff.160r-166v. *Bologna?, ca. 1350.*

Vellum. 166 ff. 29 x 21 cm. 19th-cent. morocco with crossed keys of the Abbey of Melk on spine.—Prov.: Monastery of Melk.

Ad. Lea 3: This ms. was discovered at Melk (G 38 m. 2°) by Pertz and Schottky in 1820, and a copy was made for the *Monumenta Germaniae*. This transcription served for the edition of Emmy Heller, *Die Ars dictandi des Thomas von Capua* (Heidelberg, 1929).

Ms. Lea 4 (Lat.)
BROCARDUS TEUTONICUS. Veridica Terrae Sanctae . . . descriptio, ff.1r-42v, *inc.:* Incipit prologus in libellum de descriptione Terre Sancte. Cum in veteribus ystoriis legimus.—*With* MARINO SANUDO (copied by Peregrinus de Santo Vito from a text in the possession of the archbishop of Ravenna). De modo recuperationis Terre Sancte, ff.42v-49v.—IN LIBRO MONACHORUM de temporalibus contemnendis, f.49v, *inc.:* Mens tua terrenis non inhereat atque caducis.—METRA MORALIUM PHILOSOPHORUM de virtutibus, f.50r, *inc.:* Quicquid agas ratio consulta preambulet actum . . . (8 poems of which 2 are in H. Walther, *Initia carminum*, [Göttingen, 1959], cf. his nos. 3557 and 14595).—HISTORIA BEATI ALBANI, ff.51r-55v, *inc.:* Erat olim in partibus Aquilonis (cf. Bollandists, *Bibl. hag. lat.*, [Brussels, 1898-9], I, p. 34). *Italy, 14th-cent.*

Vellum. 57 ff. (last two blank). 25 x 18 cm. Two illum. initials (ff.1r and 51r). 17th-cent. boards.—Initials P.F. on fly leaf and f.57v, traces of earlier ownership notation (L.S.M.?) on f.57v.

Ms. Lea 5 (Ital.)*
ASSIZES OF ROMANIA. (Ms. unlisted by Georges Recoura, ed., *Assises de Romanie*). *Venice?, early 16th cent.*

Paper. 43 ff. 28 x 19 cm. Contemp. vellum.—From the libraries of the Jesuit Father Matteo Canonici, and the Rev. Walter Sneyd.

Ms. Lea 6 (Lat.)
[AVIGNONESE PAPACY]. 1. JOHN XXII. Register of bulls, interdicts, etc., ff.1r-123r (42 in number, all in full, all pertaining to the struggle with the Emperor Louis of Bavaria; the prefixed "tabula," ff.1-2, *ends:* Explicit tabula in processibus contra Bavarum et adherentes eidem in occupatione imperii romani).—2. INNOCENT VI and GREGORY XI. Register of papal letters, 1352-1378, ff.125r-276v, *inc.:* Et primo littere missive et commissiones facte per cameram apostolicam de mense Januarii anno primo. (Innocent VI, 112 letters dealing mostly with affairs of England, France and Sicily, ff.125-179v; Gregory XI, 142 letters, ff.179v-243; Gregory XI, 23 letters in French, mostly to king of France, Charles V, ff.243-262; miscellaneous papal letters, mostly of Urban V, ff.263-276). *Avignon?, early 15th-cent.*

Paper. 281 ff. (ff.3-6,124,277-281 blank). 29 x 21 cm. 17th-18th-cent. mottled calf, with the arms of C.F. de Lamoignon (1644-1709).

Ms. Lea 7 (Lat.)
RAYMONDUS DE SABUNDE. Theologia naturalis. *Germany, 28 April 1487*, "per manum Johannis Vischer" (f.199r).

Paper. 199 ff. 31 x 21 cm. Boards (incunable leaf).

Ad. Lea 4, no. 1: Better known as Burchardus de Monte Sion.

Ms. Lea 8 (Lat.)

[MILAN]. Proceedings of a suit between the brothers Constantius and Daniel de Vicario, and Jacobus de Pego, syndicus fiscalis. Notarized by Jacobus de Guida. *Milan, 1470.*

Paper. 109 ff. 29 x 20 cm. H/leather.—Morbio Collection (sale 1889, no. 716).

Ms. Lea 9 (Ital.)*

ASSISE DEL ALTA CORTE DEL REGNO DE HIERUSALEM ET CYPRO, tradutte in itagliano [from the French text of Jean d'Ibelin, by Florio Bustron (cf. f.23v)]. (The date of the ms., before the printing of 1535, suggests that this may be the holograph of Florio Bustron). *Cyprus?, 3 Jan. 1533 (n.s.).*

Paper. 349 ff. 30 x 21 cm. 17th-cent. vellum.—19th cent. armorial bookplate "La vertue est la seule noblesse." Sir Harry Luke.

Ms. Lea 10 (Ital.)

[ST. URSUS]. La vita de Sancto Orso de antiquissimo codice latino fidelmente de parola in parola in vulgar lingua tradutta per il Reverendo M. Padre Alberto Bischazza, *inc.:* Nella provincia di Franza imperante Carlo per cognome Magno. (With notarial statement, but without seal or signature, by Johannes Franciscus de Platea of Vincenza. This St. Orso is a local saint venerated in the village of the same name in the district of Vicenza; cf., *Acta Sanctorum,* [Paris, 1866], May v.11, pp. 430–432). Prayer to St. Ursus on paper f. preceding the Vita. *Vicenza?, 1539.*

Vellum. 14 ff. 18 x 12 cm. Decorated initial (f.2v).—Prov.: Sir Thomas Phillipps (no.6894).

Ms. Lea 11 (Lat.)

PROVINCIALE secundum provincias, ff.1-10.—*With:* Table of contents, 26 chapters, of unidentified book on natural sciences, f.11. *Germany?, 15th-cent.*

Paper. 11 ff. 13.5 x 9.5 cm. Boards.

Ms. Lea 12 (Lat.)

BOSCO MARENGO. Statuta. *Bosco Marengo, 15th-cent.* (date 1493 on f.lxxxv); with additions in later hands.

Vellum. 6 ff. index, 1 f., 87 ff., 1 f. (= 95 ff.) 27.5 x 20 cm. Contemp. calf.—Prov.: Conte Pietro Civaleri; Walter Ashburner.—Cf. L. Fontana, *Bibliografia degli statuti dei comuni dell'Italia superiore,* (Turin, 1907), I, p. 159.

Ms. Lea 13 (Lat.)

JACOBUS RAGONA. Regulae artificialis memoriae, ff.1r-15v, *inc.:* Jussu tuo princeps. . . . —*With* JUVENCUS COELIUS CALANUS.

Historia Attilae Hunnorum regis, ff.16r-23v, *inc.:* Hunni qui et Navares. . . . *Italy, 1471* (f.23v: L.D.S. scripsit. . . . 1471).

Paper. 24 ff. (last blank). 20.5 x 14.5 cm. Contemp. vellum.—Cf. J. Rosenthal, *Bibliotheca medii aevi manuscripta* . . . Kat.90, (Munich, n.d.), no.184.

Ms. Lea 14 (Ital.)

[FLORENCE]. Gli ultimi anheliti della moribunda Republica Fiorentina rappresentati alla Maestà dell'Imperatore Carlo Quinto . . . 1535. Contains: 1. GALBOTTO GIUGNI. Narratione del processo della causa agitata appresso la Cesarea Maestà, ff.8r-95r.—2. JACOPO NARDI. Discorso esposto agl'agenti cesarei in Napoli . . . 1536, ff.99r-138r.—3. IDEM. Discorso, ff.140r-170v.—4. LETTERA de fuorusciti fiorentini all'illmo. sigr. Conte di Sifonte . . . 1535, ff.176r-192v.—5. JACOPO NARDI. Espositione del salmo quinto, ff.195r-213v.—6. ULTIMA RIMOSTRANZA o supplica della Republica Fiorentina, ff.217r-237r.—7. CAPITULA ET CONDITIONES PACIS inter . . . Clementem VII et Carolum V . . . , ff.240r-262r. *Florence?, early 17th-cent.*

Paper. 268 ff. (ff.1–5,7,96–98,139,171–175,193–194,214–216,238–239,263–268 blank). 30 x 21 cm. Contemp. vellum.

Ms. Lea 15 (Ital.)

[TURKISH-PERSIAN WAR]. Successi della guerra fra Sultan Amunat [i.e. Murad III] imperatore de Turchi, et Fach Mehemet Catanet [i.e. Mahommed Kutabanda] re di Persia, et li Georgiani christiani dalli 1577, fino 1581. *Italy, late 16th-cent.*

Paper. 28 ff. 26 x 21 cm. Boards.

Ms. Lea 16 (Lat.)

[CATHOLIC CHURCH]. 1. FORME ROMANE CURIE super beneficiis et questionibus, ff.1r-79r, *inc.:* In litteris indulgentie videlicet. —2. THOMAS (or Thomasius) OF CAPUA. Forme Romane Curie super casibus penitentie, ff.79v-104r. (Published by H. C. Lea in *A Formulary of the Papal Penitentiary in the Thirteenth Century*, [Philadelphia, 1892]). *Italy, ca. 1290.*

Vellum. 7 ff. register, 72 numbered ff. (f.22 lacking), 26 ff. (=104 instead of 105 ff.) 22 x 15 cm. H/calf.—Prov.: Henry C. Lea.—Cf. C. H. Haskins, "Two Roman Formularies in Philadelphia," in *Miscellanea Francesco Ehrle*, (Rome, 1924), IV, pp.275–286.

Ad. Lea 13, no. 1: Cf. Paolo Rossi in *Rivista critica di storia della filosofia*, XIII (1958), 163–5.—No. 2: The translation from Greek into Latin was made by Ponticus Virunius; cf. R. Sabbadini in *Giornale storico della litteratura italiana*, XLVII (1906), 36–7.

Ms. Lea 17 (Lat.)*

SUMMULA DE CASIBUS, *inc.:* Peccata que ad episcopum debent micti (cf. Schulte, *op. cit.*, II, 534). *Italy?, 1356* (cf. f.2r; correct date?).

Paper. 68 ff. (ff.1, 67 blank; ff.2 and 86 with extraneous text). 20 x 13 cm. Decorated initials. Bound in 14th-cent. vellum notarial document.

Ms. Lea 18 (Lat.)*

ST. ANTONINUS FLORENTINUS. Confessionale. *Italy, second half 15th cent.*

Paper. 208 ff. 15 x 10 cm. H/morocco.—Prov.: Presbyter Marcus Bonvesinus (16th-cent.); Conte Paolo Vimercati-Sozzi; Henry C. Lea.

Ms. Lea 19 (Lat.)

SCIENTIFIC MISCELLANY. 1. AQUA PHILOSOPHICA atque occulta, f.1r-v, *inc.:* Sunt aliqui dicentes.—2. GEBER. De investigatione magisterii, ff.2r-10r.—3. ARNOLDUS DE VILLA NOVA. Rosa novella, ff.10r-14r.—4. VASA CHEMICA, ff.14v-22v, *inc.:* Primo et principaliter in omnibus.—5. GEBER [?]. De investigatione perfectionis magisterii, ff.23r-34r, *inc.:* Consideramus in nostris voluminibus.—6. PRACTICA magni philosophi, ff.34r-44r, *inc.:* Fiat primo dissolutio.—7. OPUS UNIVERSALE, ff.44r-47r, *inc.:* In primo sublima mercurium.—8. PHILOSOPHUS PERPULCER et nobilis quo ad veram viam universalem [later hand on margin: 2ᵃ pars pholis <sic, for philos.?>], ff.47r-64r, *inc.:* Nunc in dei benedictione.—9. ANTHONIUS. Tractatus concordiarum philosophorum de lapide philosophorum M. Anthonii, ff.64r-75v, *inc.:* Philosophi de lapide philosophorum loquentes.—10. JOHANNES DE RUPESCISSA [Cf. Thorndike, *Catalogue of Incipits*, <Cambridge, 1937>, col. 424, here ascribed to RAYMUNDUS LULLUS], Liber lucis, ff.75v-80r, *inc.:* Natura seu materia lapidis.—11. UNIVERSALE quomodo corpora in primam materiam reducantur [title on margin, in later hand: MERCURIUS CORPORIS], ff.80r-93v.—12. SYNONIMA CORPORUM, spirituum et salium cum signis, ff.93v-102v, *inc.:* Sol O.—13. TRACTATUS UTILIS de materia et generatione metallorum [later hand on margin: "Est cap. 2, lib. 3ⁱⁱ ALBERTI <MAGNI> de mineralibus"], ff.102v-108v, *inc.:* Per artem autem.—14. TRACTATUS PERPULCER de generatione et corruptione metallorum, ff.109r-119r, *inc.:* Queritur utrum per adunamentum artis.—15. DIALOGUS IN MISEROS et stolidos alchymistas, ff.119v-122r, *inc.:* Spero alchimie prosperos exitus. *Germany, third quarter 15th cent.*

Paper. 122 ff. and 1 f. inserted between ff.75–76. 21 x 14 cm. Drawings of chemical apparatus and chemical symbols. H/morocco over original wooden boards.—Prov.: Georg Kloss; George T. Strong; Henry C. Lea.—Several of the

Vasa Chemica. Lea 19, f.22v.

incipits are listed from this ms. in L. Thorndike, "Additional incipits," *Speculum*, XIV, pp. 93–105, and his "Further incipits," *ibidem*, XXVI, pp. 673–95. For note on this ms. see also *Osiris*, VI, pp. 617–630.

Ms. Lea 20 (Sp.)

INFORMACIO RECEPTA SUPER CONVERSIONE SARRACENORUM ad fidem catholicam de mandato reverendi domini Joannis de Churruca, inquisitoris in civitate et diocesi Valentini . . . (f.9), preceded by 1 f. "Comission" by Don Alonso Maurique, abp. of Seville, 1 f. "Tas preguntas," signed Joannes Garcio Settius, and 1 f. "El poder del ordinario," notarized by Bartholomeo Martinez. (Official copy of the proceedings). *Valencia, 1524.*

Paper. 8 prel. ff. (5 blank), ff. I–LXXXV, LXXXV–CLII, 1 blank f. (= 162 ff.). 31 x 21 cm. Bound in 15th-cent. notarial document on vellum.—Prov.: Pascual de Gayangos, 1877; Robt. Samuel Turner sale (London, 18 June 1888, I, no.2991); Henry C. Lea.

Ms. Lea 21 (Lat.)*

GUILLAUME DE MONTLAUZUN. Sacramentale, ff.1–73r (cf. Fournier, in *Hist. litt.*, *op. cit.*, XXXV, 481). *With* ST. ANTONINUS FLORENTINUS. De excommunicatione, interdicto, suspensione, irregularitate, et penis in genere, ff.75r–149r (here attributed wrongly to Montlauzun). *Italy, 15th cent.*

Paper. 152 ff. (ff.74,150–152 blank). 32 x 22 cm. H/morocco.—Prov.: Conte Paolo Vimercati-Sozzi; Henry C. Lea.

Ms. Lea 22 (Lat.)

GUILELMUS PARISIENSIS (= ALVERNUS). De sacramentis, ff.1r–229v.—*With* IDEM. De poenitentia, ff.230r–260v.—GEORG PFEUFFER. (De interdictis, etc.), ff.261r–307v, *inc.:* Siquis ecclesiam non audieritis.—PETRUS DE PILICHDORF. Tractatus contra errores Waldenses . . . 1395, ff.308–362r (wrongly ascribed to Pilichdorf according to W. Preger, *Beiträge*, <Munich, 1875>, p. 10; cf. A. G. Little, *Initia operum*, <Manchester, 1904>, p. 52: Cum dormirent homines). *Germany, 15th cent.* (Pfeuffer dated 1477; written in several hands).

Paper. 362 ff. (5 ff. removed before numbering falling between ff.307 and 308). 30 x 21 cm. Original blind-stamped leather over wooden boards, rebacked.—Given (1560) by Johannes Regensperger to Liboritz(?) in Crailszheim; Henry C. Lea.

Ad. Lea 19, No. 5: Cf. Thorndike, *Incipits*, 2nd ed., col. 252.—No. 7: Listed by Thorndike, *ibid.*, col. 710 as Geber, Liber claritatis alchemie.—No. 8: Cf. *ibid.*, col. 965, perhaps by Rudianus.—No. 9: Cf. *ibid.*, col. 1040 and printed ed. cited under "Licet in ista."—No. 10: On this work by Johannes de Rupescissa, cf. Thorndike, *History of Magic*, III, 365–9.—No. 14: Adunamentum *read* adiuvamentum.

Ms. Lea 23 (Lat.)
JOHN DE BURGH. Pupilla oculi. *England, ca. 1400.*

Vellum. 192 ff. 25 x 18 cm. Vellum.—Belonged (15th cent.) to church St. Daniel; Sir Thomas Phillipps (no.20547); Henry C. Lea.

Ms. Lea 24 (Lat.)
[PETRUS LOMBARDUS]. Registrum primi [-quarti] libri sententiarum, (index to St. Augustine's *Civitas dei*, etc.), ff.1r-33v.—*With* NICOLAS MAGNUS DE JAUR[INO?]. Tractatus de superstitionibus, ff.35r-63v, *inc.*: Quoniam lumbi mei.—BARTHOLOMAEUS OXONIENSIS. Lecturae super "firmiter credimus" lectae in studio wienensi . . . 1414, ff.64r-154v, *inc.*: Ad laudem et gloriam in mense.—CASPAR DE CALDRINIS. Tractatus de indulgentiis, ff.155r-174r, *inc.*: Nostro postulasti.—PROHIBITIO DE PROPRIETATE TENENDA [correct title?], ff.174r-176r, *inc.*: Non dictatis.—DE HORIS CANONICIS, ff.176v-179v.—(Marginal commentaries in a contemporary hand throughout various parts of the ms.) *Germany, first half 15th cent.*

Paper. 179 ff. 30 x 22 cm. Contemp. blind-stamped calf.—Prov.: Henry C. Lea.

Ms. Lea 25 (Sp.)
[MEXICO, Inquisition]. 1. Processo gr^a Ysabel Rodriguez, natural dela Salceda en Portugal, muger de Manuel Diaz, mercader . . . de Mexico, 1, 144 ff.—2. Processo gr^a Manuel Diaz, mercader natural del Fondenel, reyno de Portugal. Vezino desta ciudad de Mexico, 154 ff.—3. Processo gr^a Sebastian Rodriguez, natural dela villa de Sanct Vicente del obispado Delaguardia en Portugal, 2, 179 ff. (Notarized original records of the proceedings of three trials, held in Mexico in 1595). *Mexico, 1595.*

Paper. 450 ff. 31 x 22 cm. H/leather.—Prov.: General Riva Palacio; Henry C. Lea. Cf. H. C. Lea, *The Inquisition in the Spanish Dependencies* (New York, 1908), p.208.

Ms. Lea 26 (Lat.)
TRENT, Council. Declarationes concilii sacrosancti Tridentini decretorum a cardinalibus . . . ad diversos episcopos et praelatos missae, seu ad alias particulares personas acscriptae . . . usque ad annum 1591. *Italy, ca. 1600.*

Paper. 1 blank, 258, 2 blank ff. 27 x 20 cm. Contemp. vellum.—Prov.: "Biblioteca dei PP. Dominicani del Convento di S. Maria della Quercia presso Viterbo"; Henry C. Lea.

Ad. Lea 24: This ms. not included in the list of mss. of the Tractatus de superstitionibus in Adolph Franz, *Der Magister Nikolaus Magni de Jawor* (Freiburg i.b., 1898), pp. 255-64.—NICOLAS MAGNUS DE JAUR[INO?] *read* NICOLAS MAGNI DE JAUER.

Ms. Lea 27 (Lat.)

OTTO III, Emperor. Diploma issued to Adam, son of Teutio; it takes Adam under imperial protection and gives him the right to live under Roman law. *Pavia, July 10, 1000.*

Vellum. 1 f. 44 x 36 cm. In frame. For text and bibliography, see J. F. Böhmer, *Die Regesten des Kaiserreiches unter Otto III*, new ed., 1956, no. 1386, indicating prov. as Archivio Magherini Graziani.

Ms. Lea 28 (Ital.)

CORRISPONDENZA ACCIAIOLI. Two separate collections: I. Four autograph letters by Niccolo Acciaioli and two autograph letters by other members of the family. 1. NICCOLO ACCIAIOLI to Jacopo di Donato and Simone di Lione Acciaioli on business affairs, Naples, 1342, 2 ff.—2. IDEM to Jacopo di Donato and Giovanni Richi on cession of Prato to Florence and founding of Certosa del Galuzzo, Naples, 1349, 1 f.—3. IDEM to Angelo Acciaioli, Jacopo di Donato and Giovanni Richi on Prato purchase, Ascoli, 1351, 1 f.—4. IDEM to same on the political situation resulting from arrival of Emperor Charles IV in Italy, Naples, 1354, 1 f.—5. NERI DI JACOPO ACCIAIOLO to Giovanni Acciaioli on family affairs, Avignon, 1360, 1 f.—6. BENEDETTO ACCIAIOLI to Lorenzo Acciaioli referring to death of Lorenzo's daughter Margarita, Naples, ca. 1390, 1 f.—II. Twenty-nine letters addressed to Donato Acciaioli, ca. 1384–1395, mostly on political matters, by Pietro Gambacorti, Jacopo d'Appiano, Gentile III da Varrano, Galleotto Tarlati, Bertoldo degli Orsini, Rinaldo degli Orsini, Federigo Gonzaga, Conrad von Anchelberg, Roberto Caracciolo, Pietro da Prata, Lodovico Aliotti, Cosimo di Migliorati (later Pope Innocent VII), etc. *Various places, 1342–1395.*

Paper. 36 ff. Various sizes. Each document in individual plastic slip-case, bound in cloth.

Ms. Lea 29 (Ital.)

[MONCADA FAMILY]. Ravaglio genealogico dell'inclita stirpe de Moncadi, ff.32r-99v, preceded by introduction and genealogical tables, and followed by Sangue reale trasfuso dalli rè antichi nelle vene de' Moncadi. *Italy, late 17th cent.*

Paper. 114 ff. 33 x 24 cm. Full-page coat of arms on f.2r. Contemp. calf with coat of arms on front and back cover.—Prov.: D. Ferdinando de Moncada.

Ms. Lea 30 (Ital.)

COSIMO III DE MEDICI. Lettere del Gran Duca Cosimo III scritte al Marchese Montauti inviato di Toscana alla corte cesarea (1694–1696), ff.1-41.—*With* FRANCESCO DE MEDICI. Lettere del Cardinale Francesco M. de' Medici scritte al Marchese Montauti inviato di

Toscana alla corte cesarea (1690, 1694–1696), ff.52–118. (Partly in cipher). *Florence, 1690–1696.*

Paper. 123 ff. (incl. some blank). 29 x 21 cm. Contemp. vellum, Medici coat of arms on front cover.

Ms. Lea 31 (Ital.)

COSIMO III DE MEDICI. Lettere di pugno di Cosimo Terzo scritte al Marchese Montauti inviato alla corte cesarea. Non ordinate. (Partly in cipher). *Florence, 1695–1698.*

Paper. 169 ff. (incl. some blank). 30 x 21 cm. Contemp. vellum.

Ms. Lea 32 (Ital.)

COSIMO III DE MEDICI. Lettere [al Marchese Montauti]. (Partly in cipher). *Florence, 1672–1693.*

Paper. 80 ff. (incl. some blank). 21 x 15 cm. Contemp. vellum.—See also Ms. Lea 198, part of the same collection, but acquired more recently.

Ms. Lea 33 (Ital.)

PAOLO SARPI. Dell'origine de'beni, e benefitii ecclesiastici, e del dominio di essi, discorso (i.e. his Trattato delle materie beneficiarie). With corrections in a contemp. hand. *Italy, 17th cent.*

Paper. 2 ff., 155 pp., 9 ff. 31 x 22 cm. In folder.

Ms. Lea 34 (Lat.)

FERRARA. Collection of notarial documents, incomplete at beginning (starting with f.126). The first five ff. are notarized copies from the year 1637; followed by three earlier documents (1589, 1518, 1506); chronologically consecutive copies, 1626–1668, and a name index (ff.88–92). *Ferrara, 1506–1668.*

Vellum and paper. 95 ff. (incl. some blank). 30 x 21 cm. Contemp. boards.

Ms. Lea 35 (Ital.)

PAOLO SARPI (supposed author). Opinione come debba governarsi internamente ed esternamente la repubblica di Venezia. (A. Bianchi-Giovini, *Biografia di Frà Paolo Sarpi*, <Basle, 1847>, pp. 479–480, no. 1 lists the *Opinione* under "opere falsamente attribuite a Frà Paolo Sarpi"). *Italy, 1615?*

Paper. 84 ff. (last blank). 20 x 14 cm. Contemp. vellum, village scene painted on back cover.

Ms. Lea 37 (Ital.)

CARLO BORGO. Anecdoti interessanti di storia e di critica sulla Memoria cattolica . . . 1787, ff.1r-137v (with contents as described for the printed edition by A. de Backer and C. Sommervogel, *Bibl. de la*

Compagnie de Jésus, [Brussels, 1890], v. I, col. 1797, no. 4).—*With* VILLEGAS DI STAIMBOURG. Lettera . . . scritta all'Abbate Lefeller, e stampato nel suo diario sotto il di 16 aprile 1790, pag. 632, ff.138–139. *Italy?, post 1790.*

Paper. 139 ff. 26 x 18 cm. Contemp. h/vellum.—Prov.: Henry C. Lea.—Incl. the text of the *Memoria cattolica* and the *Osservazioni sul Breve di Pio VI condannatorio della Memoria.*

Ms. Lea 38 (Sp.)

TASSAS DE LA CORTE DE ROMA en materia de breves y dispensaciones: I. De los impedimentos, por los quales no se puede contraher matrimonio . . . ; II. De las causas beneficiales . . . ; III. De diversas causas y materias . . . tanto in foro conscientiae, quanto in exteriori. . . . *Spain, ca. 1725.*

Paper. 49 ff. 26 x 19 cm. Contemp. vellum.—Prov.: Henry C. Lea.

Ms. Lea 39 (Sp.)

PIERRE MATTHIEU [supposed author, cf.f.7r, pencilled note of H. C. Lea]. Compendio de la vida de el Rey de España Felipe Segundo, ff.1r-45r.—*With* CESAR VICHARD DE SAINT-REAL [supposed author, cf.f.45v]. Relacion tragica y veridica de Don Carlos, principe de España. . . . En Colonia, por Federico Barbo, 1680, ff.45v-120r.—Excerpts from various 16th-century works on Don Carlos, ff.121r-213r. *Low Countries?, early 18th cent.*

Paper. 213 ff. 30 x 20 cm. H/morocco.—Prov.: Henry C. Lea.

Ms. Lea 40 (Ital.)

PIETRO DI NORES. Della guerra fra Filippo II, re di Spagna, e Papa Paolo Quarto. *Italy, 1688* ("scritto in Roma . . . 1644, e copiato da me Lorenzo di Agostini . . . 1688").

Paper. 169 ff. 26 x 19 cm. Contemp. h/leather.—Prov.: Henry C. Lea.

Ms. Lea 41 (Lat. and Ital.)

VENICE. Juramentum capitulare, advocatorum per offitia rivoalti, written "in expensis Marco Zeni . . . [et] Francisco Contarini" (f.15r). Venice, ca. 1526, in a calligraphic hand.

Vellum. 15 ff. 20.5 x 14 cm. Illuminated border, initial and coats of arms on f.1r. Vellum, decorated with the lion of St. Mark.

Ms. Lea 42 (Lat.)

LAURENTIUS CYNTHIUS. Tractatus de misericordia ad Jacobum Guicciardinum (= Jacopo di Piero, d. 1490). Epigram of 3 distychs, f.lv, *inc.:* Si cupis in coelum transcendere tramite recto; text, f.2r-9v, *inc.:* Laurentius Cynthius Iacobo Guicciardino S.P.D. Cum superioribus diebus; St. John Chrysostom. Testament (in Greek), ff.10r-v; concludes with epilogue, f.11r, *inc.*: Hec habui mi Jacobe: quae carptim de misericordiae operibus ad te scriberem. Hoc nunc ego . . . addam quod Leo pont. max. dicit in sermonibus, followed by 10 lines of Greek (Phōkyllidou . . .). *Italy, late 15th cent.*

Paper. 11 ff. 22 x 15 cm. In portfolio.

Ms. Lea 43 (Ital.)

PERUGIA, San Lorenzo. Constitutiones ecclesiae Sancti Laurentii, cathedralis Perusiae reformate, de horis canonicis quotidie in choro dicendis. *Perugia, ca. 1628.*

Paper. 33 ff. 22 x 15 cm. Contemp. vellum.

Ms. Lea 44 (Ital.)

[VINCENZO COLONNA]. Genealogica discendenza del ramo del Marchese Don Vincenzo Colonna, principiandola con più certa notizia dall'anno 950. . . . (Copies of documents establishing Vincenzo Colonna's genealogy, with notarization, testimonials, and the seal of Prince Philippus Hercolani at end). *Italy, 1706.*

Paper. 28 ff. 28 x 20.5 cm. Contemp. decorated paper wrapper.—Prov.: Prince Liechtenstein.

Ms. Lea 45 (Lat.)

PETRUS DE PALUDE. Extracts from *Liber bellorum domini*, articles 105–112 and 192–195 concerning the Albigensian Crusade, ff.1r-24r, *inc.*: Centesimus quintus articulus prime partis de bello domini contra quosdam Saracenos et contra Albigenses hereticos . . . habet tres conclusiones; and articles 142–148, concerning the eighth-century martyrs Amelius and Amicus, ff.24v-32v, *inc.*: Centesimus quadragesimus secundus articulus de bellis domini . . . habet tres conclusiones. The ms. ends: "Explicit hic liber/ de pena sum modo liber/Explicit hoc totum/ pro pena da michi potum/ Explicit expliciat/ ludere scriptor eat/. Finito libro sit laus et gloria Christo." *Southern France, first quarter 15th cent.*, by a scribe Rolandus de Monte.

Paper. 32 ff. 29.5 x 21.5 cm. 17th-cent. vellum.—A 17th-cent. note indicates that the complete work was "in bibliotheca nostra parisiensi" (f.32v). By the 18th cent. Quétif could not find the work in the Dominican convent of St. Jacques in Paris (*Script. Praed.*, I, 608). Cf. *Hist. litt. de la France*, XXXVII, 180–82.

Ms. Lea 46 (Ital. and Fr.)

[MICHELE ANTONIO VIBO CORRESPONDENCE]. Collection of 254 letters, 1670–1681, largely sent from Avignon by Cardinal Paluzzo Altieri, Michele Zaccharia, Carlo d'Anguisciola, Giaconto Libelli, Mustio Estense Giuseppe, and others to the governor of Carpentras, Michele Antonio Vibó. *Avignon and Turin, 1670–1681.*

Paper. 510 ff. 27 x 20 cm. H/calf.

Ms. Lea 47 (Fr.)

LIÈGE. Pawilhar. Collection of laws, privileges and customs of the county of Liège, ff.1r-258r, *inc.:* Alyance defencive.—*With* LIÈGE. Constitution du conseil, ff.259r-269v. *Liège, after July 27, 1521.*

Paper. 269 ff. (ff.29,30 and 132 blank). 29 x 20 cm. Full-page coat of arms (f.258v). H/calf.—Prov.: Hermann Suchier.

Ms. Lea 48 (Fr.)

DE LA BEAUME. Relation, en forme d'histoire, de la revolte des fanatiques, ou camisards. 1707. (Copied from the original ms., then in the possession of the Marquis d'Aubais). *France, 1707?*

Paper. 462 pp., plus indices at end. 26 x 18 cm. Contemp. calf.—Prov.: Antoine de Valette-Travesac.

Ms. Lea 49 (Ital. and Lat.)

VENICE. Capitolario de le parte et ordeni del officio di magistri signori tre savii areveder le raxon dela illustrissima signoria per conto del cancello de le 30 e 40 per cento. (Ff.1–5 and 19–33 in the earliest hand, with additions in various later hands). *Venice, 1519–1626.*

Vellum. 63 ff. (f.18 lacking). 33 x 23 cm. Illum. first f. with the lion of St. Mark, three coats of arms with initials I.R., I.D., F.P. and the date 11 Jan. 1519, illum. motto "nomine dissimiles non mente," three coats of arms with initials A.E., M.M., and B.B. and date 1528 on f.34r. Contemp. blind-stamped calf over wooden boards.—Book plates of John Ruskin Brantwood and Edward Cheney, with note "E.C. Venice, March 26, 1835, given to me by Rawdon Brown."

Ms. Lea 50 (Fr.)

NICOLAS DONGOIS. Recueil criminel depuis 1312 jusqu'à 1603 . . . par M. Dongois, greffier-en-chef du Parlement, qui a tiré ce recueil sur les registres du greffe criminel. *Paris, early 18th-cent.*

Paper. 3 vols. (790,660 & 630 pp.). 37 x 25 cm. Contemp. calf. Prov.: A. Taillandier?, who in writing a biogr. note for Hoefer's *Nouvelle biogr. générale* (XIV, col. 551-2) indicates that he owned a three-volume ms. of the *Recueil.*

Ms. Lea 51 (Lat.)

BULLARIUM AUGUSTINIANUM. Collection of papal letters and instruments dealing with the order of the Eremite Friars of St. Augustine, in two parts (ff.1r-69v; 71r-125v). Written "ad usum fratris Joannis Angeli de Crema [by] Antonius Melius . . . con[cepit] manu propria" (f.1r); f.71r contains an attestatur by Georgius Franciotus: "Frater Antonius de Meliis Cremensis, prior conventus St. Augustini Lucae

Ad. Lea 48: Author's full name: Charles-Joseph de La Baume. Ed. Abbé Goiffon, 2nd ed. (Nîmes, 1874).

... nobis exhibuit et ostendit quasdam litteras apostolicas . . .";
copy of notarial statement by "Antonius domini Andreae de Recaneto publicus et imperiali auctoritate notarius," f.125r. *Italy, 1505–1506.*

Vellum. 4, 134 ff. (f.1 and 134 pasted against covers of binding; prel. f.4v and ff.126, 127 contain notes by former owner Federico Patetta). 18 x 13 cm. Illum. border with portrait (Sixtus IV?) on f.1r and border on f.71r, illum. initials throughout. Contemp. stamped calf, spine repaired.

Ms. Lea 52 (Lat.)

VALPERGA. Statuta (incomplete at beginning and end). *Valperga, ca. 1400.*

Paper. 23 ff. (f.1, and one or more ff. at end, missing). 30 x 22.5 cm. Portfolio.—Cf. L. Fontana, *Bibliografia degli statuti dei comuni dell'Italia superiore*, (Turin, 1907), III, pp.260–261, describing two 14th-cent. mss., one incomplete at beginning, the other at end.

Ms. Lea 53 (Lat.)

VIGLIANO D'ASTI. Statuta communitatis Viglani edita per homines et communitatem dicti loci Viglani, diocesis and capitaneatus Astensis. *Vigliano, 18 May, 1488, and earlier.*

Vellum. 16 ff. 24 x 18 cm. Contemp. h/calf over wooden boards, vellum f. written in Carolingian minuscule (ca.1100?) used as fly-leaf. Cf. L. Fontana, *op.cit.*, III, p.356 who mentions what appears to be the identical ms., reported to him by G. Dellavalle. Ff. 4 and 8 rewritten in a different hand; at the bottom of each is the inscription "Corector ego idem Ansermus Robusti . . . rector in civitate Alexandrie," who notes on f.14 under the date 1488 that he extracted these statutes from a "certain volume" with the addition of other clauses "defficientes in dictis statutis," obtained by Aratinus(?) de Pectinaciis, of the town of Alexandria.

Ms. Lea 54 (Lat.)

CASTINO. Statuta et ordinamenta edita et condita per comunem et homines loci Castini [1471]. Primo, ut omnis tollatur litigiorum materia . . . *Castino, 1471*, with a few later additions (f.23).

Vellum. 20 ff. (f.19 missing), 3 ff. 24 x 17 cm. Illuminated initial and coat of arms (f.1). Contemp. wooden boards, vellum f. (12th-cent. missal leaf) used as fly-leaf.—Prov.: Giuseppe Combetti of Turin. Cf. L. Fontana, *op.cit.*, I, p.294, describing the identical ms.

Ms. Lea 55 (Lat.)

PHILIPUS [BRUSSERIUS] DE CIVITADEI. Descriptio Terrae Sanctae, ff.1r-11v, *inc.:* Quoniam natura humana presertim huius seculi amatorum. . . .—*With* MARCUS DE VENETIIS, Historia Hierosolimitana (1487), ff.11v-122v, *inc.:* Postquam divine propitiationis munificenter exercitus christiani. . . .—3. OTTO OF FREISING. Chronicon, ff.123r-231r. *Southern Germany, 1487.*

Paper. 231 ff. 21 x 16 cm. Contemp. blind-stamped leather over wooden boards.—Prov.: Boies Penrose II; James P. R. Lyell.

Ms. Lea 56 (Lat.)

BALANGERO, MATHI and VILLANOVA di Mathi. Statuta. (Vidimus of Duke Amadeus of Savoy, of the statutes of Balangero, Mathi, and Villanova di Mathi, issued by his mother Bona of Bourbon). *Italy, 1461–1463.*

Vellum. Rotula of 10 sheets (35 x 47 cm.) sewn together, the confirmation at end torn and somewhat incomplete. In container. Cf. L. Fontana, *op.cit.*, I, p.77, describing the identical ms.

Ms. Lea 57 (Lat.)

[CATHOLIC CHURCH]. Taxe cancellarie apostolice, *inc.:* Omnium bullarum duo sunt genera, alterum de beneficiis non consistorialibus. . . . (On the charges to be levied for various services, by the apostolic chancery). *France, ca. 1500.*

Paper. 32 ff. (ff.19–20 blank). 21 x 14.5 cm. 17th-cent. calf.—Bookplate "C.S. Iordani et amicorum." Commentary on ms. by earlier owner on 2 prel. ff.

Ms. Lea 58 (Lat.)

SONCINO. Statuta terrae Soncini. *Soncino, 17th cent.*

Paper. 6,2 blank, 159 ff. (first signature of 12 ff. missing). 20.5 x 14.5 cm. Contemp. boards.—Cf. Fontana, *op.cit.*, III, pp. 123–124.

Ms. Lea 59 (Lat.)

DE CASIBUS CONSCIENTIAE. Quarta pars doctrinae de casibus conscientiae, posita in consideratione poenarum ecclesiasticarum, ff.1r-364v, *inc.:* Consideratio poenarum ecclesiasticarum ad modum utilis est sacerdotibus.—*With* CLEMENT VIII. Literae processus S.D.N.D. Clementis papae VIII lectae die coenae domini An. 1598, [originally printed?] Romae, apud impressores camerales, MDXCVI, ff.366-379.—DE CASIBUS RESERVATIS, et nominatim de iis qui reservantur in bulla Coenae domini, ff.380r-514r, *inc.:* Quanti momenti sit haec consideratio (a long commentary on Clement VIII's bull). *France?, ca. 1598.*

Paper. 514 ff. 13 x 9 cm. Contemp. vellum.

Ms. Lea 60 (Lat.)

PERUGIA, Inquisition. Acts of the proceedings of the inquisition under the podestà of Perugia and the administration of Alessandro Zeno. Among the accused are Romanellus Egidii, Jacobus Craccii,

Augustinus Vannutii and Joannes Menchutii. Notarial copy of Johannes de Novara. *Perugia, 1448–1449.*

Paper. 14 ff. 30 x 22 cm. H/vellum.

Ms. Lea 61 (Lat.)

DE SUMMI PONTIFICIS AUCTORITATE, *inc.* (title of chap. I): Temporalis et spiritualis potestatis necessitas; (text:) Homines non ut conchas de cibo. . . . *Italy, 17th cent.*

Paper. 26 ff. 32 x 22 cm. Contemp. vellum.

Ms. Lea 62 (Lat. and Ital.)

GUILELMUS DE LAVICIA. Via salutis vel dieta, ff.1r-73r, *inc.:* Hec est via, ambulate in ea; *expl.:* Iste liber est mei Fratris Stephani Bilicich abbatis monasterii Sancti Nicolai portus Sibeicensis, quem scripsi manu propria . . . 1449. Table on ff.91v-92.—*With* STEPHANUS BILICICH. Diary, etc. about the monastery of St. Nicholas, ff.73r-75r. —MISCELLANY (probably written by the same Stephanus Bilicich) containing a code, proverbs, sayings, prayers, recipes (some in Italian), and a poem in Italian (f.88r, one line for every letter of the alphabet, beginning: Ara la arena, chi per comune pena), ff.79v-94v. *Sebenico, (Dalmatia), 1449–1453,* written by Stephanus Bilicich.

Paper. 94 ff. 21.5 x 14 cm. Illuminated initial and marginal decoration on f.1r. Contemp. vellum over wooden boards, rebacked.—Prov.: Stephanus Bilicich; Sir Thomas Phillipps (no.14870).

Ms. Lea 63 (Lat.)

FERDINAND II, Archduke of Austria. Two letters, to the Bishop of St. Severus (ambassador of Poland) and to Pope Clement VIII. With seals. *4 July 1592 and 21 Jan. 1593.*

Paper. 4 ff. 33 x 21 cm. Portfolio.

Ms. Lea 64 (Lat.)

CASTELLO. Statuta municipalia civitatis Castelli, 1261 and 1273, (the former attested "Ego Hō[norius?] Sancti Jacobi filius Monete . . . tempore capitanie domini Bernardi domini Benegratie, corrected to read Bonaventure, de Perusio). *Castello, 1261, 1273.*

Vellum. 14 ff. (incomplete at beginning and end). 42 x 27 cm. Vellum.— (Castello could not be clearly identified; municipality in the vicinity of Perugia?)

Ms. Lea 65 (Lat.)

ORDINE DE' CAVALIERI DI SANTO STEFANO. Patent issued by Ferdinand II, grand duke of Tuscany, conferring the privilege of the order upon Niccolo Zanobini (with lead seal of the order). *Florence, 12 Dec., 1639.*

Vellum. 1 f. 36 x 48.5 cm.

Ms. Lea 66 (Lat.)

LATIN CHARTERS. Three miscellaneous items:
1. JOAN I, Queen of Naples. Grant of pension to John of Sabran. *Naples, 19 April, 1371.* 1 f.
2. FRONBERG (dioc. Regensburg). St. Mary and Catherine. Indulgence to visitors of the church, issued by various cardinals. *Rome, 2 December, 1465.* 1 f.
3. JOANNA BARBAR de Ippeswiche. Acknowledgment of payment of 15 pounds from Richard Stonebey of Aldingsgate Street. *London, 7 May, 1567.* 1 f.

Vellum. The indulgence (no.2) with two original wax seals in metal containers, appended by string, of the cardinals Angelo of Santa Croce di Gerusalemme and Bernardo of S. Sabina; remnant of a third seal (cardinal John of S. Lorenzo in Damaso). Boxed.

Ms. Lea 67 (Lat.)

MONTERUBBIANO (March of Ancona). Liber sive quaternus reformationum communitatis et hominum terre Montisrubiani . . . factus, editus et compositus tempore . . . Ser. Bactiste Ser Cicchi de Pigoloctis de Firmo. . . . Scriptus et publicatus per me Angelinum Johanutti de Montegranario. *Monterubbiano, Sept., 1417-Apr., 1418.*

Paper. 70 ff. (incl. 6 blank) and one loosely inserted f. 30 x 22 cm. Contemp. vellum.—Prov.: Baptista Cicchi, whose name appears on binding.

Ms. Lea 68 (Lat.)

[JOHANN WESEL]. Trial of Johann von Wesel for heresy, 1479, *inc.:* Anno domini [MCCCC]LXXIX Reverendissimus [archiepiscopus] Moguntinus misit litteras ad universitatem Heydelbergensem et Coloniensem pro theologis examinationis articulos magistri Johannis de Wesalia de heresi suspectos. *Germany, 1479.*

Paper. 9 ff. 20 x 14 cm. H/morocco.—Cf. C. Du Plessis d'Argentré, *Collectio judiciorum,* (Paris, 1755), I(2), pp.291-298. Text of Lea ms. 68 differs in several respects from that printed by Du Plessis d'Argentré.

Ms. Lea 69 (Lat. and Ital.)

CASTELLO. Statuti. (Three 15th-century fragments, of 2, 8 and 9 ff. respectively, including lists of holidays, some ordinances, and a good many 16th-century entries in Italian; the last piece includes nominal rolls of citizens by parishes). *Castello, early and late 15th cent.*

Vellum. 19 ff. 31 x 22 cm. In portfolio.—Castello has not been identified.

Ms. Lea 70 (Lat.)

[SIENA, Monastery of St. Mary of the Angels]. Papal confirmation by Gregory XI of the grant of the late Nerius Gabrielli di Piccolomini for the construction and other matters concerning the monastery. *Rome, April 2, 1377.*

Vellum. 1 f. 21.5 x 38.5 cm. Unbound.

Ms. Lea 71 (Lat.)

PICCOLOMINI PAPERS. Collection of 64 letters and other documents addressed to or relating to members of the Piccolomini family, from the 12th through the 16th century. *Various places, 1197?–1594.*

Vellum. 64 ff. Various sizes. Boxed.—Prov.: Frederick North, Earl of Guilford, and Sir Thomas Phillipps (no.6067).—Cf. Avery D. Andrews, "From the Piccolomini Papers," *The Library Chronicle,* XXVI, pp.17–29.

Ms. Lea 72 (Ital.)

GENZANO DI ROMA. Statuta di Genzano; copia publica, promulgated by Prince Giuliano Cesarini on Aug. 19, 1562, written and notarized by Cesar Lucarellus de Albano. *Rome, 17th cent.*

Paper. 60 ff. 20 x 13 cm. Portfolio.—Cf. [Italy], Bibl. del Senato, *Catalogo della raccolta di statuti,* (Rome, 1955), III, p. 313.

Ms. Lea 73 (Ital.)

[FLORENCE]. Memorie particulari della città de Firenze e comincia l'anno MDCXIII essendo Sommo Pontefice Paolo V et Imperatore Mattia I e Gran Duca di Toscana Cosimo II, continued to 1635. (Title on spine: Diario della città di Firenze del anno 1613 al 1635. Part of longer work?, marked "XII"). *Florence?, after 1635.*

Paper. 209 ff. (ff.15–16,26–28,40,48,61–64,71–72,80,86–88,176,182,198 and 203–209 blank). 22 x 17 cm. Contemp. vellum.

Ms. Lea 74 (Ital.)

[HUNGARY]. Storia d'Ungheria, dalle origini al 1339 [actually 1539], *inc.*: De la generatione delli Ongari, sono piu oppinioni. . . . *Italy, 16th cent.*

Paper. 8 prel. ff. (3 ff. with portraits pasted in), 39 ff. (numbered pp. 3–92; title missing?), 6 blank ff. 28.5 x 19.5 cm. H/leather.—Prov.: Damiano Muoni of Milan; Giuseppe Martini.—Cf. reference to the "Storia d'Ungaria" in D. Muoni, *Archivi di Stato in Milano, con un cenno sulle particolari collezioni dell' autore,* (Milan, 1874), p.84.

Ms. Lea 75 (Ital.)

TOMMASO VIDONI CORRESPONDENCE. Raccolta di lettere della segretaria di stato, scritte à Monsig. Arcivescovo Tomaso Vidoni in tempo che era in Malta inquisitore apostolico, e poi nunzio a Firenze dal MDCLXXXVI fino al MDCXCVII.—Letters written by Alderanus Cybo and the cardinals Ottoboni, Spada and a few others, with some memoranda interspersed. *Rome, 1686–1697.*

Paper. 2 vols. 26 x 19 cm. Contemp. vellum.—Name "Joseph Marchio Vidonus, Cremonensis" inside front covers.

Ms. Lea 76 (Ital.)
FILIPPO NERLI. Comentarii de fatti civili occorsi drento [for dentro] nella città di Firenze dal MCCXV al . . . MDXXXVII (in 12 books). *Italy, early 17th cent.*

Paper. 264 ff. 29 x 20.5 cm. Contemp. vellum.

Ms. Lea 77 (Ital.)
[FLORENCE]. Miscellany. 1. ISTORIA della Signora Bianca Cappello, gran duchessa di Toscana, e di Pietro Buonaventuri, suo marito, ff.3r-29v.—2. CONGIURA di Lorenzo de' Medici contro il Duca Alessandro . . . 1536, ff.31r-43v.—3. MORTE del Duca Alessandro de' Medici . . . , ff.45r-47v.—4. VITA di Lorenzino de' Medici . . . , ff.51r-130v.—5. MORTE di Vincenzio Serzelli, ff.133r-153v.—6. VITA di Piero Strozzi . . . , ff.155r-204r.—7. VITA di Filippo di Filippo Strozzi, ff.205r-339r.—8. DISCORSO del clarissimo S. Alessandro Rinuccini . . . sopra la carestia del'anno 1619, ff.341r-354r.—9. VITA di Piero Strozzi, ff.357-413r.—10. COMPENDIO della vita della . . . Suor Maria Caterina Brondi, descritta dal Padre Abate Bambacati, ff.415r-426v. *Florence, early 17th cent.*

Paper. 2 prel., 426 ff. 32 x 21 cm. Cloth.—Prov.: "Capt. Napier, from a friend sincere, Luigi Frescobaldi, Florence, October 8th, 1838."

Ms. Lea 78 (Ital.)
GIOVANNI CAVALCANTI. Istoria di Firenze. (The first chapters have been compared with printed ed. [Florence, 1821], cf. marginal notes). *Italy, late 17th or early 18th cent.*

Paper. Prel. blank ff., 317, 2 blank ff. 27 x 19.5 cm. Contemp. vellum.

Ms. Lea 79 (Ital.)
[NICCOLÒ COSCIA]. Processi e documenti relativi alla condetta del Cardinale Coscia. (70 ff. mss., 71 ff. [9 printed titles], 5 ff. mss., 10 ff. [2 printed titles]). Incl. Pope Clement XII's bull sentencing the cardinal on May 9, 1733. *Rome, 1730–1733.*

Paper. Prel. blank, 156 ff. (a few loose inserts). Various sizes, largely 28 x 20 cm. Contemp. h/calf.—Prov.: Henry C. Lea.

Ms. Lea 80 (Lat.)
[PEDRO XIMENES]. Proceedings of the trial of Pedro Ximenes of Teruel, accused of rape and simony. *Pamplona, June 13–Sept. 13, 1267,* by Fernando Ximenes de Gongora.

Vellum. 6 sheets sewn together, measuring ca. 351 x 25 cm. Boxed.

Ms. Lea 81 (Fr.)*

[FRANCHE-COMTÉ]. Fragments of accounts rendered to Mahaut d'Artois, Countess of Burgundy, from her properties in the County of Burgundy, by Guillaume de Salins in 1307-8 and 1310-11, *inc.:* Ce sont li contes que Maistres Guillaumes de Salins rent de la terre que ma dame a en Bourgogne. *County of Burgundy, 1308-1311.*

Vellum. 11 ff. 35 x 25 cm. Portfolio.—Other fragments from these accounts are in Paris, Bibl. nat., ms. fr. 8551 and Besançon, Bibl. mun., mss. 914 and 915. Extracts made before the leaves were dispersed are in Paris, Bibl. nat., Coll. Moreau, ms. 900.

Ms. Lea 82 (Ital.)

VITA DI PAPA ALESSANDRO VI e de suoi figlioli, dedicata al Rè Cattolico. *Italy, 17th cent.*, copied from a ms. in the Vatican Library (cf.f.113r).

Paper. 126 ff. 27.5 x 20 cm. Contemp. vellum.—Prov.: Henry C. Lea.

Ms. Lea 83 (Ital.)

[VENICE]. Relazione di alcune corti fatte da gl'ambassadori alli loro soverani. (Reports of Venetian ambassadors, i.e. 1. BERNARDO NAVAGERO. Report on mission to Rome in 1558, ff.1r-75r.—2. Report on Venice sent to King Philip II of Spain, ff.77r-123v.—3. BRUNORO ZAMPESCA. Report on Crete, ff.125r-139r.—4. GIROLAMO LIPPOMANI. Report on his embassy to duchy of Savoy, 1574, ff.141r-219v.—5. MARCO FOSCARI. Report on Florence, ca. 1527, ff.221r-272v.—6. EMILIANO MARIA MANOLESSI. Report on the state, military strength and administration of Ferrara, ca. 1575, drawn up for the Doge and the Signoria of Venice, ff.273r-316v.—7. Report on negotiations with the Swiss and the form of government of the Grisons, ff.317r-338v). *Venice, late 16th cent.*

Paper. 338 ff. 25 x 19 cm. Contemp. vellum.—Prov.: Sir Thomas Phillipps (no.5552).

Ms. Lea 84 (Ital.)

[FLORENCE]. 1. ORIGINE E DESCENDENZA della casa de Medici, ff.1r-334v.—2. NICCOLO MACCHIAVELLI. Il Principe, ff.335r [f.336 numbered 334]-447v. *Italy, 17th cent.*

Paper. 449 ff. (with some errors in foliation). 28 x 19 cm. Contemp. vellum.

Ad. Lea 82: The source may be Vat. Borg. lat. 561 or Vat. lat. 12252.—Line 2: 17th *read* 18th.

Ad. Lea 83, no. 1: Cf. Antonibon, *op. cit.*, p. 97.—No. 4: *Ibid.*, p. 111.—No. 5: *Ibid.*, p. 43.—No. 6: *Ibid.*, p. 42.

[165]

Ms. Lea 85 (Ital.)

ZACCHIA. Lettere scritte da Monsignore Zacchia nella sua nuntiatura di Venetia al Signore Cardinal Ludovisio, nipote di Papa Gregorio XV, dal mese di luglio fino à dicembre dell' anno 1621. *Italy, 17th cent.*

Paper. 3 prel. ff. (incl. title), 160 ff. 30.5 x 21.5 cm. Contemp. vellum.

Ms. Lea 86 (Ital.)

[FLORENCE]. Relazione delle magistrature fiorentine fatta l'anno 1763 dal Presidente Pompeo Neri. (Copy apparently made for scholarly purposes, the text occupying the right hand column of each page, and a somewhat later English commentary, sometimes verging on an outright translation, on the left). *Florence, ca. 1800.*

Paper. 226 pp. 30 x 21 cm. H/cloth.

Ms. Lea 87 (Ital.)

[FLORENCE]. Memorie manuscritte relative alla famiglia de Medici et all' istoria fiorentina. (Nos. 1–11 deal with the Medici family, 1428–1582 <ff.3–83>; nos. 12–14 are from writings of Jacopo Nardi). *Italy, late 16th–17th cent.*, in various hands.

Paper. 119 ff. 29 x 21 cm. H/vellum.—Owned by Ottaviano Giuseppe de Medici in 1747 (cf. f.119).

Ms. Lea 88 (Lat.)

BERNARDUS PASCHUALIS. Grants Raimundus Berengarius and his wife Dulcia, certain rights in the seigneury held together in the parish of Sant Mamet de Corró in Vallés, county of Barcelona. *Corró de Munt, county of Barcelona, March 9, 1172.*

Vellum. 1 f. 21 x 8 cm. (oblong). In folder.—Cf. John F. Benton, "Two Twelfth-Century Latin Charters from Rural Catalonia in the Lea Library," *The Library Chronicle*, XXVIII (1962), no.1.

Ms. Lea 89 (Lat.)

GUILLELMUS GILABERTI DE OLIVARIIS. He and his wife Sicarda settle a dowry on their daughter Guielma and her husband Raimundus in the parish of Sant Mamet de Corró. *Corró de Munt, county of Barcelona, April 18, 1170.*

Vellum. 1 f. Ca. 23 x 15 cm. (oblong, uneven). In folder.—Cf. John F. Benton, "Two Twelfth-Century Latin Charters from Rural Catalonia in the Lea Library," *The Library Chronicle*, XXVIII (1962), no.1.

Ms. Lea 90 (Ital.)

HISTORICAL MISCELLANY. Notes and extracts (by unknown compiler). 1. JOSEPHUS FLAVIUS. Dall' istoria . . . della guerra che ebbono i Giudei co Romani, ff.11r-30r.—2. ENRICO CATERINO

DAVILA. Dall' istoria . . . delle guerre civili di Francia, ff.47r-73r.—3. DONATO GIANNOTTI. Dal Giannotti nel libro della Republica Fiorentina, ff.99r-103r.—4. GIOVANNI VILLANI. Da Giovanni Villani nelle cronache, cap. 38 [e lib. 6°], ff.117r-132v. *Italy, 17th cent.*

Paper. 142 ff. (many blank). 20 x 14 cm. Contemp. vellum.

Ms. Lea 91 (Ital.)

[VENICE]. Electoral lists of doges (f.1, etc.), procurators of St. Mark's (f.31,etc.) and patriarchs of Venice (f.240,etc.). *Venice, 18th cent.* (1795 latest date entered).

Paper. 562 ff. (many blank). 20.5 x 14.5 cm. Contemp. calf.

Ms. Lea 92 (Ital.)

CASTELLO DEL VIVARO. Statuta, (in six books). *Italy, late 16th cent.*

Paper. Ff.10–70 (ff.1–9, 25 and 71 missing), 8 ff. (6 ff. index and 2 blank ff.) 21.5 x 15 cm. Vellum.—"Ex[aminatus]; x februarii 1634 pro Pasquale q[uondam] Thome cons. Annibale Christophori. Hyacintus Calamarius, sub." (f.34r).

Ms. Lea 93 (Ital.)

VENICE, Inquisition. Copia del Capitolare delli eccelentissimi signori inquisitori di stato: con le aggionte che li sono state fatte. (Rules and regulations beginning with the proceedings of the Great Council of June 16, 1504). *Venice, ca. 1700.*

Paper. 64 ff. 24.5 x 18 cm. 18th-cent. marbled paper.—Prov.: Prince Liechtenstein.

Ms. Lea 94 (Ital.)

PAOLO SARPI (supposed author). Opinione del padre fra Paolo Seruita . . . consultore di stato datta alli ss. inquisitori di stato in qual modo debba governarsi la Republica di Venetia internamente et esternamente. . . . [Same text as Ms. Lea 35]. *Italy, first half 17th cent.*

Paper. 62 ff. 20 x 14 cm. Contemp. vellum.—Prov.: Library of the monastery of Morbio; on front cover the inscription "All' Illustrissimo Borgondio, ambasciatore dell' illustrissima città di Brescia, mio signore carissimo."

Ms. Lea 95 (Ital.)

[FLORENCE]. Nota di tutti quelli, che sono morti per via dell' ultimo supplizio in Firenze dal giugno 1435 [a luglio 1695]; in quà cavata da un' libro della Compagnia del Tempio. *Florence, ca. 1695.*

Paper. 66 ff. 29 x 20 cm. Boards.

Ms. Lea 96 (Ital.)

FRANCESCO ALBIZZI. Riposta all' Historia della sacra inquisitione composta già dal R. P. Paolo Servita [Sarpi]. *Italy, 17th cent.*

Paper. 657 (vero 646) pp. 27 x 20 cm. Contemp. vellum.—Prov.: Cardinal Giuseppe Renato Imperiali (1651–1737); Frederick North, Earl of Guilford; Sir Thomas Phillipps (no.5318).

Ms. Lea 97 (Ital.)

BARTOLOMEO DI BARTOLOMEO DA SAN MINIATO. Libro di ricordanze (front cover: Jornale, ricordi . . . D). Account book for 1495–1497. *Italy, 1495–1497.*

Paper. 285 ff. 28.5 x 21 cm. Contemp. vellum.

Ms. Lea 98 (Ital.)

[NAPLES, Inquisition]. Al Nostro Santissimo Padre Innocenzio XII, intorno al procedimento ordinario, e caninico, nelle cause che si trattano nel tribunale del Santo Ufficio nella città, e regno di Napoli.— With 4 ff., in different hand (Latin), dealing briefly with the lives of Saint Francis of Assisi and Saint Elizabeth, taken from the work of Bartholomew of Trent. *Italy, last decade 17th cent.*

Paper. 350 ff. 21 x 14.5 cm. Contemp. vellum.

Ms. Lea 99 (Ital.)

ALAMANNO DI BERNARDO DI ALAMANNI DE MEDICI. Account book and record of transactions, 1470–1488. *Italy, 1470–1488.*

Paper. 7 ff. text (numb. 1–6,11); 16 blank ff. (numb. 12–13, 15–30); 1 f. (inventory of Possessions, numb. 31), 1 blank f., 24 ff. text (numb. 31–49, 49–55). 32 x 24 cm. Contemp. vellum (document), in portfolio.

Ms. Lea 100 (Ital.)

[FLORENCE]. Cronica dopo la morte del Duca Alessandro de' Medici, fino al 1555. *Italy, 16th cent.*

Paper. 83 ff. (one or more ff. wanting at beginning). 35 x 24 cm. Contemp. vellum, rebacked.—Photostat of article by Alessandro Cutolo, "Rivalazioni di un documento inedito," *Corriere della Sera*, xx (Dec. 2–3, 1941), p.3, dealing with this ms., pasted in.

Ms. Lea 101 (Lat.)

PARMA. Constitutiones nonnullae magnificae communitatis Parmae ex suis exemplaribus summo cum labore a me Baldo Puello, archivii praefacto, excerptae et breviter quoad fieri potuit in hanc formam redactae anno virginei partus sexagesimo septimo supra millesimum et quingentesimum pridie cal. Maii . . . (includes material from 1514 to 1564). *Parma, 1567.*

Vellum. 19 pp., 4 blank ff. 24.5 x 17.5 cm. Boards.

Ms. Lea 102 (Ital.)

[FLORENCE]. Memorie, antiche e moderne; cose più notabili accadute in Firenze fino dalla fondazione. *Florence, ca. 1800.*

Paper. 6 ff. (index), 499 pp. 32 x 21 cm. Contemp. vellum.

Ms. Lea 103 (Ital.)

GIULIANO UGHI. Memorie istoriche delle cose di Firenze, scritte dal P. Fra Giuliano Ughi dalla Cavallina, dall' anno MDI all' MDXLVI, pp. 1–193.—*With* BIAGIO BUONACCORSI. Impresa di Pisa fatta da signori fiorentini l'anno MD, scritta da Biagio Buonaccorsi a Lucantonio degli Albizzi. *Florence, 17th cent.*

Paper. 4 ff., 193 pp., 1 blank f., 4 ff. (index), 16 ff. 35 x 23 cm. 18th-cent. calf.

Ms. Lea 104 (Ital.)

GREGORIO DATI. Memorie di varie guerre de fiorentini e del loro governo et ufizi, scritte da Goro di Stagio Dati, dal 1380 al 1440 [*sic!*, 1405?], pp. 1–160.—*With* FRANCESCO CEI. Notizie varie delle cose di Firenze dal 1494 al 1523, pp. 1–214 (second part). *Florence, 17th cent.*

Paper. 8 ff., 160 pp., 4 ff., 214 pp., 8 ff. 35 x 24 cm. 18th-cent. calf.

Ms. Lea 106 (Sp.)

FELIPE II, King of Spain. Notes and letters about the difficulties of the inquisition in converting the Moors of Valencia. *Spain, 1542–1565* (in late 18th-cent. copy).

Paper. 12 ff. 30 x 21 cm. In folder.

Ms. Lea 107 (Ital.)

ANCONA, Consiglio. Collection of eight documents, dealing with economic and administrative matters: 1. Selection of two citizens to be sent to Rome to attend to important business, f.2r-v.—2. Reform of the statuta regulating commerce of the city, incl. relations with oriental merchants, ff.3r-7r.—3. Minuta nova dei capitoli facta da Messer Jacomo Jaromini (dealing with "li mercati turchi et gli altri"), ff.8r-9r. —4. Copia di capitoli di sensali, f.10r-v.—5. Copia delli aggravii che li mercati sentano dalli novi capitoli, ff.11r-12r.—6. Capitoli de sensali, ff.14r-16v.—7. Capitoli per i Turchi, ff.18r-20r.—8. [Breve] Paulus Papa III, Feb. 21, 1547, ff.22r-27v. (The first 6 ff., dated March 26, 1549 and April 2, 1549 have the appearance of original documents, written in a hasty cursive; title on v. of f. 6.: Capitoli Anconitani. The remainder is clearly written; these documents are undoubtedly notarial or secretarial copies). *Ancona, 1547–49.*

Paper. 28 ff. (several blank). 30 x 22 cm. Contemp. boards, with inscription on inside back cover: "Exhibiti et admissi, Ancone die xxvii martii 1549."

Ms. Lea 108 (Sp.)

SPAIN, Consejo real. Consulta . . . a la Reyna . . . Doña Mariana de Austria . . . aprobando las comedias, dated October 6, 1666, ff.1r-14r.—*With* IDEM. Consulta echa al Señor Rey Dn. Carlos Segundo sobre la jurisdición del Santo Oficio de la Inquisición, dated May 12, 1696, ff.17r-131v.—PEDRO GARCIA. Tratado contra la opinión de los médicos en curar en comun, en suzinto panegírico, ff.134r-139v. *Spain, 18th cent.*

    Paper. 140 ff. (last blank). 21 x 15.5 cm. Contemp. vellum.

Ms. Lea 109 (Ital.)

FLORENCE, Statuta. Riforma del MDLXVI et altre provvisioni della gabella de contratti di Firenze (with copies of a few 17th-18th-cent. documents). *Florence, middle 18th cent.*

    Paper. 40, 227 pp. 42 x 27.5 cm. Contemp. h/vellum.

Ms. Lea 110 (Ital.)

FLORENCE. Diversa statuta ac leges particulares civitatis, comitatus, ac districtus Florentie. (A collection of 137 documents, nos. 114 and 136 printed, with index; title on spine: Rubrica diversorum statutorum). *Florence, 2nd half 17th and early 18th cent.*

    Paper. 8, 400 ff. 29 x 20 cm. Contemp. vellum.

Ms. Lea 111 (Ital.)

ROME, Inquisition. Proceedings of the inquisition in the Apostolic Palace in Rome on 8 July 1610, (ff.1r-37v) and Oct. 1625 (ff.38r-40v), comprising a collection of papal constitutions of the 16th and 17th century dealing with the inquisition; with additional papal letter on assorted subjects (e.g. forbidding the monks and nuns to make gifts [ff.41r-46r, an additional unpaginated signature bound at this point] and decreti of the Holy Congregation on the celebration of mass [ff.47r-62v]). At the end, a note "De excommunicatione" (ff.62v-64r); "Explicatione d'alcuni termini" (f.64r); privileges to the Capuchin order (f.64v ff.). *Italy, early 18th cent.*

    Paper. 74 ff. 20 x 13 cm. Contemp. boards.—Prov.: Sir Thomas Phillipps (no.5740).

Ms. Lea 112 (Sp.)

DISCURSO APOLOGETICO de la inquisición, en satisfacción à la carta, que contra este tribunal, escribiò el ciudadano francés Gregoire, Obispo que se titula de Blois . . . por un antirevolucionario español, *inc.:* Proemio à los españoles, habiendo llegado casualmente. *Spain, late 18th cent.*

Paper. 460 pp. 20 x 14 cm. Contemp. marbled calf.

Ms. Lea 113 (Ital.)

ROME, Inquisition. Forma moderna di fabricar li processi del Santo Offizio, pratticata hoggi dì nel supremo tribunale di Roma, *inc.:* Nel pigliare una denunzia. *Italy, 18th cent.*

Paper. 268 pp. 26 x 19.5 cm. Contemp. boards.—Prov.: Sir Thomas Phillipps (no.5336).

Ms. Lea 114 (Ital.)

GENOA. Leges, seu reformationes nove Reipublice Genuensis, facte a duodecim reformatoribus, anno 1528. (With Index capitulorum decretorum nec non declarationum . . . , pp. 297–315; Nomina civium nobilium . . . , pp. 1–150 [2nd numbering]; Index tam albergorum, et eorum numerus, quam familiarum in dictos albergos contentarum ordine alphabetica, nec non numerus dictarum familiarum, 15 ff. at end). *Genoa, early 17th cent.*

Paper. 315, 150 pp., 15 ff. 21 x 14.5 cm. Contemp. vellum.

Ms. Lea 115 (Ital.)

[INQUISITION]. Pratica del modo di procedere nelle caose spettanti al Santo Officio, *inc.:* Le cause del Sant' Offizio, o sono d'heresia, o di sospittione di essa. *Italy, ca. 1700.*

Paper. 106 ff. 25 x 18.5 cm. Contemp. vellum.—Prov.: Sir Thomas Phillipps (no.5322).

Ms. Lea 116 (Lat.)

GUILLAUME DE MANDAGOT. Libellus super electionibus faciendis et earum processibus ordinandis. *France?, ca. 1400.*

Vellum. 40 ff., last 2 blank. 18 x 12.5 cm. 18th-cent. h/calf.—Bookplate of H. Charles Barnston and Amelia Daubeney; notation on inside front cover "cost £8 at Dr. Neligan's sale in 1867."

Ms. Lea 117 (Sp.)

CONSULTAS Y RESOLUCIONES sobre controversias con los tribunales de la ynquisición. *Madrid, 7 March, 1769* (date of certification by Ignacio Esteban de Igareda, last f.)

Paper. 212 ff. 31 x 20.5 cm. Contemp. h/calf.—Signature Andrés Osequera [?] on title page, date 1849 in the same hand on fly leaf.

Ad. Lea 112: Henry Grégoire's letter to the Inquisitor General of Spain was published in Paris in 1798. This anonymous reply not mentioned in Lea, *History of the Inquisition of Spain* (New York, 1907), IV, 397–8.

Ms. Lea 118 (Lat.)

COMO. Statuta civilia causarum civitatis Comi, elargita a D. Sebastiano Perto. *Italy, late 16th or early 17th cent.*

Paper. 12 ff., 2 blank ff., 222 pp., 10 blank ff. 28.5 x 18.5 cm. Contemp. vellum.—Cf. L. Fontana, *op.cit.*, I, pp. 377–81, especially p. 379, describing several mss. in private hands of which one might be identical with this ms.

Ms. Lea 119 (Ital.)

RELATIONE DE FIRENZA et di Siena, *inc.:* Il parlare di cose di stato et il referire alla presenza della serenità vestra fu sempre riserbato. . . . *Florence, 17th cent.*

Paper. 33 ff. 30.5 x 21.5 cm. Boards.

Ms. Lea 120 (Sp.)

PEDRO DE SALAZAR DE MENDOZA. Vida, causa y sucesos prósperos y adversos del illustríssimo y sereníssimo señor D. Fr. Barttolomé de Carranza y Miranda, arzobispo de Tóledo. . . . Excrita . . . a instancia del Cm°. S. Cardenal Quiroga . . . año de 1568 [sic]. *Spain, ca. 1700.*

Paper. 277 ff. 30 x 20.5 cm. Contemp. vellum.—Prov.: Henry C. Lea.—J. Quétif and J. Echard, *Scriptores ord. praed.*, (Paris, 1721), II, p.242, col.2 mentions this biography; no printed text listed in A. Palau y Dulcet, *Manual del Librero*, but Mr. Lea added on the title of the same text, in Ms. Lea 130, "This was printed by Ant. Valadanes de Sotomayor, 1788" (and described in B.M. *Catalogue*).

Ms. Lea 121 (Port.)

PORTUGAL, Inquisition. Over forty documents (four printed) relating to the inquisition in Portugal. *Portugal, 17th and early 18th cent.*

Paper. 5 blank, 30 ff., ff.35–378 (last blank). 30 x 20 cm. Contemp. vellum.—Stamp of Pedro A. Ferreira, abbot of Miragaya.

Ms. Lea 122 (Lat. and Ital.)

SAN BARTOLOMEO DI SASSO FORTE. Statuta. (Deliberations of the "consilium generale hominum communitas jurisdictionis Sancti Bartholomei in Saxo Forte"). Stamped notarial signets throughout. *Italy, 1718–1783.*

Paper. 80 ff. (16 ff., 30 x 21 cm., bound in after f.69; numerous blank ff. interspersed, and at end of vol.). 37 x 23.5 cm. Colored coat of arms of Antonius de Affarusiis on f.1, on whose orders this ms. was written. H/vellum.

Ms. Lea 123 (Ger.)

[NÜRNBERG]. Chronica perpetua, darinnen alle und jede Malefiz-Persohnen, aus vielen alten Büchern mit mühsamen Fleiss zusammen getragen, anzutreffen sind. (Executions in Nürnberg from 1298 to March 1709; begins with "Ordnung des Halsz-Gerichts," [f.2r-v] and poem "Loch Ordnung zu Nürnberg," [f.3r-v]). *Nuremberg, ca. 1709.*

Paper. 57 ff. 34.5 x 21 cm. Boards.—Prov.: Liechtenstein Library.

Ms. Lea 124 (Ital.)

[FRANCESCO GIUSEPPE BORRI]. Abiuratione del Borri nell' anno 1661. (Trial for heresy, before the "inquisitori generali," cf. *Encycl. ital.*, v. VII, p. 510, with a short biogr. account of the alchemist and adventurer, there entered under "Borri <or Borro>, Giuseppe Francisco). *Italy, after 1661.*

Paper. 36 ff. 27 x 19 cm. Boards.

Ms. Lea 125 (Ital.)

LIBRETTO delli brevi [charms], in 24 chapters, *inc.:* Virtu delli brevi; primo, contra la fortuna del mare. . . . (Copied from a work in the possession of Francesco da Pesaro). *Italy, 2 August, 1629.*

Paper. 1, 61 ff. (2 ff. numbered 23 in error). 14 x 9.5 cm.—Prov.: "Joannes Baptista Comes a Thu . . . [illeg.] 1695 (inside front cover); "Ego Wolfgangus Theodosius Barsa Thona [?] possesor sum huius libri 1706." (front cover).

Ms. Lea 126 (Lat.)

CONVENTIO inter rectores ospitalis Civitatis Placentie et D. Antonium Franciscum Finellum. *Piacenza, 21 March 1580.*

Paper. 8 ff. (1,2 and 8 blank). 30 x 21 cm. Boards.

Ms. Lea 127 (Lat.)

NEPI. 1. LIBER STATUTORUM Nepesinae Civitatis, quae condita et publicata fuere per reverendissimum dominum Franciscum . . . illustrissimi domini Ioannis de Borgia ducis Nepesini tutorem de consensu reverendissimorum dominorum Antonietti Sanctae Praxedis, Joannis Antonii et Sanctorum Nerei et Achilei . . . et Ipoliti Estensis diaconi cardinalis contutorum, ff. 7—p. 96. (Notarial statement, signed Fulvius Sansonius, and dated 1588, p. 96, crossed out).—2. DE GIUDICI del danno dato, pp. 103–134. *Italy, 17th cent.*

Paper. 8 ff., 96 pp., 2 ff. (index in later hand), 1 blank f., 2 ff., 18 ff. (ff.2-5 cut out), 14 blank ff. 26 x 19 cm. Contemp. vellum.—Cf. similar ms. described in [Italy], Bibl. del Senato, *op.cit.*, V, pp.38-40.

Ms. Lea 128 (Ital.)

FLORENCE. Memorie delle armi pubbliche di Firenze, etc. (Collection of 137 pieces, comprising genealogical notes, documents, family trees, and descriptions of coats of arms, of Florentine families, especially the Verrazzano family and its various branches; incl. also the Buonsostegni, Donnino, Migliore, Medici; "Stratto del priorista per alfabeto" [16 ff.]; "Nota da osservarsi sopra le armi del priorista" [16 ff.] etc.) *Florence, 18th cent.*

Paper. 137 pieces of varying length and size. Boxed.

Ms. Lea 129 (Ger.)

HALL (Tirol), Congregation Mariae Verkündigung. Bericht und Satzungen (and accounts, 1763–1822). Title on front cover: Pactum Marianum Congregationis civice Halensis, 1764. *Hall, 1764–1822.*

Paper. 45 ff. (several blank). 31.5 x 20.5 cm. Contemp. vellum.

Ms. Lea 130 (Sp.)

HISTORICAL MISCELLANY. 1. PEDRO DE SALAZAR DE MENDOZA. Vida, subcesos, prósperos, y adversos de Fr.D. Bartholomé de Carranza y Miranda . . . (cf. Ms. Lea 120), ff.1–120.—2. FELIPE IV, King of Spain. Copia de dos papeles originales escritos ambos de la real mano del Señor Rey D.Ph.4. à su valido el Conde Duque de Olivares (on the birth of the King's illegitimate son [1602], later known as Alonso de Santo Thomas, Dominican and bishop of Malaga), ff.121–123.—3. DUQUE DE OLIVARES. Copia de la carta que el Duque Cardenal valido del Rey Ph.3. embió a Ph.4. quando heredó la corona, ff.124–125.—4. DISCURSO al sermón de zeniça del P. Maestro Guerra sobre las palabras sigiuentes, ff.127–142.—5. GERONIMO GASCON DE TORQUEMADA. Nacimiento, vida, prisión y muerte de D. Rodrigo Calderón (printed, Madrid, 1789), ff.143–174.—6. DIEGO CASTELLO ROS DE MEDRANO. Dictamen . . . sobre la resolución del Papa y consulta de la Iunta que de orden de S.M. se hico, en cassa del señor presidente, ff.175–181.—7. FRANCISCO DEL MELGAR. Zensura del papel que escrivió D. Francisco de Morovelli de Puebla, defendiendo el patronato de Santa Teresa de Iesús, y respondiendo a Don Francisco de Quevedo, ff.183–196.—8. FRANCISCO DE QUEVEDO. D. Reymundo el entremetido al buen entendedor, ff.199–217.—9. MEMORIAL que dió en una academia pidiendo una plaça y indulgencias . . . , ff.217–219.—10. DESPOSORIO entre el cassar y la iubentud de D. Francisco de Quevedo y Villegas, ff. 220–222.—11. CAPITULACIONES de la vida de corte y oficios entretenidos en ella de D. Francisco de Quevedo y Villegas, ff.223–244.—12. FRANCISCO DE QUEVEDO. Carta . . . a la rectora del Collegio de las Virgines, ff.245–246.—13. IDEM. Carta . . . sobre casarse, ff.247–250. *Spain, 18th cent.*

Paper. 250 ff. 20.5 x 14.5 cm. Contemp. vellum.—Prov.: Henry C. Lea.

Ms. Lea 131 (Sp. and Lat.)

MANUEL RODA Y ARRIETA. Dictamen a una consulta . . . sobre las observaciones de Dn. Gregorio Mayans y Siscar (preceded by Introduction, signed Sebastián Vilardebó, 1862), 375 pp. — *With* COMPENDIUM HISTORIAE ECCLESIASTICAE, *inc.*: Romanum Imperium sumpsit exordium a Caio Julio Caesare (to the end of the 17th cent.), 107 pp.—DE PRIVILEGIIS CISTERCIENSIBUS (brief compendium of privileges extracted from a work of three volumes), 9 pp.—DE JURE CANONICO (4 pp.) and De jure civili (8 pp.).—DE CONCILIIS (the last cited is the Council of Trent), 54 pp.—DE HAERESIBUS (including discussion of Jansenism and the bull Unigenitus; with Compendium haereticorum), 24 pp. *Spain, late 18th cent.*

Paper. 4 unnumb. ff., 375 pp., 3 ff. (last blank), 107 pp., 3 blank ff., 9 pp., 12 pp., 56 pp. (last 2 blank), 24 pp., 3 blank ff. 21 x 15 cm. Vellum.—Prov.: Sebastian Vilardebo, presbitero, Barcelona, 1862; Henry C. Lea.

Ms. Lea 132 (Ital.)

S. STEFANO. Filza di prove di nobiltà di varie famiglie nell' occasione di dovere alcuno delle medesime prender li abito della religione de Cavallieri di S. Stefano fatte nel secolo 16º. La maggior parte davanti il Sig. Raffaello de Medici, bali di Firenze, e ammiraglio di detta religione. *Florence, 1565–1579.*

Paper. 509 ff. 30 x 21 cm. 4 colored coats of arms, f.133. Contemp. h/vellum in portfolio.

Ms. Lea 134 (Fr.)

FRANCISCO HURTADO DE MENDOZA Y BABADILLA. Le Tison d'Espagne, ou origines de la plus grande partie des familles nobles de ce royaume et du Portugal issues tant d'Estoc que par femmes de Maures et Juifs convertis. Traduit de l'Espagnol. (Span. title: Tizon de la nobleza de España). *France, 18th cent.*

Paper. 73 pp. 23 x 16 cm. Contemp. calf, rebacked.—Prov.: Lord Stuart de Rothesay; Henry C. Lea.

Ms. Lea 135 (Sp.)

JOSE MOÑINO FLORIDA BLANCA. Vida política o ministerial del Conde de Floridablanca, escrita para él mismo en representasión hecha al Rey Don Carlos III y presentada después a su hijo Don Carlos IV antes de su caída. San Lorenzo, Oct. 10, 1788 (f. lllv). *San Ildefonso, September 28, 1795* (f. 115v).

Paper. 115 ff. 20 x 14 cm. H/morocco.—Prov.: Henry C. Lea.

Ms. Lea 136 (Fr.)

CHEVALIER DE L'AIGLE. Les quarante nouveaux statuts de la maçonnerie, qui fondent les pouvoirs des Chevaliers de l'Aigle. *France, after June 24, 1752.*

Paper. 31 ff. 19.5 x 15 cm. Cloth.—Prov.: Henry C. Lea.

Ms. Lea 137 (Lat.)

COLLECTIO DIVERSORUM DECRETORUM Sacre Congregationis Sancti Officii Urbis [Romae], ordine alphabetico digestorum. *Italy, ca. 1669.*

Paper. 2 blank ff., 424 (falso 423) pp., 4 ff. (index), 4 blank ff. 20 x 13 cm. Contemp. gilt vellum.—Prov.: James Lewis, LL.D., of Cambridge; Henry C. Lea.

Ms. Lea 138 (Sp.)

CHARLES V, Emperor of the Holy Roman Empire. 1. Instrucción . . . à Phelipe Segundo su hijo, dada en el año de 1543, ff.1r-27v.—2. Carta que escrivió . . . à su hijo Phelipe Segundo, 1543, ff.29r-77r.—3. Adbertencias . . . escritas . . . à Phelipe Segundo su hijo [1548], ff.79r-171v. *Spain, 17th cent.*

Paper. Title, 171 ff. H/morocco.—Prov.: Henry C. Lea.

Ms. Lea 139 (Port. and Sp.)

SPAIN AND PORTUGAL, Inquisition. Noticias recónditas y póstumas del procedimiento de las inquisiciones de Espanha y Portugal con sus presos. Part I: Alvarà del Rey Don Juan IV de Portugal: Relación portugueza de la inquisiçión de su reino. (Originally written probably at Rome, between 1667 and 1678; printed in Venice in 1750 in "Relacio exactissima pello P. Ant. Vièpra," pp. 1–95).—Part II: Reflexiones sobre la dicha relación. (Incl. Sagrada atarazano de la inquisiçión de Italia, copied from the original which was published by Sebastian Zequini in 1653; Relaçión de la prisión de Luiz Ramé en la inquisiçión de México). *Spain, 18th cent.*

Paper. 5,102, 6,146 pp. 21.5 x 16.5 cm. H/morocco.—Bookplate of Biblioteca Visnievsciana, with name in ms. Michat Ursmiewsky(?); Henry C. Lea.—See H. C. Lea, *History of the Inquisition of Spain*, III, 284–5.

Ms. Lea 140 (Lat.)

LUDOVICUS. De indulgentiis et censuris (written in 1643). *Italy, 17th cent.*

Paper. 12 ff. (ff.1–2, 6–12 blank), 254, 3 ff. 19.5 x 13.5 cm. Contemp. vellum. —Prov.: Henry C. Lea.—Cf. A. de Backer and C. Sommervogel, *op. cit.*, IV, col.1754.

Ms. Lea 141 (Sp.)

PAPELES VARIOS. 1. CHARLES V, Emperor of the Holy Roman Empire. Cartas (to his son Philip II) 1523, ff.1r-26r.—2. IDEM. Orden . . . para detener al Gran Capitán, el Rey, 1515, [misbound:] ff.37r-40v, 27r-30r.—3. IDEM. Instrucción . . . en 9. de julio de 1557 al Señor Rey Don Phelipe II . . . sobre el particular tratamiento de los grandes de Castilla, f.31r-36v.—4. FERDINAND V. Copia de carta que . . . escribió al Conde de Rivagorza, ff.42r-46v, with "Comento," and "Otra carta" and "Advertencias," ff. 46v-56r.—5. EPISTOLAE NOTABILISSIMAE quae [sic] refert Stephanus Auferius . . . ad Clement[em] I, ff.56v-58r.—6. FELIPE II, King of Spain. Carta . . . sobre la prisión del Príncipe Don Carlos . . . 1568, ff.59r-64r.—7. BARTOLOME DE CARRANÇA. Copia de una carta . . . a su Mag. del Rey Don Felipe 2° [1569], ff.60r-63v.—8. ANTONIO ZAPATA DE MENDOZA. [Carta] al Rey Dn. Felipe 3. en los espolios de los obispos, ff.64r-67v [69v?].—9. SPAIN, Consejo real. Discurso . . . sovre èl remedio dela despoblaciòn de España, ff.70r-90v.—10. JUAN ANTONIO ENRIQUEZ. Enciclopedia marítima o diccionario; asuntos del diccionario, ff.92r-100r.—11. Four printed pamphlets. *Spain, 17th-18th cent.*

Paper. 103 ff. 20.5 x 14 cm. Contemp. vellum.—Prov.: Henry C. Lea.

Ms. Lea 142 (Sp.)

RELACION de lo acaecido en España en tiempo y con motibo de la expulsión indispensable del P. Juan Everardo [Nidardo] de la Compañía llamada de Jesús, confesor de la reyna, madre y tutora del Señor Carlos 2°. *Spain, late 17th cent.*

Paper. 372 pp. 21 x 15 cm. Boards (titling on spine: Nitardo, instead of Nidardo).—Prov.: Henry C. Lea.

Ms. Lea 144 (Lat. and Eng.)

PERPETUAL CARD, (prel. ff.1-6).—*With* VATICINIA VARIA, pp. 1-192.—EXPLANATION of the tables of the planets, 3 ff. *London, 1688.*

Paper. 6 ff., 193 pp. (last blank), 11 ff. (8 ff. blank). 15 x 9.5 cm. Diagrams and pen-and-ink drawings throughout. Contemp. gilt calf, rebacked.—Prov.: Richard H. Buel; Henry C. Lea.

Ms. Lea 145 (Lat.)

DE IMPOSTURIS religionum breve compendium, descriptum ab exemplari manuscripto, quod in bibliotheca Joh. Frieder. Mayeri Berolini anno 1716 publice distracta deprehensum et a principe Eugenio de Sabaudia LXXX imperialibus redemptum fuit. *Germany, ca. 1716.*

Paper. Title, 54 pp. (last blank). 20 x 16 cm. Contemp. calf, rebacked.—Prov.: Henry C. Lea.

Ms. Lea 146 (Lat.)

BENEDICTIONES et exorcismi, begins with Benedictiones pro shedulis immaculatae conceptionis beatissimae virginis Mariae, followed by Exorcismus super chartam, calamum, atramentum, sigillum contra omnia maleficia, with benedictions and prayers. *No place or date* (*Germany?, ca. 1700?*).

Paper. 28 ff. (last 5 blank). 16 x 9.5 cm. H/morocco.—Prov.: Henry C. Lea.

Ms. Lea 147 (Rhaeto-Roman)

ENGADIN. Statuts civils, criminels et matrimoniels (with list of officials, to 1729). *Engadin, ca. 1762.*

Paper. 6 blank ff., 185 ff., 1 blank f., 11 ff. (index), 12 blank ff., 17 ff. (list of officials), 13 blank ff. 17 x 11.5 cm. Contemp. calf.—Prov.: Henry C. Lea.

Ms. Lea 148 (Lat.)

DUPIN. Tractatus de jure, justicia, ac de legibus, traditus a Reverendo Patre Dupin, Soc. Jesu, anno . . . 1696 et scriptus . . . 1699 ad usum Petri Lajaunye, *expl.:* Dictavit hunc tractatum R. P. Dupin . . . 1695. *France, 1699.*

Paper. 4 ff. (ff.2,4 blank), 295 (vero 290) pp., 2 blank ff. 16 x 11 cm. Engravings pasted on title and f.3v. Contemp. calf.—"Ex libris Jacobi Doazan;" John Trotter Brockett; Henry C. Lea.—Not in A. de Backer and C. Sommervogel, *op.cit.*

Ms. Lea 149 (Ital.)

RISTRETTO circa li delitti piu frequenti à giudicarsi nel S. Officio.—*With* REGOLE GENERALI per le cause del S. Officio. *Italy, ca. 1600.*

Paper. 2 ff. (f.1 blank), 178 (vero 181) pp., 4 ff. (3 last blank). 16.5 x 11.5 cm. H/morocco.—"Ex bibl. Ios. Ren[ato] Card. Imperialis;" Henry C. Lea.

Ms. Lea 150 (Sp.)

MEMORIAL ajustado del processo, y causa de Antonio Pérez, secretario de Ph⁰ Segundo, sobre la muerte del secretario Escobedo, y otras cosas. *Spain, 18th cent.*

Paper. 176 ff. (last 2 blank). 19.5 x 14 cm. Contemp. calf.—Prov.: Manuel Lopez Alguacil; Francisco Carminas; Sebastian Vilardebo; José Vilardebo; Henry C. Lea.

Ms. Lea 151 (Sp.)

PROCESO que se hizo, a Antonio Pérez, secretario de estado, y del despacho del Rey Don Phelipe 2º, que tubo principio en el año del 1578. Juez, el lizenciado Rodrigo Vázquez de Arze, presidente del consejo de hacienda; escrivano Antonio Márquez. *Spain, 17th cent.*

Ad. Lea 148: A catalogue description in the Lea Library attributes this tract to Louis Ellies Dupin, who was, however, not a Jesuit.

Paper. Ff.64–146 (with previous numbering 101–185). 21 x 15 cm. H/morocco.—Prov.: Henry C. Lea. Apparently the same text as Lea ms. 150.

Ms. Lea 152 (Lat.)*
JOHANNES GERSON. Opuscula varia, with the addition of items (12–20) not identified in Gerson's *Opera omnia*. Southern Germany (Memmingen?), *1466* (cf. f.142v; some parts probably slightly earlier; ff.157v–9 perhaps somewhat later). Written in several hands.

Paper. 159 ff. (ff.27–8 and 82 missing; ff.1, 95–8, 121 and 143–6 blank). 30 x 21.5 cm. All, except ff.2–3 and 157v–9r, in two cols. Contemp. pigskin over wooden boards. *Prov.:* Johannes Frank ("hunc librum dedit dominus Johannes Frank socius divinorum apud Sanctum Martinum in Memmingen fratribus ordinis Carthusiensis in Buchsheim"); Carthusian monastery, Buxheim (sign. 2FI); Ludwig Rosenthal, Cat. 120 [1909], no. 127; unidentified catalogue, no. 186; F. Valée; Henry C. Lea.—Contents: 1. JEAN GERSON (Celestinus). Opuscula et tractatus ipsius magistri Johannis Gerson [i.e. Annotatio II, Jean Gerson, *Oeuvres complètes*, ed. Mgr. Glorieux, (Paris, Desclée, 1960), pp.29–33, with variations], ff.2v–3v.—2. JEAN GERSON (cancellarius Parisiensis). De oratore, ff.4r–12v. (His *Opera Omnia*, ed. L. Ellies du Pin, The Hague, de Hondt, 1728, v. III, cols. 247–62).—3. IDEM. Dialogus de perfectione cordis, ff.12v–20r (*Opera*, v. III, cols. 436–49).—4. IDEM. Tractatus de sollicitudine ecclesiasticorum, ff.20r–28v (icplt., ends with "particula" 44; *Opera*, v. II, cols. 597–609).—5. IDEM. Regulae morales, ff.29r–41r (icplt., begins with "regula" 56; *Opera*, v. III, cols. 88–106).—6. IDEM. De vita spirituali animae, ff.41v–94r (index on ff.41v–44v; *Opera*, v. III, cols. 1–72).—7. IDEM. De audienda confessione, ff.99r–103r (*Opera*, v. II, cols. 446–53).—8. IDEM. Tractatus de injungenda poenitentia contra recidivum, ff.103r–5r (*Opera*, v. II, cols. 457–9).—9. IDEM. Tractatus de praecepta confessione et scientia mortis, ff.105r–15r (*Opera*, v. I, cols. 427–42).—10. IDEM. Tractatulus secundus de confesione sacramentali, ff.115v–9r (*Opera*, v. I, cols. 442–7).—11. IDEM. Opusculum pro conquerenda noticia bene moriendi, ff.119r, 124v-6r (*Opera*, v. I, cols. 447–50).—12. QUAESTIO utrum hoc possit scire se esse electum . . . ad civitatem dei . . . , ff.119v–20r.—13. MODUS DISPONENDI se ad mortem . . . , f.122v.—14. REGISTRUM historiarum ewangeliorum de libro magistri Nicolai organiste, *inc.:* Sciendum . . . , ff.123r–4v.—15. SPECULUM MORTIS sanctae peccatoris S. Augustini, *inc.:* Quoniam . . . , ff.126r–9r.—16. ARTICULI propter quos prohibetur altaris communio, rubricated: Hiis sequentibus altaris communio est prohibenda, ff.129r–32r.—17. BREVILOGIUM de malis huius mundi, *inc.:* Stet speculator . . . , ff.132r–3v.—18. BREVILOGIUM de vana huius mundi oblectatione, *inc.:* Omnes amatores, ff.133v–4r.—19. TRACTATUS de incarnatione, *inc.:* Inclinavit se Jesus, ff.135r–42v.—20. DECLARATIO et expositio arboris consanguinitatis, *inc.:* Ad arborem . . . , ff.147r–57r. (With 3 schematic drawings).—21. JEAN GERSON. Tractatus de confessione Mollitiei, ff.157v–8r (*Opera*, v. II, cols. 444–5).—22. IDEM. Responsio super questione sibi facta . . . de statuto ordinis Carthusiensium, f.158r–v (*Opera*, v. II, cols. 460–1).—23. IDEM. De eodem statuto, f.158v (*Opera*, v. II, cols. 461–2).—24. IDEM. Avisamentum per modum confessionis in religioni sub . . . audiendi, ff.158v–9r (*Opera*, v. II, col. 462).

Ms. Lea 153 (Sp.)

ANTONIO PEREZ. Política (i.e. his Summa de preceptos justos, necesarios y provechosos en Consejo de Estado, v. I, ff.2r-85r.—Discurso al Rey Felipe, Terzero de España al ingreso à la corona . . . con advertencias para governarse, v. I, ff.87r-290v.—Máximas políticas, v. II). *Spain, second half 17th cent.*

Paper. 2 vols. 20 x 16 cm. Contemp. vellum.—Prov.: Henry C. Lea.

Ms. Lea 154 (Ital.)

ISTORIE TRAGICHE. 1. AVVERSITÀ NOTABILISSIMA di Papa Paolo Quarto e de suoi nepoti con il successo memorabile della casa Caraffa, 1 f., 145 pp.—2. DUODECIM CAPITA PROCESSUS Card. Caroli Carafae, 3 ff., 106 pp.—3. NARRATIONE del successo della morte della Duchessa Violante di Cardona . . . ; Eseguita dal detta duca e dal Conte d'Aliffee e dà Don Leonardo di Cardines, p. 107, 34 pp.—4. RELATIONE della giustitia fatta di Onofrio Santacroce l'anno 1601, al quale fù tagliata la testa per haver acconsentito al matricidio di Paolo suo fratello in persona della Signora Costanza Santacroce, 1 f., 7 pp.—5. JOSEPH BLONDO (or Biondi). Raguaglio della prigionia, e morte del Signor Troilo Savelli . . . 1592 (A. de Backer and C. Sommervogel, *op. cit.*, v. I, col. 1546), 1 f., 75 pp.—6. EFFETTI della maleditione paterna nel racconto delle morti de figliuli del Marchese de Massimi, 1 f., 15 pp.—7. IL RACCONTO del grave delitto del Centino, nipote del Cardinale d'Ascoli e compagni, per far morire Papa Urbano 8º, 1 f., 30 pp.—8. VITA & MORTE di Papa Sisto V, 3 pp. (incomplete). *Italy, ca. 1700.*

Paper. 1 vol. 19 x 11 cm. Contemp. vellum.—Prov.: Henry C. Lea.

Ms. Lea 155 (Fr.)

RÉPONSE, ou avis des conseaux à Son Altesse Serenissime l'Archiduchesse Marie Elisabeth sur le projet de placcart, touchant les livres defendus, stipulé par les ecclésiastiques du Pais-Bas. *Low Countries, post 1730.*

Paper. 96 ff. 19.5 x 16 cm. Contemp. calf.—Prov.: Henry C. Lea.

Ms. Lea 156 (Sp.)

ALONSO DE PEDRAÇA. Instrución para actuar los comissarios y notarios de el Sancto Officio (dedicated to Juan Eberardo Nidhardo, and letters to the author, signed, by Pedro de Espinosa, Iacinto de Urturi y Ibáñez and Bartolomé Francisco de Villaviciosa). *Cuenca, 1667.*

Paper. 14 ff. (first blank), 104 pp., 4 ff. 23.5 x 17 cm. Illum. dedication with coat of arms (f.2). Contemp. gilt leather.—Prov.: San Pablo de Cuenca; Henry C. Lea.

Ms. Lea 157 (Sp.)

JUAN DE MARIANA. Tratado y discurso sobre la moneda de vellón, que al presente se labra en Castilla, y de algunos desórdenes y abusos, escrito . . . en idioma latino e traducido en castellano . . . e impreso en Colonia año de 1609. *Madrid, 1799.*

Paper. 90 ff. (ff. 1, 86–90 blank). 21.5 x 15.5 cm. 19th-cent. calf.—Prov.: Henry C. Lea.

Ms. Lea 158 (Ital.)

[INQUISITION, Rome]. Processi overo copie delle confessioni fatte nell'alma città di Roma dal P. Anello Arciero, da Sor Giulia de Marco et da Gioseffo de Vicariis nell'anno MDCXV, a 12. die Luglio. *Rome, ca. 1615.*

Paper. 1, 55 ff. (last blank). 18.5 x 13 cm. Contemp. vellum.—Prov.: Henry C. Lea.

Ms. Lea 159 (Ger.)

[VIENNA]. Judenschafft, so nit privilegiret hier zu sein (punishment of 12 begging Jews who entered Vienna without permission), signed Nicolaus Prinz [?]. *Vienna, 1721.*

Paper. 1 f. 42.5 x 29 cm. Cloth.—Prov.: Henry C. Lea.

Ms. Lea 160 (Sp.)

[MEXICO, Inquisition]. Processo y causa criminal da Ysabel de Montoia, mulata o castiza (llamada La Centella). *Mexico City, 1652–1661.*

Paper. 2 vols. (194, 157 ff.). 32 x 21.5 cm. H/morocco.—Prov.: Henry C. Lea.

Ms. Lea 164 (Ital.)

NICOLO CAPASSO. Ragionamenti intorno al tribunale della inquisizione, nei quali metodicamente si dimostra con quanta ragione gli onorati cittadini napolitani si siano sempre opposti à tentativi degli ecclesiastici d'introdurre nella città a regno [di Napoli] il detto tribunale. *Naples, post 1711.*

Paper. 149 ff. (incomplete at end). 26.5 x 18.5 cm. H/vellum.—Prov.: Henry C. Lea.

Ms. Lea 165 (Ital.)

NICOLO CAPASSO. Ragionamenti. *Naples, 1717.*

Paper. 1 f., 161 pp., 1 f. 30 x 21.5 cm. Contemp. vellum.—Prov.: Henry C. Lea.

Ms. Lea 166 (Lat.)

[NAPLES]. 1. NICOLO CAPASSO. Disputationes orthodoxae de nova, absurdaque forma judicii a quaesitoribus fidei in coërcendis haereticis usurpata (Latin version of the Ragionamenti, cf. Lea 164–165).—2. DISSERTATIONES JURISDICTIONALES anonimae (De jurisdictione capellani maioris; Consultatio in materia immunitatis; De remediis regi competentibus adversus prelatos turbantes jurisdictionem; Explicactio in bullam Gregorii XIIII; Explicactio in bullam caenae domini; De bigamia; De jurisdictione quam ecclesiae habent in regno; De impensis seu meliorationibus feudo factis; An judex laicus possit cognoscere clericos ex causa rebellionis; De visitatione et exemptione hospitalium; An papa sit supra imperatorem). *Naples, ca. 1715.*

Paper. 5 ff., 206 pp., 4 ff., 229 ff. (several ff. blank). 28 x 20 cm. Contemp. vellum.—Prov.: Henry C. Lea.

Ms. Lea 167 (Ital.)

GIUSEPPE VALLETTA. Al nostro SS. Padre Innocenzio XII intorno al procedimento ordinario, e canonico nelle cause che si trattano nel tribunale del S. Ufficio nella città, e nel regno di Napoli. *Naples, ca. 1700.*

Paper. 223 ff. 28 x 20 cm. Contemp. vellum.—Prov.: Thomas Vargas Macciucca; Henry C. Lea.

Ms. Lea 168 (Ital.)

PIETRO GIANNONE. [Apologia dell'Istoria civile di Napoli]. Trattato de rimedi contro le scomuniche invalide e proibizione de libri che si decratone in Roma. . . . *Naples, ca. 1750.*

Paper. 1 f., 451 pp. 29.5 x 22.5 cm. Contemp. vellum.—Prov.: Henry C. Lea.

Ms. Lea 169 (Ital.)

GIUSEPPE VALLETTA. Valletta al nostro Santissimo Padre Innocenzo XII intorno al procedimento ordinario, e canonico nelle cause che si trattano nel tribunale del S. Officio. *Naples, ca. 1700.*

Paper. 170 ff. 22.5 x 16.5 cm. Contemp. boards.—Prov.: Henry C. Lea.

Ms. Lea 170 (Ital.)

GIUSEPPE VALLETTA. Al nostro Santissimo Padre Innocenzio XII intorno al procedimento ordinario, e canonico nelle cause, che si trattano nel tribunale del S. Officio nella città, e nel regno di Napoli. *Naples, ca. 1700.*

Paper. 1, 175 ff. 21.5 x 15.5 cm. Contemp. vellum.—Prov.: Henry C. Lea.

Ms. Lea 171 (Ital.)

PIETRO DE FUSCO. Per la fedelissima città di Napoli negli affari della Santa Inquisizione, ff.1–41.—*With* GIACINTO DE MARI.

Discorso indrizzato all'Eccellenza del Sig. Duca d'Alva (on heresy), ff.42–80.—IDEM. Riflessioni contro le stesse osservazioni impugnate nell' antecedente scrittura . . . in difesa della città, a regno di Napoli in exclusione del ritorno del ministro delegato del tribunale dell' Inquisitione di Roma, ff.81–104. *Naples, 2nd half 17th cent.*

Paper. 104 ff. 24 x 17.5 cm. Contemp. vellum.—Prov.: Rodrigo Nolli; Henry C. Lea.

Ms. Lea 172 (Ital. and Sp.)

ANTONIO CASTALDO. Istoria . . . delle cose occorse del S. Ufficio in tempo che vi fu vicere D. Pietro di Toledo.—*With* FERDINAND VI, King of Spain. Edicto [contra Franc-Masones] 8 de Julio de 1751 (in Spanish).—Undated edict, in Italian, against public assembly.—NICOLO CAPASSO. Ragionamenti (partial copy).—PEDRO DE HONTALBA. Report on controversies over article 23 of the concordat between the Holy See and the royal court in Madrid, 1738–1739. *Spain, 18th cent.*

Paper. 32, 2 blank, 3 ff. (last f. blank), 129 pp., 26 ff. (all but ff.8–14 blank). 25 x 17 cm. Contemp. vellum.—Prov.: And. Tontoli; Henry C. Lea.

Ms. Lea 173 (Ital.)

VITA, MORTE E MIRACOLI di Bartolomeo Garosi detto Brandano e volgarmente detto il Pazzo di Gesù Christo, pp. 1–51.—*With* LA MORTE di Cecco d'Ascoli seguita in Firenze l'anno mille trecento venti octo, pp. 53–58.—MORTE di Giuliano de Medici . . . 26 Aprile 1470, pp. 59–64. *Italy, ca. 1600.*

Paper. 1 f., 64 pp. 21.5 x 16 cm. Contemp. vellum.—Prov.: Henry C. Lea.

Ms. Lea 175 (Sp.)

ABRAHAM GUER DE CORDOVA. Fortaleza del yudaísmo e confussión del christianismo. *Spain or Netherlands, 17th cent.?*

Paper. 2, 158, 1 ff. 24.5 x 18 cm. Boards.—Prov.: Henry C. Lea.

Ms. Lea 176 (Lat.)

BRICCI. Disputationes de poenitentia. *Italy, 17th cent.*

Paper. 200 pp. 27.5 x 19.5 cm. Contemp. vellum.—Prov.: "Rome, . . . des Français" (stamp on p. 1); Henry C. Lea.

Ms. Lea 177 (Sp.)

MELCHOR DE MACANAZ. Refutación jurídica é histórica de la consulta, que hizo el R. Consejo de Castilla al Rey Nostro Señor [1708]. *Spain, 18th cent.*

Paper. 120 ff. 29 x 19.5 cm. Contemp. calf.—Prov.: Henry C. Lea.

Ad. Lea 173: For bibliography on item 2 see Thorndike, *History of Magic*, II, 951.

Ms. Lea 178 (Sp.)

MELCHOR DE MACANAZ. Proposiciones que de orden de Su Magestad hizo Don Melchor de Macanas al consejo para que consultase lo que fuese conveniente para el concordato que se estava tradando en París con la corte de Roma [Dec. 19, 1713]. *Spain, 18th cent.*

Paper. 71 ff. 20.5 x 15 cm. Boards.—Prov.: Henry C. Lea.

Ms. Lea 179 (Sp.)

[FROILAN DIAZ]. Causa de Fr. Froylán Díaz, confesor que fue del Signor Carlos 2º. *Spain, 18th cent.*

Paper. 65 ff. 30 x 20.5 cm. H/leather.—Prov.: Henry C. Lea.

Ms. Lea 180 (Sp.)

[FROILAN DIAZ]. Hechizos de Carlos 2º. Debates entre el ynquisidor general y consejeros de la suprema. Papel histórico político de casos veconditas del gavinete de Carlos 2º. Informe de la causa y proceso fulminando contra el Padre . . . Froilan Diaz. . . . *Spain, 18th cent.*

Paper. 243 ff. 19 x 15 cm. H/leather.—Prov.: Marquis de Morante; Henry C. Lea. "This is actually the same as the 'Processo criminal . . . ,' Madrid, 1788. There is some difference in the documents at the end," pencilled note on fly-leaf.

Ms. Lea 181 (Lat. and Ital.)

TORELLI [=Taurelli] FAMILY. Memorie dei Conti Torelli, signori di Guastalla. (45 legal documents incl. contracts, deeds, an inventory, investitures, etc., plus 1 printed proclamation of Empress Maria Theresa <Mantua, 1765>; most documents are notarized). *Lombardy, 1454-1665.*

Vellum and paper. 2 vols. Various sizes (bound in bindings measuring 30.5 x 22.5 cm.). Notarial signets. H/calf.

Ms. Lea 182 (Ital.)

DEODATO BARTOLINI. Vita e miracoli di S. Mauro, abate . . . insieme con la storia del monastero di Glannafoglio. *Italy, 17th cent.*

Paper. 78 ff. (numbered 25–102; misbound in the following sequence: ff. 1–67, 97–102, 90–96, 68–89). 28.5 x 20 cm. Boards.—Prov.: Henry C. Lea.

Ms. Lea 183 (Ital.)

RELAZIONE DEI TRIBUNALI di Roma, pp. 1–248.—*With* ALCUNE REGOLE per decidere le questioni più frequenti, che vertono avanti l'uditore della segnatura, pp. 253–291.—Indice, 4 ff. at end. *Italy, post 1770.*

Paper. 2 blank ff., 291 pp., 10 ff. (ff.5–10 blank). 26 x 18.5 cm. Contemp. h/calf.—Prov.: Giacomo Calidi; Silvio Bocca; Henry C. Lea.

Ms. Lea 184 (Ital.)

DESIDERIO SCAGLIA. Prattica per le cause del Sant'Offitio. *Italy, 17th cent.*

Paper. 3 ff. (ff.1 and 3 blank), 51, 6 blank ff. 26 x 19 cm. Contemp. vellum.—Prov.: Henry C. Lea.

Ms. Lea 186 (Ital.)

VINCENZO MARIA CORONELLI. Libro d'oro ossia delle famiglie nobili venete. *Venice, ca. 1712.*

Paper. 321 pp. (with 12 ff. tipped in, some cancels and pasted-in corrections and additions). 28 x 20.5 cm. Engraved coats-of-arms pasted in throughout; several coats in pen-and-ink. Contemp. calf.

Ms. Lea 187 (Ital.)

GIUSEPPE VALLETTA. Al nostro Santiss. Padre Innocenzio XII^{mo} intorno al procedimento ordinario, e canonico nelle cause, che si trattano nel tribunale del S. Ufficio nella città, e nel regno di Napoli [preceded by Latin title:] De his quae Neapoli, Hispaniae, ac Romanae per Neapolitanos, vel scripta fuere, gesta pro vitanda, impediendaque introductione procedendi. . . . [Title on spine:] Trattati per la introducione del S. Officio. . . . *Italy, ca. 1700.*

Paper. 2 vols. 33.5 x 22.5 cm. Contemp. vellum.—Prov.: Thomas Vargas Macciucca; Henry C. Lea.

Ms. Lea 188 (Ital.)

PIETRO GIANNONE. Professione di fede scritta . . . al P. D. Giuseppe Sanfelice, Giesuita. . . .—*With* IDEM. Abbiura, ff.89–96. *Italy, 18th cent.*

Paper. 96 ff. 31 x 21 cm. Contemp. vellum.—Prov.: Henry C. Lea.

Ms. Lea 189 (Ital.)

PIETRO GIANNONE. Racconto della sollevazione di Napoli accaduta nel 1647 distribuito per giornali sino al tempo che furono introdotti li Spagnoli, in cominciando dalli 7. luglio 1647 . . . e finisce ab aprile 1648. . . . Di più s'aggiunge altri successi derivati dall'istessa sollevazione, e durorno fino all'anno 1655. . . . *Naples?, late 17th cent.*

Paper. Title, 172 ff. 31.5 x 21.5 cm. H/morocco.—Prov.: Henry C. Lea.

Ms. Lea 190 (Sp.)

CARTA escrita a un cavallero de Cordova sobre los cavallos e ginetes de la America Meridional, ff.1–6.—*With* JUAN DE LA CERDA. Carta al marques señor [sobre] el ganado bacuno de la America

---

Ad. Lea 184: For analysis of this ms. see Lea, *Materials toward a History of Witchcraft*, pp. 963–6.

Meridional con otras particularidades, y frequentes disgressiones en varia literatura, ff.9–131.—IDEM[?] Carta 2ª . . . sobre usos y particularidades de la America Meridional, ff.132–346.—IDEM. Notas del traducttor señore. El cantto primero, ff.348–352.—IDEM. Addiciones, ff.354–364.—RAPHAEL DE CORDOVA. Copies of reports, 1756 and 1764, ff.365–375 (the author, but not these writings mentioned in A. de Backer and C. Sommervogel, *op. cit.*, II, cols. 1446–7). *South America?. 2nd half 18th cent.*

Paper. 375 ff. 29 x 20.5 cm. Contemp. calf (rebacked).—Prov.: Henry C. Lea.

Ms. Lea 191 (Lat.)

HERMANN À KERSSENBROCH. Furoris anabaptistici Monasterium [Münster] inclytam Westphaliae metropolim evertentis historica narratio. *Germany, ca. 1700?*

Paper. 369 ff. 32.5 x 21 cm. Cloth.—Prov.: Henry C. Lea. The version which appeared in I. B. Mencken's *Scriptores rerum germanicarum* (Leipzig, 1728–1730), III, cols. 1503 ff., under the title "Narratio de obsidione monasteriensi seu de bello anabaptistico" is considerably abbreviated and quite different in some sections.

Ms. Lea 192 (Ital.)

[NAPLES]. Congiura de'baroni. (Copy of the "Processo contra Antonello de Petruciia," his sons, and Francisco Coppula, originally printed in Naples by the "Germani fidelissimi," July 14, 1487 [Hain 13382], pp. 1–174, followed by the text of the "Processo contra Pyrrum de Baulio, Antonellum de S. Severino, Johannem Carazolum," etc., printed *ibidem*, June 30, 1488 [Hain, 13383], pp. 179–340). *Italy, 1731.*

Paper. 340 pp. 27.5 x 20 cm. Contemp. vellum.—Prov.: Henry C. Lea.

Ms. Lea 193 (Sp. and Portug.)

[LISBON, Inquisition]. 1. RELACIÓN de los reos que se han de saler al auto particular de fee que se ha de celebrar en esta corte Domingo 23. de Feb. de 1682, 2 ff.—2. LISTA das personas que has de ouuir suas sentenças do auto publico da fee que se celebra no terreiro do paço desta cidade Domingo, 10. de mayo de 1682, 8 ff. (last 3 blank). Bound with printed *Relación verdadera del auto general de la fè, que celebrò el Santo Oficio de la Inquisicion de la ciudad de Lisboa, en el terreno de palacio de dicha ciudad, el Domingo 10. de mayo . . . 1682*, (Lisbon, 1682), 6 ff. *Lisbon, 1682.*

Paper. 16 ff. 30.5 x 21.5 cm. H/cloth.

Ms. Lea 194 (Lat.)

FRIULI. Quaternus protocollorum [title on back cover; alternate title on f.1r:] Quaternus notarum Petri de Monastero, notarii, filii S.

Odorici, notarius de civitate Austriae. 1397. (Collection of documents dealing with investitures, purchases, donations, etc., bearing the names of various notaries; the name Ottoboni occurs in various documents). *Friuli, 1397.*

Paper. 115 ff. 15 x 11.5 cm. Bound in vellum document, dated 1385.

Ms. Lea 195 (Fr.)
JEAN MARTIN LAUBARDEMONT. Collection of three letters, reporting the proceedings against, and condemnation of, Urbain Grandier, curé of Loudun, accused of perverting the Ursulines of Loudun to witchcraft, addressed to Cardinal Richelieu. *Loudun and Tours, August 20 and November 28, 1634; August 28, 1636.*

Paper. 5 ff. (ff.1r and v, 3r and v, and 5r containing the reports). 33.5 x 23 cm. Portfolio.

Ms. Lea 196 (Lat. and Ital.)
[MISCELLANEA AUTOGRAPHICA ECCLESIASTICA ITALIANA]. 30 documents and letters, 1503–1770, incl. items by members of the Borgia, Caraffa, Della Rovere, Grimaldi and Farnese families. *Rome, etc., 1503–1770.*

Paper and vellum. 43 ff. Various sizes in portfolio.

Ms. Lea 197 (Fr. and Lat.)
[FRENCH LEGAL DOCUMENTS]. 1. Sale of property in Caen by "Johanna dicta La Fromme" to "Raginaldus Colli Rubei," 1256, 1 f.— 2. Feudal rights granted by "Thiebaus de Maliers, seigneur du Châtel en Ardenne," to "Gervais de Donchery" and his wife, 1300, 1 f.—3. Receipt of payment by "Bertran de Tarride" from "Jaques Lempereur" for military services, 1355, 1 f.—4. Similar receipt by "Jehan de St. Germain," 1360, 1 f.—5. Receipt by "Sarrazius de Bethencourt" of gift from "la Comtesse de Flandres et Artoys" through "Michiel de Cambier," 1370, 1 f.—6. Real estate transaction between "Jehan duc de Berry" and his "neveu le duc de Orleans," 1411, 1 f. *France, 1256–1411.*

Vellum. 6 ff. Various sizes. Portfolio.

Ms. Lea 198 (Ital., etc.)
DISPACCI DIPLOMATICI inviati dalla corte granducale di Toscana ad Antonio Francesco Montauti (ambassador to the imperial court Vienna). 1. COSIMO III, grand duke of Tuscany. Dispacci, Sept. 17, 1689–Nov. 14, 1699 (279 items).—2. IDEM. Lettere di cancellaria, Jan. 2, 1690–Nov. 21, 1699 (32 items).—3. APOLLONIO BASSETTI. Lettere scritte . . . al Marchese Montauti, Sept. 4, 1691–April 18, 1699 (355 originals and 355 sep. bound copies).—4. FRANCESCO

MARIA DE' MEDICI. Lettere, May 1, 1688–Nov. 10, 1696 (152 items), bound with: PAOLO ANTONIO CONTI. Lettere, Oct. 8, 1689–Oct. 16, 1699 (229 items).—5. FRANCESCO MARIA DE' MEDICI. Lettere, Jan. 6, 1691–Oct. 31, 1699 (140 items).—6. FRANCESCO PANCIATICHI. Lettere . . . scritte al Marchese Montauti, Oct. 16, 1691–Oct. 11, 1699 (280 items).—7. GIOVANNI GASTONE. Lettere, Sept. 13, 1689–May 29, 1706 (27 items).—8. Lettere varie (Cosimo III, Cardinal Francesco Maria de' Medici, Count Palatin Johann Wilhelm, Emperor Leopold I, etc.), 1690–1744 (36 items).—9. Copie di dispacci riguardanti il feudo di Filattierra (involving Leopold I and Cosimo III, etc.), primarily of the years 1698–1699 (51 items).—10. Cifrari, 1689 and 1694 (etc.), (4 items).—11. Copie di dispacci vari pervenuti al Montauti, etc., 1650–1734 (132 items).—12. *With* COSIMO III, grand duke of Tuscany. Lettere scritte a Alessandro da Verazano, 1696–1703 (279 items). *Various places, 1650-1744.*

Paper. 13 vols. Various sizes (all in folio bindings or portfolios). Contemp. vellum (6) and portfolios (7).—Original letters and documents, and copies; some autograph, others signed, many with seals, some in code. As far as known the entire collection of "dispacci" remains unpublished. See also Ms. Lea 30–32, part of the same collection, but acquired earlier.

Ms. Lea 199 (Lat.)

BARTOLOMEO CHIOCCARELLI. Magni archivii scripturarum pro regali jurisdictione Regni Neapolis ex omnibus regiis archiviis Philippi. IV. . . . mandatis, et acuratissima diligentia . . . exceptarum . . . et in unum collectarum, tomus I [–XVIII].—*With* IDEM. Notitia elaborata, et absolutissima, and printed *Indice compendioso* (Venice, 1721). *Italy, second half 17th cent.*

Paper. 18 vols. in 16 (of the main work), 1 vol. (Notitia) and 1 vol. (Indice) = 18 vols. 32.5 x 23 cm. (Indice: 22.5 x 16.5 cm.) Contemp. vellum.—Prov.: Marquis Salsa. Niccola Fraggianni's *Lettera circolare . . . intorno al modo di procedere in causa di fede*, printed Naples, 1761, tipped in at end of vol. 10.

Ms. Lea 200 (Lat.)

BARTOLOMEO CHIOCCARELLI. Same collection as the preceding, but vols. 3–18 of the main work only. *Italy, second half 17th cent.*

Paper. 16 vols. 30 x 21 cm. Contemp. vellum.—Prov.: Henry C. Lea.

Ms. Lea 201 (Ital.)

FERDINAND II, Grand Duke of Tuscany. Viaggio del Serenissimo Gran Duca di Toscana da Fiorenza insino a Roma. *Italy, 17th cent.*

Paper. 20 ff. 28 x 21 cm. Boards.

Ms. Lea 202 (Fr.)*

MATHURIN DE MONTALAIS, seigneur de Chambellay (Maine-et-Loire). Feudal rents from his properties of "Seaulx, la Fillotiere, Crisse, et Langevine." *France, early 16th cent.*

Paper. 280 ff. 35 x 25 cm. Contemp. vellum.

Ms. Lea 203 (Sp.)

[BARCELONA, Inquisition]. Sobre los procedimientos y relaxade vida del canónigo de Castelló [de Ampurias] Antonio Navarro, notario de este Santo Oficio (addressed by the "inquisidores" to the bishop of Urgel, signed Jerónimo de Escóbar, Juan de Ribera, etc.) *Barcelona, May 16, 1671.*

Paper. 2 ff. (f.2 blank except for archival marking). 30 x 21 cm. Portfolio.

Ms. Lea 204 (Ital.)

[PIACENZA]. Notarial document of 1531, respecting the marriage agreement between Constantia, daughter of Hyronima and the late Albericus Malvicini de Fontana, and Matteo, son of Filippo Fori. *Piacenza, 1531.*

Vellum. 4 ff. 20 x 17 cm. Portfolio.—Prov.: Morbio Collection.

Ms. Lea 205 (Lat.)

[PIACENZA]. Two notarial documents of 1534 and 1540. 1. Acknowledgment of a sum of 1000 pounds as a dowry for Lucia de Medicis, who is to marry Innocentius, son of Antoninus Antonii.—2. Document drawn "in pallatio magno super scalis" respecting the completion of notarial documents of the deceased notary, Leonardus Casalis, by the notary Albertus Penna. The notaries are Albertus Penna (1) and Bartholomeus Casalis (2). *Piacenza, 1534, 1540.*

Vellum. 2 ff. 24.5 x 18 cm. Portfolio.—Prov.: Morbio Collection.

Ms. Lea 206 (Port.)

[INQUISITION]. Sentenças proferidas pelo Santo Officio. (Accounts of trials held at Lisbon, Goa, Coimbra, Rome, etc., 1603–1706). *Lisbon, ca. 1750.*

Paper. 4, 112, 4 blank ff. 24 x 17 cm. Contemp. calf.—Prov.: John Foster sale (Sotheby June 25–28, 1878).—"Tomo primeiro" only (same as in 1878).

Ms. Lea 207 (Ital.)

PIETRO GIANNONE. Trattato de'rimedi contro le scomuniche invalide, e proibizioni de libri, che si decretano in Roma . . . coll'occasione della invalida censura contro di lui fulminata dal vicario di

Napoli per aver fatto quivi imprimere i libri della storia civile di quel regno senza sua licenza, e della proibizione de medesimi decretata in Roma nel di 1. luglio 1723. *Naples, 1723.*

Paper. 283 ff. 29 x 21 cm. Contemp. calf.—"Ex libris Orontii Mello."—Cf. Lea mss. 168, 188–9.

Ms. Lea 208 (Ital.)
CHERUBINO CHIRARDAZZI. Istoria di Bologna, parte terza, manuscritta, ed estratta della Libreria del Convento di S. Giacomo Maggiore di Bologna, l'anno 1734. Continuation of two printed volumes, beginning with some additional material left out of printed books 27, 28, and 29 and covering the years 1393 to 1425 (pp. 1–22), continuing with [unpublished?] books 30 (p.23)–38 (ending p.1174); followed by notes "Aggiunta à questo tomo manoscritto" (pp.1175–1202) and "Tavola generale" (pp.1203–36). *Italy, 1734.*

Paper. Title, 1236 pp. 29 x 20 cm. Contemp. vellum.—Prov.: Biblioteca Banzi.

Ms. Lea 210 (Ital.)
[SLAVERY]. Ruolo di tutti li schiavi che anno predato le sei galere di S.A.S. [Cosimo II, Grand Duke of Tuscany] in quest'anno in Levante, tanto masti quanto femine, il quale comincia alli 6 di maggio 1611 all'Isola di Storonisse in Levante fino alli 22 detto a sigra di Mitelino. (List of 202 slaves, giving in each case the name, origin, age and general description of the captive and the name of the person to whom he or she has been assigned). *Florence?, 1611.*

Paper. 16 ff. 31.5 x 21.5 cm. Boards.—Cf. no. 353.

Ms. Lea 211 (Ital.)
VINCENZO MEDICI. Report to Cosimo II on his activities as "depositario generale" of a "zecca" from 1595 to 1609, dealing with economic questions, e.g. purchase and sale of grain, benefices, etc. *Tuscany, Oct. 19, 1609.*

Paper. 2 ff. 30 x 21 cm. (folded). Boards.—Cf. mss. 243–50, 294–5.

Gondi-Medici Business Records

Numbers 212–355 were acquired as a collection. They are arranged more or less chronologically, within the following series: Medici records in regular folio; narrow folio; smaller sizes.—Amadori records.—Arrigucci and Gondi records.—Textile trade records.—Miscellaneous records. All volumes were originally part of the Gondi archives, specifically of that part which was left to the Ritiro della Quiete in Florence by Caterina and Elisabetta, descendants of Giuliano il Vecchio, cf. Roberto Ridolfi, *Gli archivi delle famiglie fiorentine* (Florence, L. S. Olschki, 1934).

Ms. Lea 212 (Ital.)

CASA MEDICI. Ricordanze di beni et immobili di casa Medici, 1456–95 (a variety of sections: ff.2r–4v, 1456–76; ff.10r–12r, 1458–68; ff.13v–14r, 1473–4; f.24r–v, 1458–70; ff.25r–26v, 1463–73; f.27, 1464; ff.30r–32v, 1464–95; ff.38v–39r, 1463–72[?]; f.48, 1465–70; f.50, 1471–8–[?]; f.52, 1473–92; f.53, 1479–80; f.54r without date; ff.64r–65v, 1474–93; ff.66r–68r, 1493–4). [Giornale] A. *Italy, 1456–95.*

Paper. 144 ff. (ff.1, 16–9 wanting, as are the following, probably blank ff., ff.56–7, 69–71, 74–6, 86–91, 94–102, 108–13, 135.—Ff.5–9, 20–3, 33–7, 40–7, 50, 55, 58–63, 72 are blank). 28 x 22 cm. Contemp. vellum, no. 22[?] on spine, no. 242 on front cover.

Casa de Medici. Ricordanze. Lea 212, f.3r (detail).

Ms. Lea 213 (Ital.)

[CARLO DE MEDICI?]. Quaderno di cassa, debitori e creditori, 1532–3. [Giornale] C. *Italy, 1532–33.*

Paper. 64 ff. (ff.36–64 blank). 28.5 x 21.5 cm. Contemp. vellum, no. 130 on spine, no. 225 on front cover.

Ms. Lea 214 (Ital.)

CARLO DE MEDICI. Giornale di chassa, 1°, debitori e creditori, 1533–4. *Italy, 1533–34.*

Paper, except first and last f., vellum. 2, 240 ff. (ff.121–70 blank), 1 f. 33.5 x 23 cm. Contemp. vellum, no. 27 on spine, no. 295 on front cover.

Ms. Lea 215 (Ital.)

———. Quaderno di chassa, 3°, debitori e creditori, 1534–5. *Italy, 1534–35.*

Paper. 1 f. vellum, 111 ff. (ff.107–11 blank). 33.5 x 23.5 cm. Contemp. vellum, no. 30 on spine, no. 293 on front cover.

Ms. Lea 216 (Ital.)

BIVIGLIANO D'ALAMANNO DE MEDICI. Libro in sul quale fara schrivere e sua beni . . . e altre cose importante. . . . *Italy, 1534–44.*

Paper. 64 ff. (ff.42–64 blank). 26.5 x 20.5 cm. Contemp. vellum, no. 52 on front cover.—Deals primarily with real estate.

Ms. Lea 217 (Ital.)

[CARLO DE MEDICI?]. Quaderno di chassa, 7°, debitori e creditori, 1536–7. (Assigned to "Vincenzo de Medici?" by previous owner). *Italy, 1536–37.*

Paper, except first and last f., vellum. 2, 175 ff. (ff.108–75 blank), 1 f. 33 x 23.5 cm. Contemp. vellum, no. 131 on spine, no. 289 on cover.

Ms. Lea 218 (Ital.)

CARLO DE MEDICI. Quaderno di chassa, 6°, debitori e creditori, 1536–7. *Italy, 1536–37.*

Paper, except first and last f., vellum. 2, 239 ff. (ff.123–239 blank), 1 f. 33.5 x 23 cm. Contemp. vellum, no. 29 on spine, no. 290 on front cover.

Ms. Lea 219 (Ital.)

[CARLO DE MEDICI?]. Quaderno di cassa, 8°, debitori e creditori, 1537–8. (Assigned to Carlo de Medici by previous owner; among the accounts are those of Carlo and Francesco da Barberino; Ottaviano and Lorenzo de Medici; Spedale di Santa Maria Nuova; Anastasio and Giovanni Pitti; Francisco di Girolamo Rucellai; Mariotto de Medici). *Italy, 1537–38.*

Paper, except first and last f. of text, vellum. 18 ff. (index, in vellum wrapper), 2, 237 ff. (ff.116–237 blank), 1 f. 33 x 23 cm. Contemp. vellum, no. 133 on spine, no. 288 on front cover.

Ms. Lea 220 (Ital.)

[_____]. Quaderno di cassa, debitori e creditori, 1538–9. (Assigned to "Carlo de Medici?" by previous owner; among names appearing are Antonio and Giovanni Pitti; Spedale di Santa Maria degli Innocenti; Giuliano, Francesco, Mariotto and Gregorio de Medici; Anastasio de Buonacorso; Alessandro di Nicolo Antinori). *Italy, 1538–39.*

Paper, except first and last f., vellum. 1, 18 ff. index, 1, 239 ff. (ff.99–239 blank), 1 f. Contemp. vellum, no. 286 on front cover.

Ms. Lea 221 (Ital.)

SALINA DI PISTOIA. Li signori quattro commisari sopra le cose di Pistoia, 1539. *Pistoia, 1539.*

Paper. 1 f. 29 x 21 cm. In portfolio with ms. Lea 259.

Ms. Lea 222 (Ital.)

[CARLO DE MEDICI?]. Quaderno di chassa, 12°, [debitori e creditori], 1539–40. (Assigned to Luigi de Medici by previous owner; among the accounts are Anastasio de Buonacorso; Spedale di Santa Maria Nuova; Santa Maria del Fiore; Carlo de Simone Benzoni; Giovanni di Baldo; Mariotto di Gregorio de Medici; Ottaviano de Medici). *Italy, 1539–40.*

Paper, except first and last f., vellum. 2, 223 ff. (ff.107–223 blank), 1 f. 33 x 23 cm. Contemp. vellum, no. 135(?) on spine, no. 304 on front cover.

Ms. Lea 223 (Ital.)

[_____]. Quaderno di cassa, 13°, debitori e creditori, 1539–40. (Assigned to "Luigi de Medici?" by previous owner; among accounts are those of the Spedale di Santa Maria Nuova; Santa Maria del Fiore; Anastasio di Buonacorso Pitti; Mariotto di Gregorio de Medici; Antonio di Giovanni Pitti; Francesco Legnaiolo; Giovanni d'Ottaviano Doni; Diegho de Chastro spagnolo; Francesco and Matteo Manucci). *Italy, 1539–40.*

Paper, except first f., vellum. 2, 95 ff. (and 144 blank ff.). 33.5 x 23 cm. Contemp. vellum, no. 136 on spine, no. 303 on front cover.

Ms. Lea 224 (Ital.)

CARLO DI FERDINANDO DE MEDICI. Quaderno di debitori e creditori. [Giornale] B, 1540–56. *Italy, 1540–56.*

Paper. 208 ff. 28.5 x 20.5 cm. Contemp. vellum, no. 31 on spine, no. 122 on front cover.

Ms. Lea 225 (Ital.)

[CARLO DE MEDICI?]. Quaderno di cassa, 18°, debitori e creditori, 1542–3. (Assigned to "Carlo de Medici?" by previous owner; among the names appearing are Rafaello di Miniato; Santa Maria del Fiore; Pagolo Giovanni Gondi; Buonacorso Pitti; Mariotto di Gregorio de Medici; Spedale di Santa Maria Nuova). *Italy, 1542–43.*

Paper, except first and last f., vellum. 1, 140 ff. (misnumbered; ff.85–140 blank), 1 f. 33.5 x 23 cm. Contemp. vellum, no. 142 on spine, no. 285 on front cover.

Ms. Lea 226 (Ital.)

[_____]. Quaderno di cassa, 21°, debitori e creditori, 1543–4. (Assigned to Carlo de Medici by previous owner; among the accounts are those of Alessandro di Nicolo Antinori; Anastasio di Buonacorso Pitti; Spedale di Santa Maria Nuova; Jacopo d'Alamanno; Alamanno di Bernardo de Medici). *Italy, 1543–44.*

Paper, except first f., vellum. 2, 143 ff. (ff.82–143 blank). 33 x 23 cm. Contemp. vellum, no. 143 on spine, no. 296 on front cover.

Ms. Lea 227 (Ital.)

[_____]. Quaderno di cassa, 20°, debitori e creditori, 1543-4. (Assigned to "Carlo de Medici?" by previous owner; among the names appearing are Santa Maria del Fiore; Mariotto di Gregorio de Medici; Alessandro Antinori; Spedale degli Innocenti; Santa Maria Nuova; Bernardo di Piero Brandolini; Guerardo and Piero d'Alamanno Salviati). *Italy, 1543-44.*

Paper. 1, 95 ff. (ff.91-5 blank). 33.5 x 23.5 cm. Contemp. vellum, no. 144 on spine, no. 297 on front cover.

Ms. Lea 228 (Ital.)

CARLO DE MEDICI. Quaderno di cassa della suventione del anno 1543[-6]. [Giornale] B. *Italy, 1543-46.*

Paper. 1, 47 ff. (ff.36-47 blank). 33 x 23 cm. Contemp. vellum, no. 33 on spine.

Ms. Lea 229 (Ital.)

_____. Quaderno di cassa, 22°, debitori e creditori, 1544-5 (and 1 entry each 1546 and 1559). *Italy, 1544-59.*

Paper. 1, 95 ff. (ff.87-95 blank). 34 x 23 cm. Contemp. vellum, no. 34 on spine, no. 306 on front cover.

Ms. Lea 230 (Ital.)

CARLO BERNARDO ALAMANNI DE MEDICI. Libro di contracti, no. 9, 1552-69 (Beni di Volterra, etc.) *Italy, 1552-69.*

Paper. 1, 49 ff. (last blank). 28 x 21 cm. Contemp. vellum, no. 126 on spine.

Ms. Lea 231 (Ital.)

[ARTE DELLA LANA]. 3 documents, 1552 to late 16th cent. 1. Addressed to the "illustrious and most excellent Duke" [of Tuscany] by Lelio T., a "supplica" concerning Giovanbattista Bettini, Amerigo Carnesecchi and Luigi Bettini, dated 1552.—2. Addressed to the same, unsigned, concerning Giovanbattista Bettini, n.d.—3. "Supplica" of Nicolo and Fabrizio di Luigi de Medici to the Grand Duke [Cosimo II?] concerning a Camilla lor'zia paterna, n.d. *Italy, 1552-late 16th cent.*

Paper. 3 ff. Ca. 29 x 21 cm. Portfolio.—Cf. mss. 327 ff.

Ms. Lea 232 (Ital.)

CARLO DI BERNARDO DE MEDICI. Conto di tutti debitori [e creditori] divisi delle ragioni di Giovanbattista Bettini . . . , Pandolfo de Medici . . . , 1553-60, 1570. [Giornale] A. *Italy, 1553-70.*

Paper. 1, 63 ff. (ff.33-49, 54-63 blank). 27.5 x 21 cm. Contemp. vellum, no. 36 on spine, no. 126 on front cover.

Ms. Lea 233 (Ital.)

NICOLO and FABRIZIO (figlioli di Luigi) DE MEDICI. Libro di debitori e creditori, ricordi e altro, 1566–8. [Giornale] A. (Contains also "copie di conti," "conti co[l] lavoratori delle ricolte e vantaggi," "entrata e uscita di grani e biade e altro"). *Italy, 1566–68.*

Paper. 1, 175 ff. (ff.113–23, 131–43, 167–75, blank); 2 ff. doc. concerning Rinaldo di Falente, lavoratore, 17 Feb. 1565, laid in. 33.5 x 23 cm. Contemp. vellum, no. 14 on spine, no. 137 on front cover, 1 f. from incunable sewn in front cover.

Ms. Lea 234 (Ital.)

LUISA (moglie di Luigi) DI BIVIGLIANO DE MEDICI. Libro di debitori e creditori, ricordi, etc., 1566–73. [Giornale] A. (Debitori e creditori, prel. f.1v–104r; ricordi e copie di conti, ff.104v–22v; conti co lavoratori del podere di Castagnolo, ff.124v–38r; entrata e uscita di grani e biade e altre, ff.144v–88r). *Italy, 1566–73.*

Paper. 1, 191 ff. (ff.123, 139–43, 189–91 blank). 33 x 23 cm. Contemp. vellum, no. 25 on spine, no. 112 on front cover (folio ms. leaf <15th cent.> on vellum preceding and following account book, fragment of incunable leaf stitched inside front cover).

Ms. Lea 235 (Ital.)

NICOLO and FABRIZIO (figlioli di Luigi) DE MEDICI. Libro di debitori e creditori. [Giornale] B, 1568–75. *Italy, 1568–75.*

Paper. 1, 191 ff. (ff.187–91 blank). 33.5 x 23 cm. Contemp. vellum, no. 16 on spine, no. 138 on front cover.

Ms. Lea 236 (Ital.)

CARLO DI BERNARDO DE MEDICI and FRANCESCO DI STEFANO DI RISALITI. Libro di entrata e uscita, 1573–6. [Giornale] A [also $\frac{a}{2}$]. *Italy, 1573–76.*

Paper. 240 ff. (ff.48–50, 68–89, 117–39, 175–240 blank; numbering irregular). 32.5 x 23 cm. Contemp. vellum, no. 69 on spine, no. 48 and signet "C F" on front cover.—Cf. nos. 332–5.

Ms. Lea 237 (Ital.)

ANDREA DI CARLO DE MEDICI. Entrata [e uscita] prima delle rede di Carlo de Medici tenuta per me Andrea di Carlo de Medici, 1573–80. [Giornale] A. (Name Vincenzo Medici, in later hand, on front cover). *Italy, 1573–80.*

Paper. 144 ff. (ff.22–75, 132–44 blank). 33 x 23 cm. Contemp. vellum, no. 49 on spine, no. 229 on front cover.

Ms. Lea 238 (Ital.)

CARLO DE MEDICI [Heirs?]. Libro di debitori e creditori, 1573-80. [Giornale] A. *Italy, 1573-80.*

Paper. 1, 207 ff. 32.5 x 23 cm. Contemp. vellum, no. 38 on spine, no. 9 on front cover.

Ms. Lea 239 (Ital.)

GIORNALE [di entrata e uscita?] A, 1573-80. (Among the names appearing are Bartolomeo Ricci; Pietro Parrini; Carlo de Medici; Giovanni Bertelli; Francesco di Matteo Bracchi). *Italy, 1573-80.*

Paper. 48 ff. (ff.40-8 blank). 33 x 23 cm. Contemp. vellum, no. 148 on spine, no. 230 on front cover.

Ms. Lea 240 (Ital.)

NICOLO and FABRIZIO (fratelli, figlioli di Luigi) DE MEDICI. Libro di debitori e creditori. [Giornale] C, 1575-84. With alphabetical index at beginning. *Italy, 1575-84.*

Paper. 18 ff. (index), 1, 237 ff. (ff.226-37 blank). 33.5 x 24 cm. Contemp. vellum, no. 13 on spine, no. 136 on front cover.

Ms. Lea 241 (Ital.)

———. Ricordi e conti de contratti con lavoratori, e entrata e uscita di grano, vino e altro, 1575-82, with added Ricordi, 1582, 1584. [Giornale] C. *Italy, 1575-84.*

Paper. 1, 191 ff. (ff.171-4, 177-91 blank); 1 large f. of additions laid in between ff.83-4. 33.5 x 23 cm. Contemp. vellum, no. 17 on spine, no. 139 on front cover.

Ms. Lea 242 (Ital.)

FABRIZIO DI LUIGI DE MEDICI. Libro di debitori e creditori, 1579-1612. [Giornale] C. *Italy, 1579-1612.*

Paper. 1, 191 ff. (ff.176-91 blank), 4 ff. (2 blank) laid in between ff. 31-2, corrections and calculations inserted throughout, 6 letters or docs. of Fabrizio and a printed form in envelope at end. 33 x 23 cm. Contemp. vellum, no. 18 on spine, no. 87 on front cover.

Ms. Lea 243 (Ital.)

VINCENZO and ANDREA DE MEDICI (cf. f.158v). Libro di possessione, 1581-3. [Giornale] B. (Ff.1-111 deal with the territory and possessions "fuora della possessione di Valdenievole e delle spese attenante a bestiami et altre;" ff.112-157 with the "possessione di Valdenievole.") *Italy, 1581-83.*

Paper. 1, 191 ff. (ff.159-91 blank). 33 x 23 cm. Contemp. vellum, no. 96 on spine, no. 10 on front cover.

Ms. Lea 244 (Ital.)

VINCENZO MEDICI. Giornale della possessione di Valdenievole, 1583–92. [Giornale] C. *Italy, 1583–92.*

Paper. 64 ff. (ff.45–64 blank). 33.5 x 24 cm. Contemp. vellum, no. 98 on spine.

Ms. Lea 245 (Ital.)

VINCENZO and ANDREA DE MEDICI [f.25r]. Giornale C del libro, debitori e creditori, e libro di possession, 1583–92. (Assigned erroneously to "Carlo de Medici" <father of Vincenzo and Andrea> by previous owner). *Italy, 1583–92.*

Paper. 80 ff. (ff.16–24, 77–80 blank). 33 x 23.5 cm. Contemp. vellum, no. 150 on spine.

Ms. Lea 246 (Ital.)

———. Entrata e uscita del' libro di debitori e creditori e del libro di possessione, 1583–92. [Giornale] C. *Italy, 1583–92.*

Paper. 112 ff. (ff.8–20, 49–56, 76–83 blank). 33.5 x 23.5 cm. Contemp. vellum, no. 51 on spine, no. 251 on front cover.

Ms. Lea 247 (Ital.)

———. Entrata e uscita del libro . . . B, 1585–90 (and 1 entry each for 1593 and 1594, and 2 for 1614; concerns transactions of textile business). *Italy, 1585–1614.*

Paper. 94 ff. (ff.24–72, 83–94 blank). 34 x 24 cm. Contemp. vellum, no. 53 on spine, no. 34 and signet VA on front cover.—Cf. nos. 327 ff.

Ms. Lea 248 (Ital.)

VINCENZO DE MEDICI. Quaderno di possessione dell'anno 1595[–6]. *Italy, 1595–96.*

Paper. 1, 62 ff. (ff.3, 12–4, 26–9, 44, 62–3 blank). 30 x 21 cm. Contemp. vellum, no. 101 on spine, no. 239(?) on front cover.

Ms. Lea 249 (Ital.)

VINCENZO and ANDREA DE MEDICI. Giornale e ricordi B, 1597–1605. *Italy, 1597–1605.*

Paper. 352 ff. (ff.304–11, 323–52 blank). 34 x 23 cm. Contemp. vellum, no. 55(?) on spine.

Ms. Lea 250 (Ital.)

———. Entrata e uscita, 1597–1605, with summaries 1603–7, 1617 and 1621. [Giornale] D. *Italy, 1597–1621.*

Paper. 256 ff. (ff.238–56 blank). 35.5 x 25 cm. Contemp. vellum (no. on spine unreadable).

Ms. Lea 251 (Ital.)

COSIMO II, Grand Duke of Tuscany. 9 documents relating to the grain trade: 1. Habbiamo rivisto il conto à Marcello Strozzi . . . 1595-1600. . . . Dalla gabella delle farine, dated Florence, 1601 (2 ff., 2nd blank).—2. Relazioni . . . per conti rivisti . . . 1594-1605. . . . Supplica Strozzi, 1605 (6 ff.).—3. Li figlioli di Marcello Strozzi . . . sono molestati dal proveditore delle farine, Florence, 1605 (2 ff., 2nd blank).—4. Document concerning the same "figlioli," 1605 (2 ff., 2nd blank).—5. Haviamo rivisto il conto del consumo della casa . . . 1604-5. . . . Supplica, 1605 (1 f.).—6. Supplica of Francesco Giraldi, 1606 (1 f.).—7. Supplica of Giulio Franceschi to the Grand Duchess, 1609 (2 ff.).—8. Supplica of Giovanbattista Squarci, undated (1 f.).—9. Supplica referring to a letter of Jacopo Riccardi di Pisa, to the Grand Duchess, 1610 (1 f.). *Italy, 1601-10.*

Paper. 18 ff. Ca. 30 x 21 cm. In portfolio.

Ms. Lea 252 (Ital.)

[MEDICI MINT]. Six documents, dated 1602, 1603, 1609, 1612 and 1635(?) addressed to the Grand Duke of Tuscany, "sulla zecca medicea, contratti, approvazioni," etc. *Italy, 1602-35*(?).

Paper. 1+6+2+4+1+1 ff. (=15 ff.). Ca. 30 x 22 cm. In portfolio.—Cf. ms. Lea 211.

Ms. Lea 253 (Ital.)

VINCENZO DE MEDICI. Giornale e ricordanze, 1603-6. [Giornale] B. *Italy, 1603-6.*

Paper. 142 ff. (last blank). 42 x 28 cm. Contemp. vellum, no. 59 on spine, no. 221 on front cover.

Ms. Lea 254 (Ital.)

[MEDICI?]. Riscontro di banchi, 1603-6. [Giornale] B. (Assigned to "Carlo de Medici?" by previous owner; main firms mentioned are Giovanbattista Medici and Vincenzo de Ricci, and Francesco and Lorenzo Medici). *Italy, 1603-6.*

Paper. 1, 95 ff. (ff.41-95 blank). 29 x 20.5 cm. Contemp. vellum, no. 54(?) on spine.

Ms. Lea 255 (Ital.)

VINCENZO and ANDREA DE MEDICI. Libro di cambi, 1605-16. [Giornale] C. *Italy, 1605-16.*

Paper. 257 (vero 256) ff. (ff.251-7 blank). 33 x 23.5 cm. Contemp. vellum (rubbed and slightly broken, title and number unreadable).

Ms. Lea 256 (Ital.)

_____. Ricordanze e tintore, 1605–26. (The "ricordanze" occupy the first 4 ff. only and end with the year 1620). [Giornale] C. *Italy, 1605–26.*

Paper. 158 (vero 160) ff. (ff.150–8 blank). 34 x 22 cm. Contemp. vellum, no. 64(?) on spine, no. 29 on front cover.—Cf. nos. 327 ff.

Ms. Lea 257 (Ital.)

_____. Libro sig. C corregie verde si chiama portate, 1605–33. [Giornale] C. *Italy, 1605–33.*

Paper. 576 ff. (ff.565–76 blank). 29 x 20.5 cm. Contemp. vellum, no. 66(?) on spine.

Ms. Lea 258 (Ital.)

_____. Giornale e ricordi C (in several sections: ff.1r–111v, 1605–10; 112r–46v, 1605–12; 147r, 1620 [for 1610?]; 147r–98v, 1610–3; 190r–2r, 1612–6; 193r, 1633; 202r–24r, 1613–6; 224r–5r, 1614–24; 225v–6v, 1631; 229r–59r, 1616–29; 259v, 1632.—Large parts deal with the Capponi-Medici branch in Pisa). *Italy, 1605–33.*

Paper. 273 (vero 272, irregularly numbered) ff. (ff.194–201, 227–8, 260–73 blank). 33 x 23 cm. Contemp. vellum, no. 67(?) on spine.

Ms. Lea 259 (Ital.)

VOLTERRA. Two letters from the "rappresentanti della città di Volterra" to Cosimo II, Grand Duke of Tuscany, May–June, 1606. (Concern the "gabella di sale"). *Volterra, 1606.*

Paper. 2 (second blank) +2 ff. 28.5 x 21 cm. In portfolio with ms. Lea 221.

Ms. Lea 260 (Ital.)

VINCENZO DE MEDICI. Memoriale $\frac{0}{3}$ . . . per la zecca; negozi dello depositario Medici, 1608–9. *Italy, 1608–9.*

Paper. 1, 87 ff. (misnumbered <and misbound> 1–11, 13–48, 56–9, 54–9, 59–87). 31 x 20 cm. Contemp. vellum.

Ms. Lea 261 (Ital.)

[MEDICI]. Riscontro con li banchi, 1609–11. [Giornale] D. (Among the banking houses and large accounts are those of Francesco Medici; Capponi Medici <Rome>; Vincenzo Medici <Pisa?>; Adovardo Acciauoli; Francesco Salvetti; Bernardo Riccardi; from a slip laid in as a suppl. to 1610 it appears that the following branches are involved: Genoa, Milan, Florence, Venice, Rome, Naples, Palermo, Messina, Lyons, Bologna and Ancona). *Italy, 1609–11.*

Paper. 1, 47 ff. (ff.32–47 blank). 29.5 x 20.5 cm. Contemp. vellum, no. 259 on front cover.

Ms. Lea 262 (Ital.)

[_____]. Quaderno di cambi, 1609–11. [Giornale] D. (Transfers of large amounts to [Medici branches] Capponi-Medici, Pisa, Rome, Naples, etc.). *Italy, 1609–11.*

Paper. 32 ff. (ff.28–32 blank), ff.65–80 (ff.79–80 blank). Two signatures (ff.33–64) removed? 42 x 27.5 cm. Contemp. vellum, no. 154 on spine, no. 220 on front cover.

Ms. Lea 263 (Ital.)

VINCENZO DE MEDICI. Giornale e ricordanze, 1609–11. [Giornale] D. *Italy, 1609–11.*

Paper. 146 ff. 41.5 x 27.5 cm. Contemp. vellum, no. 98(?) on spine, no. 264 on front cover.

Ms. Lea 264 (Ital.)

COSIMO II, Grand Duke of Tuscany. 4 documents relating to the "monte di pietà," 1609–11 (one undated). *Italy, 1609–11.*

Paper. 1+1+1+2 ff. (=5 ff.). Ca. 31 x 21.5 cm. In portfolio.

Ms. Lea 265 (Ital.)

ANDREA DE MEDICI. Libro . . . intitulato intrata, uscita e giornale . . . tenuto per mano de Domenico di Giovanni Mongali, fattore del' Andrea de Medici alla sua possessione di Valdenievole, 1623–9. [Giornale] A. *Italy, 1623–29.*

Paper. 96 ff. (numbered ff.1–8, pp.9–58, 58–155, 1 blank p., pp.156–84). 34 x 23.5 cm. Contemp. vellum, no. 106 on spine, no. 82 on front cover.

Ms. Lea 266 (Ital.)

[VALDENIEVOLE]. Giornale della fattoria di Valdenievole, 1626–9. [Quaderno] C. *Italy, 1626–29.*

Paper. 288 pp. (pp.167–8 omitted, p.169 used twice). 34 x 24 cm. Contemp. vellum, no. 76 on front cover, no. 107 on spine.

N.B.: End of first Medici series

Ms. Lea 267 (Ital.)

ALAMANNO DE MEDICI. Libro e chiamasi giornale [e ricordi], 1466–94. *Italy, 1466[1465 on f.1r]–94.*

Paper. 144 ff. (ff.107–12, 126–44 blank); various slips in volume and 9 docs. (incl. letters) in envelope. 34 x 11.5 cm. Vellum, no. 11 on spine and front cover.

Ms. Lea 268 (Ital.)

LUIGI DE MEDICI. Giornale . . . , spese minute . . . , debitori e creditori . . . , entrate minute. . . . (Ff.1–8, 1495–7; f.10, 1484;

ff.12–7, 1519–44; ff.69–72, 1496–7; f.77, 1496; ff.85–6, 1496–7). [Giornale] B. *Italy, 1495–1544.*

Paper. 100 ff. (ff.18–68, 73–6, 78–84, 87–100 blank). 28.5 x 10.5 cm. Vellum, no. 165 on strip attached to spine.

Ms. Lea 269 (Ital.)

[FERNANDO?] ALAMANNI DE MEDICI. Libro di debitori e creditori, 1521–34. Giornale A. *Italy, 1521–34.*

Paper. 1, 142 ff. (numbering somewhat irregular; ff.49–64, 101–19, 124–7, 137–42 blank). 28.5 x 11 cm. Vellum, no. 164 on slip attached to spine.

Ms. Lea 270 (Ital.)

LUIGI DI BIVIGLIANO DE MEDICI. Entrata e uscita, 1533–8. [Giornale] A. *Italy, 1533–38.*

Paper. 1, 132 ff. (ff.14–49, 95–132 blank). 22 x 15.5 cm. Contemp. vellum, no. 22 on spine.

Ms. Lea 271 (Ital.)

FRANCESCO DI DOMENICO DI NANNI [for (brother of) ALAMANNO DE MEDICI]. Conti e spesi per le più di genere agricolo, 1535–44. (Ff.3v and 4r: "da Alamanno mio fratello;" f.86v: "Questo libro si e di Francesco di Domenico di Nanni . . ."). *Italy, 1535–44.*

Paper. Ff.14–86 (ff.14–41 also numbered 1–28), 1 final f., blank except for ownership inscription of Francesco di Domenico (several times repeated) and figures of additions. 28 x 11 cm. Vellum.

Ms. Lea 272 (Ital.)

RICEVUTE di raccolti di grano, 1537–56 (without name of firm responsible for the transactions; assigned to Alamanno de Medici or Carlo de Medici by previous owner). *Italy, 1537–56.*

Paper. 50 ff. 28 x 11 cm. Contemp. vellum, no. 165 on spine.

Ms. Lea 273 (Ital.)

[CARLO DE MEDICI?]. Ricordi e conti, 1535–6. (Assigned to Carlo de Medici by previous owner. Among the names appearing are Ottaviano de Medici; Carlo Gondi; Carlo de Medici; Francesco Rucellai; Agnolo Doni; Filipo Capponi). *Italy, 1535–36.*

Paper. 47 (vero 48) numb. ff.+48 blank ff. (=96 ff.) 33.5 x 11 cm. Vellum.

Ms. Lea 274 (Ital.)

[_____]. Ricordi e conti, 1535–6. (Assigned to Carlo de Medici by previous owner. Among the names appearing are Francesco Rucellai; Carlo, Ottaviano and Niccolo de Medici; Ludovico Alamanni; Federigo de Ricci; Francesco Ettolino). *Italy, 1535–36.*

Paper. 96 ff. (ff.50–96 blank). 33.5 x 11.5 cm. Vellum, no. 164 on contemp. slip pasted on spine.

Ms. Lea 275 (Ital.)

[_____]. Ricordi e conti, 1536–7. (Assigned to "Carlo de Medici?" by previous owner. Among the names appearing are Carlo Rucellai; Pietro Salmati; Ottaviano, Tommaso and Niccolo de Medici; Marco Mannelli). *Italy, 1536–37.*

Paper. 96 ff. (ff.36–96 blank). 34 x 11 cm. Vellum, no. 164 on contemp. slip pasted to spine.

Ms. Lea 276 (Ital.)

[_____]. Ricordi, no. 9, 1537–8. (Assigned to Carlo de Medici by previous owner. Among the names appearing are Francesco Bandini; Francesco Guicciardini; Ottaviano de Medici; Francesco Rucellai; Alamanno de Medici; Filippo Gondi). *Italy, 1537–38.*

Paper. 96 ff. (ff.43–96 blank). 33 x 11.5 cm. Contemp. vellum, no. 164 on spine.

Ms. Lea 277 (Ital.)

[_____]. Ricordi, 11°, e conti, 1539. (Assigned to "Carlo de Medici?" by previous owner. Among the names appearing are Ottomano Alamanno and Carlo de Medici; Jacopo della Fonte; Giuletto Francesco and Girolamo Rucellai; Giovanbattista Bettini; Spedale di Santa Maria Novella). *Italy, 1539.*

Paper. 96 ff. (ff.44–96 blank). 33 x 11 cm. Contemp. vellum, no. 164 on spine.

Ms. Lea 278 (Ital.)

[_____]. Ricordi e conti, 1538–40. (Assigned to Carlo de Medici by previous owner. Among the names appearing are Francesco Mirandola; Iacopo Guicciardini; Gianfranco Baroncelli; Rafaello di Miniato; Francesco Bandini; Giuletto Rucellai; Carlo di Fernando de Medici). *Italy, 1539–40.*

Paper. 96 ff. (ff.46–96 blank). 33 x 11 cm. Vellum, no. 164 on contemp. slip pasted to spine.

Ms. Lea 279 (Ital.)

[_____]. Ricordi e conti, 1540–1. (Assigned to Carlo de Medici by previous owner. Among the names appearing are Carlo de Medici; Tommaso Martelli; Alamanno de Medici; Giulelmo Ubaldini; Tommaso Cavalcanti; Iacopo Guicciardini; Francesco and Pandolfo Rucellai). *Italy, 1540–41.*

Paper. 1, 47 (recto 48) numb. ff.+47 blank ff. (=96 ff.). 33.5 x 11 cm. Vellum, no. 164 on contemp. slip attached to spine.

Ms. Lea 280 (Ital.)

[_____]. Ricordi e conti, 1541–2. (Assigned to Carlo de Medici by previous owner. Among the names appearing are Carlo de Medici; Tommaso Cavalcanti; Francesco Rucellai; Bartolomeo Ugholini; Giovanni Boni; Iacopo Guicciardini; Ricasoli di Firenze; Alamanno de Medici; "monachi di San Lorenzo"). *Italy, 1541–42.*

Paper. 1, 95 ff. (ff.55–95 blank). 33.5 x 11 cm. Vellum, no. 164 on contemp. slip pasted to spine (damaged).

Ms. Lea 281 (Ital.)

[_____]. Ricordi, 1542–3. (Assigned to Carlo de Medici by previous owner. Among the names appearing are, besides Carlo de Medici, Jacopo Guicciardini; Francesco Rucellai; Carlo Acciauoli; Jacopo della Fonte; Leonardo de Fornari; Alessandro Antinori). *Italy, 1542–43.*

Paper. 48 ff. (ff.44–8 blank). 33 x 11.5 cm. Vellum, no. 164 on contemp. slip pasted to spine.

Ms. Lea 282 (Ital.)

[_____]. Ricordi, 1542–3. (Assigned to Carlo de Medici by previous owner. Among the names appearing are, besides Carlo de Medici, Francesco and Giuletto Rucellai; Alessandro Antinori; Filippo Salviato; Iacopo Guicciardini; Filippo Gondi). *Italy, 1542–43.*

Paper. 96 ff. (ff.44–96 blank). 33.5 x 11.5 cm. Vellum, no. 164 on contemp. slip pasted to spine.

Ms. Lea 283 (Ital.)

[_____]. Ricordi, 20°, e conti, 1543–4. (Assigned to Carlo de Medici by previous owner. Among the names appearing are, besides Carlo de Medici, Alessandro and Lorenzo Antinori; Francesco, Giovanni, Giuletto and Mariotto Rucellai; Elbrardo di Ricasoli; Mainardo Cavalcanti). *Italy, 1543–44.*

Paper. 96 ff. (ff.55–96 blank). 33.5 x 11.5 cm. Contemp. vellum, no. 164 on spine, no. 281 on front cover.

Ms. Lea 284 (Ital.)

[_____]. Ricordi e conti, 1543–6. (Assigned to Carlo de Medici by previous owner. Among the names appearing are Simone Lotti; Antonio Cavalcanti; Antonio Baldovinetti; Andrea Mannucci; Vincenzo Ferrini; Francesco Lapi; la communità di Volterra, Bibiena, etc.) *Italy, 1543[1544 on f.1r]–46.*

Paper. 80 ff. (f.80 blank). 33 x 11.5 cm. Vellum, no. 164 on contemp. slip pasted to spine (torn).

Ms. Lea 285 (Ital.)

[_____]. Ricordi XXII, 1544–5. (Assigned to Carlo de Medici by previous owner. Among the names appearing are Francesco, Carlo and Agostino Medici; Francesco Ruccellai; Bernardo Buonaccorsi; Bernardo Ricasoli; Bartolomeo Gondi). *Italy, (1543)1544–45.*

Paper. 48 ff. (ff.40–8 blank); 2 ff. "debitori 1544" laid in. 34 x 11.5 cm. Contemp. vellum, no. 164 on spine.

Ms. Lea 286 (Ital.)

CARLO DE MEDICI. El conto; quaderno di possessioni, 1546–70. *Italy, 1546–70.*

Paper. 116 ff. (ff.39–76, 108–16 blank). 20.5 x 14 cm. Contemp. vellum, no. 90 on spine.

Ms. Lea 287 (Ital.)

[CARLO DE MEDICI?]. Ricordi e conti, 1547–59. (Assigned to "Carlo de Medici?" by previous owner. Among the names appearing are Alessandro Antinori; Mariotto Rucellai; Pietro Vettori; Giovanbattista and Giovanantonio Deti; Battista Sabatini; Alamanno de Medici). *Italy, 1547–59.*

Paper. 70 ff. 33 x 11.5 cm. Vellum, no. 165 on spine.

Ms. Lea 288 (Ital.)

CARLO DE MEDICI. Quadernuccio terzo . . . , debitori e creditori, 1549–66. [Giornale] C. *Italy, 1549–66(72).*

Paper. 70 ff., 4 ff. additions (f.1r: 1570–2; 1v–4v: 1556–70) and 1 folded sheet laid in. 33 x 11.5 cm. Contemp. vellum, no. 165 on spine.

Ms. Lea 289 (Ital.)

[CARLO DE MEDICI?]. Ricordi e conti, 1557–77. (Assigned to Carlo de Medici by previous owner. Among the names appearing are Giovanni and Bastiano Castelli; Piero Parrini; Giovanni Bertelli; Matteo Brocchi; Niccodemo di Giotto). *Italy, 1557–77.*

Paper. 60 ff. (ff.43–56, 59–60 blank); 2 ff. additions, Nov. 1568, laid in. 33 x 11.5 cm. Contemp. vellum, no. 165 on spine.

Ms. Lea 290 (Ital.)

FABRIZIO DE LUIGI DE MEDICI. Giornale e ricordanze, 1559–79. *Italy, 1559–79.*

Paper. 192 ff. (ff.180–92 blank). 35 x 14 cm. Contemp. vellum (leaf of 14th cent. ms.).

Ms. Lea 291 (Ital.)

NICCOLO DE LUIGI DE MEDICI. Quadernuccio di entrata e uscita di possessione . . . per mano di Fabrizio de Medici, 1567–72. *Italy, 1567–72.*

Paper. 68 ff. (ff.30–43, 52–68 blank). 20 x 13.5 cm. Contemp. vellum, no. 92 on spine and back cover.

Ms. Lea 292 (Ital.)

TRESPIANO, Spedale di San Bartolomeo. Libro di debitori e creditori e ricordi del . . . rettore . . . Nicolo di Luigi de Medici, 1567–78, 1585–8. [Giornale] A. *Italy, 1567–88.*

Paper. 1, 96 ff. (vero 95 ff.; ff.49–60, 66–96 blank; foliation irregular; several leaves inserted). 23 x 16.5 cm. Contemp. vellum, no. 15 on spine, no. 191 on front cover.

Ms. Lea 293 (Ital.)

FABRIZIO DI LUIGI DE MEDICI. Quadernuccio di ricordi, debitori e creditori, 1579–1612. [Giornale] C. *Italy, 1579–1612.*

Paper. 208 ff. (ff.201–8 blank). 34.5 x 14 cm. Contemp. vellum, no. 19 on spine, no. 89 on front cover; guards (front and back) early printed leaves, one on vellum.

Ms. Lea 294 (Ital.)

[VINCENZO DE MEDICI?]. Libro di possessione. [Giornale] A. (In several sections: ff.1v–2r, 1594–5; 2v–5v, 1634–7; 19v–49r, 1594–1633; 49v–64r, 1594–1636; 74v–80r, 1596–9; 80r–2r, 1634–7; 99v–155r, 1594–1636). *Italy, 1594–1637.*

Paper. 192 ff. (numbered somewhat irregularly; ff.6–18, 66–74, 84–99, 156–92 blank). 25 x 18 cm. Contemp. vellum, no. 100 on spine.

Ms. Lea 295 (Ital.)

VINCENZO and ANDREA DE MEDICI [cf. f.83r]. Quadernuccio di creditori e debitori, ricordanze, 1595–1603. *Italy, 1595–1603.*

Paper. 97 ff. (vero 96, f.29 omitted in numbering; ff.87–97 blank; various account calculations, notes, and one letter laid in). 34.5 x 12 cm. Vellum.

Ms. Lea 296 (Ital.)

QUADERNO DI SPESE, 1721–5. (Medici household? — Day by day account of expenditures by Francesco Patavini, "spenditore"). [Giornale] A. *Italy, 1721–25.*

Paper. 257 (vero 258) ff. (ff.245–50 blank). 40 x 13.5 cm. Contemp. vellum, no. 154 on spine.

Ms. Lea 297 (Ital.)

QUADERNO DI SPESE, 1695–7. Spese di camagiari, verse, gabelle e vetture. (Medici household? — Day by day account of expenditures by Luca Mecocci, "spenditore"). *Italy, 1695–1697.*

Paper. 272 ff. (some blank). 42 x 13.5 cm. Contemp. vellum, no. 56 on spine.

N.B.: End of second Medici series

Ms. Lea 298 (Ital.)
BIVIGILIANO DE MEDICI. Quadernuccio di debitori [e creditori], 1513–4. ("Domino M. Francesco Ac[c]olti . . ." on f.1r). *Italy, 1513–14 (date 1534 on cover, in later hand, in error).*

Paper. 96 ff. 14 x 10.5 cm. Contemp. vellum, no. 9 on spine.

Ms. Lea 299 (Ital.)
[CARLO DE MEDICI?]. Quadernuccio di creditori e debitori, 1530–5 (date 1525 on f.1r, in error? Assigned to Carlo de Medici by previous owner). *Italy, 1530–35.*

Paper. 96 ff. 10.5 x 7 cm. Contemp. vellum (fragment of ms.).

Ms. Lea 300 (Ital.)
FRANCESCA DI BIVIGLIANO DE MEDICI. Libro . . . di debitori e creditori, 1534–44, with Ricordi, 1555–62. [Giornale] A. *Italy, 1534–62.*

Paper. 95, 16 ff. (f.59 and last 10 ff. blank). 16.5 x 11 cm. Contemp. vellum, no. 26 on spine.

Ms. Lea 301 (Ital.)
LUIGI DI BIVIGLIANO DE MEDICI. Quadernuccio titolato giornaletto . . . seguitarsi per Bivigliano suo padre per essere piaciuto a dio tirarlo a se addi 11 di novembre 1538, 1538–41 (with alphabetical index bound in at beginning). [Giornale] B [D?]. *Italy, 1538–41.*

Paper. 20, 192 ff. 16.5 x 11 cm. Contemp. vellum, nos. 9 and 6 on spine.

Ms. Lea 302 (Ital.)
BIVIGLIANO DI ALAMANNO DE MEDICI. Quaderno septimo sul quale scriverà le facende accadute giornalmente, 1542–7. [Giornale] H. *Italy, 1542–47.*

Paper. 20 ff. index (first and last blank; within fragment of 15th cent. ms.); 18 ff. (second index, mostly blank; within 14th cent. ms. fragment), 222 ff. 16.5 x 11 cm. Contemp. vellum, no. 9 on spine, no. 50(?) on front cover.

N.B.: End of Medici series

Ms. Lea 303 (Ital.)
ANDREA DI LORENZO AMADORI. Libro di debitori e creditori. [Giornale] A (ff.1–81).—Ricordi (ff.88–95), 1506–14. *Italy, 1506–14.*

Paper. 1, 95 ff. (ff.82–7 blank). 22.5 x 16.5 cm. Contemp. vellum, no. 172 on spine.

Ms. Lea 304 (Ital.)
ANDREA and LORENZO DI FRANCESCO AMADORI. Libro di debitori e creditori, 1515–48. [Giornale] A [?]. *Italy, 1515–48.*

Paper. 84 ff. (ff.50–9 blank). 27 x 19.5 cm. Contemp. vellum, no. 175 on spine.

Ms. Lea 305 (Ital.)

ANDREA DI LORENZO AMADORI. Quadernuccio di debitori e creditori, 1522–8. [Giornale] C. *Italy, 1522–28.*

Paper. 1, 87 ff. 21 x 14 cm. Contemp. vellum, no. 173 on spine.

Ms. Lea 306 (Ital.)

——————. Ricordi 1522–37; quadernuccio seg. b [B on front cover]. *Italy, 1522–37.*

Paper. 1, 77 ff. (f.76 blank). 21.5 x 14.5 cm. Contemp. vellum, no. 191 on back cover.

Ms. Lea 307 (Ital.)

——————. Quadernuccio di debitori e creditori, 1528–37. [Giornale] D. *Italy, 1528–37.*

Paper. 1, 95 ff. 21 x 14 cm. Contemp. vellum, no. 174 on spine.

Ms. Lea 308 (Ital.)

——————. Quadernuccio . . . di debitori e creditori, 1537–44. [Giornale] E. (Letter to Piero Amadori laid in). *Italy, 1537–44.*

Paper. 2, 94 ff. 21 x 14 cm. Contemp. vellum (using earlier doc.), no. 197 on spine.

Ms. Lea 309 (Ital.)

——————. Quadernuccio. . . .— Giornale e ricordi C, 1537–52. *Italy, 1537–52.*

Paper. 1, 95 ff. 21 x 14 cm. Contemp. vellum (using earlier doc.), no. 177 on spine.

Ms. Lea 310 (Ital.)

ANDREA and LORENZO DI FRANCESCO AMADORI. Libro di debitori, creditori e ricordi, 1537–56. [Giornale] C. *Italy, 1537–56.*

Paper. 2, 149 ff., ff.151–95 (wrongly numb. 193; ff.161–95 blank); 2 f. ("Inst. . . . ." concerning property of Antonio di Taddeo Datti [=Dati, Deti?, cf. nos. 327–31] of Florence, 1548, and 1 f. "conto" of Lionardo[?] Santini, laid in). 28.5 x 21 cm. Contemp. vellum, no. 176 on spine.

Ms. Lea 311 (Ital.)

BARTOLOMEO AMADORI. Libro de debitori, creditori e ricordanze, 1543–6. [Giornale] A. *Italy, 1543–46.*

Paper. 192 ff. (f.99 omitted, f.124 repeated, f.192 blank). 29 x 21.5 cm. Contemp. vellum, nos. 178 and 17 on spine.

Ms. Lea 312 (Ital.)

ANDREA AMADORI. Libro . . . sul quale si scriverà tutti li conti [e ricordi] di Santo Stefano e della capella . . . in Castelfranco . . . , 1547 [cf. f.70v etc.]–52. [Giornale] A. *Italy, 1547–52.*

Paper. 1, 95 ff. (ff.83–95 blank). 22 x 17 cm. Contemp. vellum (document of 1377?), no. 192 on spine.

Ms. Lea 313 (Ital.)

ANDREA DI LORENZO AMADORI. Giornale e riccordi D, 1552–66. *Italy, 1552–66.*

Paper. 1, 143 ff. (ff.132–9 blank). 21 x 13 cm. Contemp. vellum, nos. 193 and 32 on spine.

Ms. Lea 314 (Ital.)

_____. Quadernuccio . . . di debitori e creditori, 1556–66. [Giornale] 6 [G?]. *Italy, 1556–66.*

Paper. 2, 158 ff. (last blank). 20.5 x 14 cm. Contemp. vellum, no. 181 on spine.

Ms. Lea 315 (Ital.)

FRANCESCO DI ANDREA AMADORI. Quadernuccio . . . in sul quale si ferra conto di tutte quello e quanto si spendera in acconcimi del podere e nelle case di dello podere . . . dal Sig. Don Antonio Montalvo . . . , 1566–72. *Italy, 1566–72.*

Paper. 1, 95 ff. (ff.74–8, 90–5 blank). 20.5 x 14 cm. Contemp. vellum (document of 1503), no. 201 on spine.

Ms. Lea 316 (Ital.)

NICCOLO and FRANCESCO AMADORI. Quadernuccio di debitori e creditori, 1585–93. [Giornale] A. *Italy, 1585–93.*

Paper. 140 ff. 33 x 14 cm. Contemp. vellum, no. 184 on spine.

Ms. Lea 317 (Ital.)

[NICCOLO AMADORI?]. Quaderno di cambi, 1600–9. [Giornale] B. (Previous owner concludes from slip addressed to Niccolo Amadori <Piacenza>, that this is his account book. Among names appearing are Vincenzo de Medici; Lorenzo Riccardi; Lorenzo and Vincenzo Ricasoli; the Carrara and Strozzi). *Italy, 1600–9.*

Paper. 1, 127 ff. (ff.122–4, 127 blank). 34 x 23.5 cm. Contemp. vellum, no. 153(?) on spine.

Ms. Lea 318 (Ital.)

NICCOLO AMADORI. Scartafaccio de fiera di Niccolo Amadori fatta d'Agosto in Piacenza 1608. *Piacenza, 1608.*

Paper. 72 ff. (ff.17, 40–4, 47, 61–3 blank). 34 x 23 cm. Contemp. vellum.

Ms. Lea 319 (Ital.)

[NICCOLO AMADORI?]. Quaderno di cambi, 1609–12. [Giornale] C. (The assigning to N. A. is based on letters and documents addressed to Amadori, found in this volume). *Italy, 1609–12.*

Paper. 1, 143 ff. (ff.30–79, 104–43 blank; 15 docs. in fol. and 11 small slips in envelope laid in). 34.5 x 23 cm. Contemp. vellum, no. 155 on spine.

N.B.: End of Amadori series

Ms. Lea 320 (Ital.)

DONATO ARRIGUCCI. Giornale e ricordanze, 1521–4. [Giornale] G. *Italy, 1521–24.*

Paper. 1, 181 ff. (ff.69–129, 145–69, 173–81 blank). 28.5 x 21 cm. Contemp. vellum (damaged), no. 218.2 on spine.

Ms. Lea 321 (Ital.)

ANDREA DI FILIPPO ARRIGUCCI (Heirs). Libro del lavoreria della eredità d'Andrea di Filippo Arrigucci, 1528–45. *Italy, 1528–45.*

Paper. 144 ff. (ff.62–99, 123–44 blank). 28.5 x 21 cm. Contemp. vellum, no. 207 on spine.

N.B.: End of Arrigucci series

Ms. Lea 322 (Ital.)

SIMONE GONDI. Administrazione di Simone Gondi delle cose di Federigo Gondi, 1533–5. *Italy, 1533–35.*

Paper. 50 ff. (ff.5–7 <blank?> missing, ff.4, 11–5, 39–50 blank). 28.5 x 21 cm. Contemp. vellum (f. from 14th cent. ms.); title on front cover in a later hand (no sep. title page); no. 283 in upper left-hand corner; no. 127 on back cover.

Ms. Lea 323 (Ital.)

LORENZO DI MARIOTTO GONDI (and successors). Conto della pigione che riscossi e fara pagare a frati di Santa Maria Novella. . . . Inventario et ricordi (cont. by Antonio, Lorenzo's brother. In several sections: prel. f. and ff.1r–4r, 1542–53; 4r–16v, 1559–86; 20v–71r, 1542–1618; 80r–90v, 1556–1617). [Giornale] 1542 A. no. 1. *Italy, 1542–1618.*

Paper. 1, 95 ff. (ff.17–8, 72–9, 91–5 blank). 20 x 14 cm. Contemp. vellum, marked "Nº4 Libro per conto della casetta . . . Filippe Gondi . . . Lorenzo Gondi . . . ;" no. 77 on spine.

Ms. Lea 324 (Ital.)

ANTONIO FRANCESCO DI LORENZO GONDI. Libro di possessione, 1558.—Ricordi, 1558–60. [Giornale] A. *Italy, 1558–60.*

Paper. 1, 127 ff. (ff.107–11, 123–7 blank). 23 x 17 cm. Contemp. vellum, no. I on spine; "1558, B. no. I" on lower left corner of front cover.

Ms. Lea 325 (Ital.)

GIULIANO GONDI. Libro di spese di casa ed altre, 1608–22. [Giornale] A. *Italy, 1608–22.*

Paper. 126 (vero 124) ff. 35 x 14 cm. Contemp. vellum, no. 278 on spine.

Ms. Lea 326 (Ital.)

LODOVICO DI MARIOTTO GONDI. Spese giornali di vitto del anno 1664[–8]. (A final section lists payments for services). *Italy, 1664–68.*

Paper. 96 ff. 32 x 11 cm. Contemp. vellum, no. 31 on spine.

N.B.: End of Gondi series

Ms. Lea 327 (Ital.)

GIOVANBATTISTA and GIOVANMARIA DETI (=Dati, Dedi, Detti?). Quadernuccio, 1547–55. [Giornale] A. (With long list of Cristofano Cibioni's "panni," and their prices, ff.183–216, 1548–53). *Italy, 1547–55.*

Paper, first and last f., vellum. 1, 182 (vero 184) numb., 24 unnumb. ff. (last 10 blank), 1 f. 33 x 22.5 cm. Contemp. vellum, no. 228 on spine, no. 166 and signet D on front cover.

Ms. Lea 328 (Ital.)

_____. Libro di entrata e uscita e quaderno di cassa, 1551–3. [Giornale] A. *Italy, 1551–53.*

Paper. 48 ff. (ff.5–19, 40–8 blank). 33.5 x 23 cm. Contemp. vellum, no. 221 on spine, 181 on front cover.

Ms. Lea 329 (Ital.)

_____. [Dedi on cover in later hand]. Quadernuccio, 1553–61. [Giornale] B. *Italy, 1553–61.*

Paper, first and last f., vellum. 1, 240 ff. (ff.204–17, 232–40 blank), 1 f. 33.5 x 23.5 cm. Contemp. vellum, no. 229 on spine, no. 163 and signet D on front cover. With extensive listings of woolen goods, with prices, salaries, etc. Cf. also no. 346.

Ms. Lea 330 (Ital.)

_____ and CAMILLO DI CARLO DE MEDICI. Quadernuccio signato, 1559–66. *Italy, 1559–66.*

Paper. 351 (vero 352) ff. 28 x 21 cm. Contemp. vellum, no. 114 on spine, no. 186 and signet D on front cover; 13th cent. ms. fragment used as guards. With lists of woolens, serge, etc., with prices.

Ms. Lea 331 (Ital.)

_____. Libro di entrata e uscita, 1565–8. [Giornale] C. (The accounts were entered by Girolamo di Domenico Vanni). *Italy, 1565–68.*

Paper. 96 ff. (ff.24–83, 90–6 blank). 33 x 23 cm. Contemp. vellum, no. 227 on spine, no. 171 and signet D on front cover.

Ms. Lea 332 (Ital.)

FRANCESCO DI STEFANO RISALITI. Quaderno di manifattori, 1550–8. [Giornale] A. (This textile manufacturing enterprise may be identical with the firm Deti, since it uses the same mark, D in a triangle). *Italy, 1550–58.*

Paper, first f., vellum. 2, 158 (slightly misnumbered) ff. (ff.152–8 blank). 33 x 23.5 cm. Contemp. vellum, no. 250 on spine, no. 67 on front cover.

Ms. Lea 333 (Ital.)

──────. Libro di debitori e creditori, 1550–60. *Italy, 1550–60.*

Paper. 110 ff. (ff.100–10 blank). 33.5 x 23 cm. Vellum.

Ms. Lea 334 (Ital.)

──────. Quaderno di cassa de la tinta, 1554–65. [Giornale] C. *Italy, 1554–65.*

Paper. 84 (vero 83) ff. (followed by blank ff.) 33 x 11 cm. Contemp. vellum, no. 254 on spine.

Ms. Lea 335 (Ital.)

──────. Libro di debitori e creditori, 1559–66. [Giornale] C. *Italy, 1559–66.*

Paper. 1, 192 ff. (ff.116–92 blank), 1 f. (13th cent. ms. on vellum) used as end guard. 33 x 23 cm. Contemp. vellum, no. 257 on spine, no. 68 on front cover.

Ms. Lea 336 (Ital.)

LODOVICO CASSO [or Cassi, Casto?]. Quaderno di cassa, 1616–21. [Giornale] A. *Italy, 1616–21.*

Paper. 1, 94 ff. (ff.58–94 blank; some errors in numbering). 37.5 x 25 cm. Contemp. vellum, no. 233 on spine, no. 99 on front cover.

Ms. Lea 337 (Ital.)

──────. Libro di ricordanze e tintori, 1616–21. [Giornale] A. *Italy, 1616–21.*

Paper. 95 (vero 96) ff. (ff.3–25, 69–95 blank), some corrections on separate slips laid in. Contemp. vellum, no. 108 on front cover.

Ms. Lea 338 (Ital.)

──────. Compere (account of textile business transactions), 1621–5. [Giornale] B. *Italy, 1621–25.*

Paper. 96 ff. (ff.43–96 blank). 33.5 x 22.5 cm. Contemp. vellum, no. 244 on spine, no. 3 on front cover.

Ms. Lea 339 (Ital.)

``_____``. Entrata e uscita del taglio, 1621–37, with additions 1640–4, 1648, 1651–2. [Giornale] B. *Italy, 1621–52.*

Paper. 336 ff. (ff.202–88, 315–36 blank). 35 x 25 cm. Contemp. vellum, no. 236(?) on spine.

N.B.: End of textile trade section

Ms. Lea 340 (Ital.)

BERNARDO [?] MUGNAIO. Libro di ricordi, 1461–6, 1498. *Italy, 1461–98.*

Paper. 87 ff. (ff.8–16, 18–30, 32–75, 77–9, 81–5 blank). 14 x 11 cm. Contemp. vellum; no. 169, and names of Alessandra Pandolfini and Meglio Vedovadi in a later hand, on front cover.

Ms. Lea 341 (Ital.)

BARTOLOMEO DI STEFANO già Spedalingo. Ricordanze.—Spese di Trespiano, 1514–22. [Giornale] A. *Italy, 1514–22.*

Paper. 1, 94 ff. (ff.55–73, 85–93 blank, f.87 torn out). 21 x 14 cm. Contemp. vellum, no. 127 on spine.

Ms. Lea 342 (Ital.)

TOMMASO RIDOLFI. Giornale, x°. A. (Ff.1–41, 1522–49; ff.65–72, 1528; ff.89–92, 1526–9). *Italy, 1522–49.*

Paper. 95 ff. (ff.42–64, 73–88, 93–5 blank). 29 x 21.5 cm. Contemp. vellum, no. 129 on spine, "Giornale A, n°. 190" on front cover.

Ms. Lea 343 (Ital.)

GUGLIELMO PECCORI. Libro di debitori e creditori, 1523–5, 1528, 1531, 1535, 1543, 1556–7. *Italy, 1523–57.*

Paper. 1, 95 ff. (ff.51–63, 67–95 blank). 28.5 x 21.5 cm. Contemp. vellum, no. 264 on spine.

Ms. Lea 344 (Ital.)

PARRINO and MARCO SECRANI [or Seccrani]. [Libro de conti?], 1543–9 (with monthly summaries, 1545–56 on ff.42v–6r and recto of back cover). *Italy, 1543–56.*

Paper. 46 ff. 29 x 10.5 cm. Contemp. vellum, no. 165 on spine.

Ms. Lea 345 (Ital.)

PIERANTONIO GUASCONI. Libro proprio di debitori e creditori d'agosto 1544 [—maggio 1549; 1552–7]. *Italy, 1544–57.*

Paper. 133 numb. ff. (ff.96 and 129 missing?), followed by unnumb. f.134 and 5 blank ff. 28 x 21.5 cm. Contemp. vellum.

Ms. Lea 346 (Ital.)

GIOVANBATTISTA and GIOVANMARIA DETI. Quadernuccio di chassa, 1553–8. *Italy, 1553–58.*

Paper. 99 ff. (ff.75–7 omitted), 64 blank ff. (last ff. damaged). 28 x 11 cm. Vellum, no. 165 on contemp. slip attached to spine.—Cf. nos. 327–31.

Ms. Lea 347 (Ital.)

FRANCESCO DAVANZATI [?, cf. inside front cover; "Francesco di P̃. Casa di Medici" on f.1r]. Libro di entrata e uscita, 1555–9. (The date 1563 on front cover, in a later hand, appears to be a misreading). [Giornale] A. *Italy, 1555–59.*

Paper. 159 (vero 160) ff. (f.121 = 2 ff.; ff.87–120 blank). 33 x 22.5 cm. Contemp. vellum, no. 147 on spine, no. 223 on front cover.

Ms. Lea 348 (Ital.)

VINCENZO CRISTOFANO. Libro de debitori e creditori, 1555–60. [Giornale] A. (Date 1501–1513, in later hand, in error). *Italy, 1555–60.*

Paper. 179 (wrongly numb. 181), 1, 16 blank ff. (=196 ff.). 33 x 23 cm. Contemp. vellum, no. 128 on spine, no. 254 on front cover.

Ms. Lea 349 (Ital.)

ALAMANNO DI GIOVANBATTISTA GIRALDI. Quaderno di ricordi e cambi, 1563–5. (Contents: "Da 1 à 15, rimesse che verranno di fuora; 15 à 30, tratte che mi saran fatte; 30 à 70, tratte e rimesse che si faranno; 70 à 90, copia di lettere di formenti; 90 à 130, debitori e creditori . . . ; 130 alla fine, diversi ricordi . . ."). [Giornale] C. *Italy, 1563–65.*

Paper. 1, 144 (partly misnumbered) ff. (ff.7–14, 28–9, 58–68, 85–9, 91–129, 135–44 blank). 35 x 24.5 cm. Contemp. vellum, no 15(?) on spine.

Ms. Lea 350 (Ital.)

COSIMO GIONI (Cosimo di . . . [undeciphered] Gioni e Cramasi). Libro di debitori e creditori, 1568–81. *Italy, 1568–81.*

Paper. 96 ff. 21 x 14 cm. Contemp. vellum (front cover defective), no. 266 on spine.

Ms. Lea 351 (Ital.)

GIORNALE A. (Among the many names are Nicolo Marmelli <f.1r>; Nicolaio di Lorenzo Morelli <ff.9r, 15r, etc.>; Boz[z]olini <f.24v>; Federigo de Ricci <f.46r>); consists of several sections: ff.1r–7v, 1569–70; 9r–11r, idem; 15r–32r, 1570–8; 32v–8r, 1584–95; 41v–51r, 1576–92; 53r–4r, 1569–74; 54v–7v, 1593–6; 59v–77r, 1655–8; 88v–91v, 1655; 92r–4v, 1577–8; 94v–6v, 1656). *Italy, 1569–1658.*

Paper. 96 ff. (ff.12–4, 23, 39–40, 52, 78–87 blank). 16.5 x 11.5 cm. Contemp. vellum.

Ms. Lea 352 (Ital.)

NICOLÒ GALIOTTI. Quaderno della ricolta di casse, 1583 [—4] di M. Vincenzo de Medici e fratelli di tutti i loro lavatori al tempo di me Nicolò Galiotti da Pescia, fattore di detti . . . *Italy, 1583–84.*

Paper. 67 ff. (+2 ff. inserted between ff.42–3). 28.5 x 22 cm. Contemp. vellum (document relating to Matteo Galiotti <1545> on inside), no. 97 on spine.—Cf. nos. 294, etc.

Ms. Lea 353 (Ital.)

[SLAVERY]. Five documents dealing with the slave trade: 1. Nota di 60 schiavi . . . dalla galera pisana . . . , viaggio di Spagna, 20 March 1602, 2ff.—2. Nota di 151 [161?] schiavi, e schiave, ragalzi, e ragalze, consignati al sereno Giuliano Sirigatti per condurre a vendere in Spagna, et al Signore Arrigo Arrighi, 13 October 1610, 6ff.—3. Nota di 21 schiavetti di Bona che sono in Pisa, n.d., 2ff.—4. Ruolo di schiavi che si ritrovano nell'arsenale di Pisa . . . descritti dall'ill^{mo}. Sig. Amiraglio Inghirami . . . , n.d., 6 ff.—5. Nota di n°. 87 schiavi . . . a vendere . . . a Napoli, Messina, e Palermo, fatti imbarcare . . . su galere di S.A.S. dall'illmo. Sig^e. Geronimo Serloni [?], n.d., 7 ff. *Italy, early 17th cent.*

Paper. 23 ff. Ca. 30 x 22 cm. Each doc. in boards.—Cf. no. 210.

Ms. Lea 354 (Ital.)

VINCENZO QUARATESI. Calculo e saldo della ragione d'arte de lana cantante in Vincenzio Quaratesi . . . in Firenze (and Jacopo Quaratesi, Andrea de Medici and Lorenzo Bamberini; notarized by Tullio Signorini). *Florence, 1628.*

Paper. 8 ff. (last blank). 28 x 20.5 cm. Boards.—Cf. nos. 327 ff.

Ms. Lea 355 (Ital.)

[EMBASSY TO THE CURIA]. Spese fatte li serenissimi Fabbio Guinigi, Bartolomeo Frangioni, Raffaelo Mansi, ambasciatori a Roma a Papa Clemente IX. *Rome?, 1669.*

Paper. 2 blank, 65 ff. 34.5 x 24 cm. Contemp. vellum.

N.B.: End of Medici-Gondi collection

Ms. Lea 356 (Ital.)

[PAUL V, Pope]. Varie opere et compositioni fatte da diversi theologi, legisti, et altri, in occasione, & per causa dell' interdetto, & censure publicato della Santità . . . contra la Republica, & signori di Venezia. 1. COMMINATORIA dell'interdetto . . . tradotta dalla linga latina nella volgare, ff.1r–9v.—2. RUDOLF II, emperor. Lettera di S. Maiestà Christianissima scritta al suo ambasciatore . . . in Roma

... per causa delli decreti ... contra la libertà ecclesiastica, ff.11r–18r.—3. DISCORSO delle cose concernenti le differenze tra H.S. Papa Paulo V et li signori venetiani, ff.19r–26r.—4. SENTENZA d'un clarissimo senator veneto ... nel Consiglio de pregati, ff.27r–37r.—5. GENOA. Lettura scritta dalla Republica di Genova a quella di Venetia, ff.39r–42v. (All other tracts are printed.) *Italy, ca. 1606-7.*

Paper. 7ff. (title and contents of 5-vol. collection), 42 ff. (ms.) 20.5 x 14.5 cm. Contemp. vellum.—Prov.: Dr. Joseph Schweizer.—Shelved as 16.1.

Ms. Lea 358 (Fr.)

SIMON MORIN. Déclaration de Morin depuis peu delivré de la Bastille, sur la révocation de ses pensées, donnez au public par les mauvais souffles, empoisonnemens et enchanteries que les démons lui avoient donné pour tromper les hommes, sous prétexte de religion. Nouvellement désabusé par Monsieur l'Abbé de Lorette de Montmorancy, sur le sujet de son livre intitulé Les pensées de Morin ... Paris, Claude Morloz, 1649. Ms. copy of printed book.—With a second "Déclaration," 1649 [also originally published in 1649], Procès verbal ... 1663, and L'Errata des quatrains. *Paris, 18th cent. (post 1725).*

Paper. 24 ff. (ff.13–24 blank). 16 x 10.5 cm. 18th-Cent. armorial morocco.—Prov.: M. Woodhull, 1795 (purchased at "Christie's auction"); Henry C. Lea.—Bound with Morin's *Pensées,* 1647, and *Arrêt de la Cour de Parlement,* 1663. Shelved as J.4.29.

Ms. Lea 359 (Ital.)

FRANCESCO MARIA II, Duke of Urbino. Vita di Francesco Maria 2º della Rovere, sesto ... duca d'Urbino, divisa in due parti, la prima da lui medesimo con titolo di Sommario della sua vita [also titled Compendio], la 2ª da Antonio Donato ... con titolo di Devolutione alla santa chiesa degli stati d'Urbino [alla sede apostolica; with "Breve del Papa al Duca" and "Patente del Duca"]. *Urbino, ca. 1630.*

Paper. 62 ff. (ff.1, 61–2 blank). 27 x 19 cm. Contemp. vellum with the arms of Pope Urban VIII. Presentation copy to the Pope? Printed from a different ms. in *Nuova raccolta di opuscoli scientifici e letterari* (Venice, 1774), v. XXIX.

Ms. Lea 360 (Ital.)

COLLECTANEA opusculorum eruditorum et historicorum, in Italian and Latin. 1. [ORATIO] AD CAROLUM V ... post victoriam bello germanico partam ..., ff.1–13.—2. VINCENZO CORONELLI. Rifflessioni ... sopra il Danubio, ff.14–32 (incl. engr. portrait of Charles VI, etched dedication, 2 folded ms. maps and double-page illus. of embankment).—3. SOMMARIO delle vere croniche di Venetia, ff.35–49, (ms. dated 24 Aug. 1563).—3A. [Section not listed in contents at beginning of vol.] Poems, some apparently autograph, incl.

one dedicated to Pope Paul V, a "Canzon al ser. principe de Venetia" (dated 1606), ff.49–56.—4. RELATIONE di stato de Milano del ano 1589, ff.57–71.—5. CARMINA AMALTHEORUM, beginning with "Maximiliano II, imperatori," and incl. "Serenissimi Principis Memmi creatio" (in a different hand), "Carmen contra Hispanos," "In vaccanza della sede apostolica per la morte di Clemente VIII, sonetto da Bastone," etc., ff.73–81.—5A. Miscellaneous items, incl. "Modo gentile per tinger di color rosso li vasi da Naranzeni," and various poems, e.g. one dedicated to Card. Borromeo, to Pope Pius V, Cornelio Frangipano, and several dealing with Venetian affairs, ff.83–103.—6. TORNEO di cento dame genovesi, ff.104–8.—7. MANIFESTO per la Republica di Venezia in materia d'Iscochi, ff.111–4.—8. MANIFESTA, il re . . . le regione dell'armi sue incaminate nel Regno di Napoli, ff.117–8.—9. OTTAVIO LAVELLI. Copy of letter to Card. Valiero, 1623, ff.118–9.—9A. MONITORIUM [jocular exhortation for a person named Longerioni], f.120.—9B. LOUIS XIV, King of France. Copy of letter, 1657, f.121.—10. VIAGGIO di Edoardo, duca di Parma, a Fiorenza, ff.123–4.—11. GIUSEPPE MORESINO. Copia di lettera [al] serenissimo prencipe [no name of addressee, or place], Galleazza dal Moglietto . . . 1656, f.125.—12. [Procuratore FOSCOLO]. Officio del proc. Foscolo detto capitan general per la guerra di Candia, ff.126–8 (with poems on the victory of Venetians, 1655, by Giovanni Antonio Ceruti; naval victory over the Turks, 1656, by Lorenzo Marcello, etc.)—13. UFFICIO fatto dal Marchese Villa . . . 1668, ff.129–30.—14. OFFICIO di Monsignor Aivoldi, nuncio apostolico in Venetia, 1675, and Narrativa della morte del Doge Nicolò Sagredo . . . , 1676, ff.131–2.—14A. Sopra il chiamar li banditi per la guerra di Candia contro 'l Turco, and other poems, ff.133–5.—15. BERNARDUS SYLVESTER. . . . De cura et regimine rei familiaris, ideo in hoc apposita volumine, quod nonnulli eam a Sancto Bernardo esse compositam, ff.137–8.—16. INQUISITIO pro rebus magicalibus, ff.140–3.—17. RIME VARIE del secolo XVII, incl. Livius de Comitibus, "Carmen exile" for Venetian anatomists Florio de Bernardis and Antonio Molinetto (1649); "Sopra l'intrepidezza dell'avocato Ambrosio Bellato" (1667); "Per il sacco di Mantova del 1630"; Leonardo Querini, "Volge le spalle al mondo," etc., ff.144–52.—18. POCCOBELLI. Oratio funebris . . . in collegio d.d. physicorum Venetiarum . . . 1660, ff.153–5.—19. [ORATIO] Venetiis in aedibus . . . fratrum praedicatorum, 1674, ff.157–9.—20. DESCRITTIONE del rinoceronte da Bergamo, ff.160–1.—21. ANTONIO STILLIO. Paraphrases in septem sectiones Aphorismorum [et in libros Prognasticorum] Hippocratis, ff.162–5.—22. DISCORSO academico, ff.166–8.—23. GASPARO MARINO. Decreto di Zaccaria Valier[o], 1709, ff.169–70.—23A. CORRISPONDENZA delle monete, 1736, ff.171–4.—24. ZACCARIA BONDUMIEVO. Revisione de conti [Venetian territories], 1626–9, ff.175–81.—24A. Copy of contracts concerning "capitulum sanctorum apostolorum," Venice, 1550–81, ff.182–9.—25. DELLA CONGIURA di Bagiamonte Tiepolo ex libris . . . Petri Pradenico, [1310], ff.190–215. *Italy, 16th–18th cent.*

Paper. 215 ff. (a few blank). Various sizes (in vol. measuring 33.5 x 22 cm.) 18th-cent. vellum.—Prov.: Walter Sneyd.

Ms. Lea 361 (Ital.)

LA TROMBA SACRA overo invito à signori prencipi christiani a collegarsi contro el Turco. *Italy, 17th cent.*

Paper. Title page, 58 pp. (pp.1–2, 55–8 blank). 27 x 20 cm. Contemp. paper covers in 19th-cent. boards. Old shelf marks pasted on paper cover; ex bibliotheca Colonna; Phillipps ms. 6389.

Ms. Lea 362 (Ital.)

HISTORICAL MISCELLANY. 1. IL DRITTO della S. Sede apostolica sopra il Regno di Napoli, pp. 1–15.—2. DICHIARAZIONE dell' investitura del Regno di Napoli . . . , pp.15–122.—3. PROFEZIE del pazzo di Cristo, pp.122–8.—4. BENEDICT XIII, Pope. Lettera . . . all'imperatore [Charles VI], pp.129–30.—5. TITOLARIO posto nelle patenti date dal Duca di Monte Mileto . . . [and] RENDITE del Duca, pp.131–4.—6. MEMORIALE date dal S. Coll. de'cardinali a Papa Benedetto XIII contro la promozione di Mon. Bichi, nunzio in Portogallo, pp.134–8.—7. ELOGIO del Card. Annibale Albani, pp.138–40.—8. ECÒ des montagnes des environs d'Embrun, pp.141–2.—9. VATICINIA data Sigismundo . . . a quodam Arabo, pp.143–54.—10. MICHAEL NOSTRODAMUS. Vaticinia, pp.154–63.—11. VATICINIUM de religione patrum Soc. Jesu (Sanctae [H]Ildegardis), pp.164–7.—12. S. MALACHIA. Vaticinia, pp.168–71.—13. S. JOANNES A CAPISTRANO. Vaticinia, pp.172–6. —14. CARD. FINI. Iscrizione sotto la statua di S. Domenico, pp.177–8.—15. Ven. BEDE. Vaticinium, p.179.—16. DIALOGO fra il confessore del imperatore et un gesuita, pp.180–94.—17. RISTRETTO della vita del Card. Giuseppe Renato, pp.195–203.—18. MANIFESTO del re di Sardegna [1714?], pp.203–14.—19. DICHIARAZIONE agli elettori, ed ai principi del S.R.I., pp.214–6.—20. MOTIVI delle risoluzioni del re christ. [Louis XIV], pp.216–30 *with* COPIA della dichiarazione, 1733 (p.230); DICHIARAZIONE dell'imperatore [Charles VI], (p.231); COPIA declarationis imperatoris (p.233); LETTERA del rè al primate, 1733 (p.236); DICHIARAZIONE agli elettori (p.238).—21. POTOSKI. Manifesto del primate di Polonia, 1733, pp.24–52.—22. NOTITIA delle ragioni che anno obligato la maiestà cattolica a mover guerra all'imperatore data . . . al suo ambasc. in Londra, pp.253–63.—23. OSSERVAZIONE dell' impera-

Ad. Lea 360, no. 15: For authorship see note to Lat. 61.

tore sopra i motivi delle risoluzioni del re di Francia, pp.264–83.—24. TESTAMENTO di Mantova, pp.283–8.—25. RISTRETTO dell'atto di confederazione fatto nella dieta di convocazione . . . 12 maggio 1733, pp.289–91.—26–45. [WAR OF POLISH SUCCESSION, 1733–5]. 21 further documents and "relazioni" dealing with the claims of Stanislas Leszczynski and Frederick August of Saxony, pp.291–457.—46. INSINUAZIONE fatta al Conte Filippi dal maestro di ceremonie del re di Sardegna, p.458.—47. RISPOSTA alla scrittura intitolata Memoria per l'ambasciator del re cattolico alla corte della Gran Bretagna, pp.459–509.—48. PHILIP V. Lettera del re di Spagna all'infante D. Carlo, pp.510–5.—49. PIETRO METASTASIO. Lettera al marito della Romanina, pp.515–9.—50. IDEM. Lettera a suo fratello, pp.519–21.—51. MASCHERATA de' principi dell'Europa, pp.521–4.—52. PROFEZIA di S. Brigita, pp.524–5.—53. PROFETIA ex Ioanne Luxembourg, pp.525–6.—54. CHARLES VI. Lettere . . . al Papa [Clement XII], 1736, pp.526–30.—55. SIXTUS V, Pope. Bulla de non coronandis regibus haereticis, pp.539–50.—56. DE LANGOBARDORUM ORIGINE . . . compendiosa narratio ed. ab Angelo Breventano . . . et denuo in lucem edita a Petro Stephanonio, pp.555–79. *Italy?, 18th cent.*

Paper. 585 pp. (wrongly numb. 577). 19 x 13 cm. Contemp. vellum.—Morbio Collection.

Ms. Lea 363 (Lat.)
ELECTIONE dell'notaro [Giovanni] Aldini. (Diploma issued by the prior of the Collegium judicum et advocatorum, Dionysius Fontanesius, 9 Nov. 1685, and notarized by Ludovicus Jacobus Pubius). *Reggio, 1685.*

Vellum. 1 f. (folded). 40 x 50 cm. Illus. border on margins, notarial signet. In folder.

Ms. Lea 364 (Ital.)
FRIGNANO. Legal documents and ms. additions to *Statuta, constitutiones ac decreta ducalis provinciae Friniani*, printed in Reggio, H. Bartholus, 1587. *Frignano, 1547–1602.*

Paper. 7 ff., following printed text. 30 x 20 cm. H/morocco, shelved with printed volume.

Ms. Lea 365 (Lat.)
SETTE COMUNI [Asiago, Enego, Foza, Gallio, Lusiana, Roano and Rotzo]. Liber privilegiorum septem comunium montanearum Agri Vicentini ut patet. . . . (Includes statutes from 1339 to 1568, with some additions to 1657). Exemplatus fuit per me presb. Bartholomeum de Velo Luxiane, notario eccl. St. Jacobi. *Italy, 1568–1657.*

Paper. 94, 25 (blank) ff. 21 x 15 cm. Contemp. calf.—Cf. Fontana, *op. cit.*, III, 112–113, who does not record any statuta earlier than the printed ed. of 1620.

Ms. Lea 366 (Lat.)

CLEMENT VII, Pope. Document addressed to Nicolas, cardinal deacon of SS. Vitus and Modestus, appointing him administrator of the church of Viterbo on the death of its bishop. Signed L. de Torres. *Rome, 16 Dec. 1532.*

Vellum. 1 f. (folded). 53 x 68 cm. In folder.

Ms. Lea 367 (Fr.)

CHARLES VII, King of France. Letter to his councillors and treasurers respecting the territories of the late Amaury de Serrac, which had been held illegally by Jean d'Armagnac, but which henceforth were to be united with the royal domain. Given at Razilly, 26 Aug. 1446.—*With* Letter of the treasurers to the seneschal of Rovergue instructing him to carry out the king's wishes, dated 18 Jun. 1446 (1447). *France, 1446–1447.*

Vellum. 2 ff. 20 x 39 and 9 x 36.5 cm. In folder.—Prov.: Archives de l'Ordre de Malthe.

Ms. Lea 368 (Fr.)

LIVRE DES TROIS IMPOSTEURS avec son histoire ou la réponse à la dissertation de Mr. de la Monnoye sur ce traité . . . imprimée à la Haye . . . 1716 et dans J. G. Krause. . . . On y a ajouté Le jugement de Mr. de la Croze . . . et aussi une collection de quelques autheurs, qui ont écrit sur ce traité. *Germany?, 18th cent.*

Paper. 40 ff. (last blank). 19.5 x 16.5 cm. Contemp. calf.—Prov.: F. F. Pappe; Henry C. Lea.—"Auctores, qui de famoso hoc libello . . . conferendi sunt," f.2r–3r, lists 73 references.

Ms. Lea 369 (Ital.)

VINCENZO DE MEDICI. Supplica to the Grand Duke of Tuscany, Cosimo II, relating to the recovery of credits from Philip III, King of Spain, by Capt. Romena. Each section with notations by chancellor Belisario Vinta. At end his remark "tutto sta bene . . ." and sign. of the Grand Duke. *Italy, 1611.*

Paper. 2 ff. 30.5 x 21.5 cm. In folder.—Cf. nos. 243 *et al.*

Ms. Lea 370 (Ital.)

ANTONIO BOCCANEGRA. Letter to Scipione del Carretto, promising support, and referring to a letter Boccanegra had written to Giovanni Andrea Costa of the podestà of Alassio. *Genoa, August, 1580.*

Paper. 2 ff. 28 x 21 cm. In folder.

Ms. Lea 371 (Sp.)

ANDREW THORNDIKE COLLECTION of inquisition and other documents, in eight boxes: 1. Inquisition trials, Barcelona, of Egidius

Taris (1532); Joaquin Ballel (1542–3); Johannes Requesenus (1598); Anthonio Morell (1649); Miguel Salbany (1662); Margarita Altamira (1681–2); and Relación espontanea of Fr. Gabriel de Jesu Maria de Cataluña, ord. Carm. (1646).—2. Trials in various places of Antonio Piña (1684); Esteban Ramoneda (1690–1700); Antonio Vives (1596–7); Ignazio . . . (1698); Estebanillo F. (1698–1700); Josef Boxeda (1704); Thomas Itagre (1715–6); Esteban . . . (1716); N. Serra (1721–8).—3. Trials in various places of Felix Duarde de Andrade (1725); Fr. Juan T., ord. Aug. (1741); Maria Ombrera (1744); Matheo Monfort (1745); Pablo Planas (1747); Jayme Sans (1749); Ramon Closa (1749–51); Maria Angela T. (1751); undeciphered (1751); Antonio Adorno (1756); Agostin Tamarit (1757); Juan Goveru (1761); and 16 other legal documents, incl. one concerning the "guardias Walonas" and another the "Universidad de Cervera."—4. 50 miscellaneous items, incl. Sale of Jesuit property (1770); Repuesta del Ex°. S°r. Conde de Florida Blanca, controversy over the sound "Noot" (1790); Augustin de la Florida, capture of a brigantine, Charlestown (1793); two fragments of account books (1556 and 1559–63); Extract from "Venditionum primum regis Martinis de anno 1398 ad 1409" (sale of property in 1401 to Guillermus de Rocabertino, copied in 1769), etc.—5. 65 miscellaneous documents, largely legal and commercial, incl. account book (1571–3) and ledger of Josef and Raymundo Murtza (1753); various privileges (1754, etc.); Resumen de Testos (1784, etc.); Contra heredes et possessones Mansi Serra (1669); printed billets for army (1797), etc.—6. 15 "limpiezas" (genealogies) as follows: Joan Aulet (1570); Antonio Gorch (1573); Marçal Traneria [?] (1581); Phederiche Comete (1583); Miguel Pelayre (1586); Jayme Rocabruna (1591–2); . . . Pages (1597); Pablo Font (1604); Gili Seguer (1604); Joan Mascaro (1615); Miguel Pusol (1618); Garau Artinbau (1645); Joan Ventos (1647); Bernat Boris (1650–1); Llorens Godo (1651).—7. "Limpiezas" of Hiacinto Mascaro (1670); Francesco Cotxet (1681); Francesco Baptista de Arrise (1747; receipt for payment); Maria Pons (relative of Hiacinto Mascaro, 1685); Pablo Castell y Ravella (1769); suit over inheritance from Joan Baptista Aragonés Don Pare (1762).—8. 23 miscellaneous documents incl. Conversion of Richard Payne (1633); Edict of denunciation (1758); Proceso contra Rafael Rocha (1664–7); undated inventory of books in unnamed "estampa"; list of books confiscated in the bookshop of Pedro Fullá [or Tullá?] by the inquisition in Barcelona (1788). *Spain, 1532–early 19th cent.*

Paper. In excess of 195 documents of various lengths (from a few to 204 ff.), several incl. printed forms, a few in Latin. Various sizes, mostly folio. Unbound, in boxes.—Prov.: Preserved by Andrew Thorndike in 1820–1 when the inquisitorial palace was stormed, and given by his son, G. Herbert Thorndike, to the American Philosophical Society in 1840, and presented to the Lea Library by the American Philosophical Society in 1962.

Ms. Lea 372 (Ital.)

VENICE. Procedura civile (without formal title for the entire work, but with subtitles, e.g. Cause si tractano al zudega de' proprio senza comandamento, f.4), *inc.:* Sententiar ponti de testamenti. . . . *Venice, first half 16th cent.*

Paper. 56 ff. (ff.48, 51–6 blank). 16 x 11 cm. H/calf.—Prov.: Frederick North, 5th Earl of Guilford; Giuseppe Martini.

Ms. Lea 373 (Ital.)

[ANCONA]. 1. BONCAMPAGNO (Buoncampagno; Potthast: Boncampagni). Liber de obsidione Anconae . . . 1172, transl. into Italian by Oddo di Biagio, ff.1r–16v, *inc.:* De una aspera obsidione facta contra Ancona . . . , *incl.* Un altra obsidione de Ancona facta da li populi Convicini (ff.15v–6v).—2. DE UNA CONTROVERSIA bellicosa tra li Anconitani et Venetiani ex chronicis Venetorum tractum est, ff.17r–21r, *inc.:* Quemadmodum latine proverbio . . . Et pero li Venitiani . . . , *incl.* Ancona da li Saraceni oppugnata (f.21r).—3. ODDO DI BIAGGIO. Chronica de la edificatione et destructione del Cassaro Anconitano . . . , ff.25r–130r, *inc.:* Se la diligentia de le scripture. . . .—4. COLUCCIO SALUTATI. Lettera di li Fiorentini in laude de li Anconitani [1383], ff.130v–2 (icplt. at end), *inc.:* (f.130v): De la victoria havuta . . . , (f.131r): Magnificis viris Antianis. . . . Excussistis tandem amici. . . . *Italy, 2nd half 15th cent.*

Paper. 132 (wrongly numb. 129) ff. (ff.22–4 blank). 20.5 x 14.5 cm. Contemp. vellum.—Prov.: Rosenheim Coll.; John C. William; Giuseppe Martini (with his notes laid in).

Ms. Lea 374 (Sp.)

CASTILE. Copia de los reales decretos expedidos al real y suprema Consejo de Castilla en 22 de septiembre de 1746 noticiandole . . . la creacion del govierno politico y militar de Madrid. . . . *Spain, 18th cent.*

Paper. 14 ff. (preceding printed official documents). 30 x 20.5 cm. Buckram (shelved as S.29.6.15).—Prov.: Henry Charles Lea.

Ms. Lea 375 (Sp.)

JUAN DE AVELLANEDA. Fabula de Eneas y Dido (9 ff. in verse).— *With* MAHOMA en Granada (18 ff.) *Spain, 16th cent.*

Paper. 27 ff. (following printed Diaz de Ribas, Piedra da Cordova, and other pamphlets). 21.5 x 15 cm. Contemp. vellum (shelved as S.25.4.14).—Prov.: Henry Charles Lea.

Ms. Lea 376 (Ger.)

CONCUBINATUM CLERICORUM, Bedenken der Concubinen wegen. Legal opinion rendered for Count Fugger by an official H. F.,

15–25 April 1589, interpretation of canon and imperial law, in a case involving, it appears, "des Kramers Köchin." *N.p., 1589.*

Paper. 2 ff. 32.5 x 21.5 cm. In folder.

Ms. Lea 377 (Sp.)

JOAN OF ARAGON, Queen of Sicily. Letter to the Count of Palamos, respecting her planned visit with Ferdinand and Isabella of Spain which now had to be delayed for various reasons until the following spring. *Naples, 1 Nov., 1498.*

Paper. 1 f. 28 x 21 cm. In folder.

Ms. Lea 378 (Ger.)

LORENTZ PSCHERER. Verzeichnis der Gesiecht unnd Erscheinung do mir Evangelisch Schulmeister Lorentz Pscherer zur Alten Statt [Altenstadt?, and Nürnberg] . . . 1627 . . . 1628 zur unterschiedlichmahlen erschiennen unnd begegnet. *Franconia, ca. 1628.*

Paper. 10 ff. 22 x 17.5 cm. Boards.

Ms. Lea 379 (Sp.)

TOLEDO, Inquisition. Causa de Isabel de Medina, hija de Gaspar de los Reyes e Isabel de Medina, de nacion portuguesa, de estado doncella residente en Madrid de 14 años (accused of the "crimen de la heregia y apostacia"). Original documents (1652–8) with 19th-cent. transcript. *Spain, 1652–19th cent.*

Paper. 62 ff. (last blank), 82 ff. 32 x 22 cm. Leather.

Ms. Lea 380 (Sp.)

CORDOVA, Inquisition. Memoria del auto dela fe que se hizo en la ciudad de Cordova . . . año de 1595. (List of persons accused of a variety of offenses, blasphemy, judaism, etc.) *Cordova, 1595.*

Paper. 6 ff. (last blank). 31 x 21 cm. Paper cover.

Ms. Lea 381 (Sp.)

CORDOVA, Inquisition. Memoria de el auto que se hico en la noble ciudad de Cordova . . . 1625. (Minutes, and list of persons, mostly Portuguese, accused of apostasy, etc., with penalties imposed). *Cordova, 1625.*

Paper. 4 ff. (numbered 7–10). 31 x 21 cm. H/cloth.

Ms. Lea 382 (Sp.)

[FROILAN DIAZ]. Causa [y prision] del Maestro Fr. Froilan Diaz, confesor de Carlos segundo, año de 1695. Y causa del yllustrissimo S. D. Bartolomeo Carranza, arzobispo de Toledo, año de 1558. Ambos del

Ordine de Predicadores. Madrid, por N. N.—*With* HISTORIA del . . . P. F. Froilan Diaz. *Spain, post 1704?*

Paper. 190 ff. (ff.2, 187–90 blank). 20 x 15 cm. Contemp. calf.

Ms. Lea 383 (Lat.)°

LUCCA, Confraternita della S. Croce, Ospedale della Misericordia (attached to St. Nicolas). Copies of documents, 1346–1489, concerning the hospital for the poor and infirm, established by Nicolao, Piero and Matteo Busdraghi, the first with *inc.*: Frater Guilelmus Dei et apostolice sedis gratia episcopus Lucanus dilectis nobis in Christo filiis confratribus societatis ditte di Cruce in . . . loco hospitalis misericordie de Luca positus intra portam Sti. Donati. . . . *Lucca, late 15th cent.*

Paper. 47 ff. (first blank, last few ff. in poor condition). 32 x 22 cm. Boards.

Ms. Lea 384 (Ital.)°

MISCELLANEA ad historiam Poloniae saec. XVI pertinentia. 1. NOTAMENTO per la restitutione del stato di Bari e Rossano; Discorso of Giovanni Lorenzo Papacoda; Copia delle pretensioni del Serenissimo Re Filippo; NOTA DE CAPI PRINCIPALI per i quali il Ser. Re Cattolico pretende de ritenere li stati di Bari, et Rossano; Riposta; Primum privilegium . . . Bari et Rossani (Lat.); NOTA in che forma et tempo fu concesso il ducato di Bari et principato di Rossano all'Illma. Isabella d'Aragona; INDEX privilegiorum; COPIA d'una informatione al Signor Vargas ambasciatore di sua Maestà Cattolica al tempo che si parte di Roma; COMPROMISSUM super statu Bari . . . 1562 (Lat.); Relatione di Scipio Catapani, etc., the whole section relating to the claims of King Sigismund II of Poland, son of the duchess of Milan, Bona Sforza, especiallyto Bari and Rossano, ff.1–108.—2. PROCESSUS factus per R. D. Aloysium Lip[p]omanum, nuntium in regno Poloniae, contra Jacobum episcopum Vladislaviensem suspectum de haeresi; PROCESSUS [eiusdem] contra D. Andream episcopum Cracoviensem; RESPONSIONES rev. dom. praelatorum, canonicorum et capitulorum cathedralium Guesnensis, Posnaniensis, Vladislaviensis et Plocensis . . . super negotio fidei; STATUTA REGNI Poloniae contra haereticos [1424–1550]; NOVUM JUDAEORUM CRIMEN in Calisiensi civitate [1556–1564], etc. (all in Lat.), ff.111–91.—(Index on f.192). *Italy?, ca. 1600.*

Paper. 196 ff. (ff.109–10, 193–6 blank; part of f.172 cut out). 31.5 x 21.5 cm. Contemp. vellum.

Ms. Lea 385 (Ital.)°

MEDICI. In questo libro sono registrati privilegi, decreti imperiali, bolle pontificie, coronazione di principe grande, instruzioni, renunzie, instrumenti, rogiti di benedizion[e] coniugale, relazioni, investiture, scritture diverse, lettere, missive e responsive; il tutto attenente nel principio alla casa de Medici e poi della casa reale di Toscana. (Documents covering the period 1443–1711, fragmentary for the early period and extensive for the late period). *Italy, first half 18th cent.*

Paper. 688 pp. (pp.1–20, 22–4, 513–28, 658–88 blank); 6 ff. index in late 19th-cent. hand laid in. Arms of Medici on title page (p.21). Gilt contemp. morocco with arms of Medici on front and back cover.—Prov.: Antonio Peregrino Colombani; Principe Pietro Ginori-Conti.

Ms. Lea 386 (Ital.)°

FLORENCE, St. Vincentio (called Annalena). Le constitutione delle suore della penitentia di Sto. Domenico del terzo ordine del Monasterio di Sto. Vincentio di Firenze, vocato Annalena. *Florence, 2nd half 15th cent.*

Vellum. 17 ff. (ff.16–7 blank); lower margin of f.1 replaced, presumably after removal of coat-of-arms. 25 x 17 cm. Vellum.—Prov.: Principe Pietro Ginori-Conti.

Ms. Lea 387 (Sp.)°

PHILIP II, King of Spain. Decreto para que ningun vasallo suyo sè este en la corte de Roma en tiempo de Paulo Quarto, dada en la villa de Valladolid à 13 dia del mes de enero de 1557, ff.1–7v.—*With* IÑIGO DE CARDENAS. Razone que sè ofrecen para mayor inteligencia del rey y regno de Francia, Paris, 4 de dec.[?] 1621, ff.7v–14r. *Spain, 17th cent.*

Paper. 14 ff. (originally numb. 300–313). 19.5 x 14.5 cm. Boards.—Prov.: Henry C. Lea. Originally classified as S-25.5.30.

Ms. Lea 388 (Fr.)°

[GERARD DIDELOT, dit de RONCOURT]. Procès criminel contre Gerard [or Girard] Didelot, "sur plusieurs oultraiges et blasphemes" at Saint Diey [i.e. St. Dié?], 1569–70, signed by Rasaille, Gardette, Le Brecq, Mainbourg, etc. *St. Dié?, 1569–70.*

Paper. 21 ff. 30 x 21 cm. Boards.

Ms. Lea 389 (Ital.)°

[CANON LAW]. TRATTATO DELLE COMMENDE, dealing in 72 chapters with ecclesiastical benefices held "in commendam." *Italy, late 17th cent.*

Paper. 6, 393 ff. (ff.6, 392–3 blank). 32 x 21.5 cm. Contemp. vellum. Apparently part of a larger collection, presumably on canon law, since the *inc.* reads: Trattarò in questo decimo quarto titulo primo della prima origine delle com[m]ende.

Ms. Lea 390 (Lat.)°

[CATHOLIC CHURCH]. Collectio diversorum decretorum Sancti Officii urbis [Romae] à Sacra Congregatione eminentissimorum diversis temporibus editorum, quae novissime ordine alphabetico digesta sunt. *Italy, 2nd half 17th cent.*

Paper. 462, 4 (tabula; last blank) ff. 26.5 x 19.5 cm. Prov.: Phillipps ms. 5321. See also ms. Lea 137.

Ms. Lea 391 (Ital.)°

FERDINAND, Prince of Tuscany. Lettere dell' A. R. del Principe Ferdinando di Toscana a Lodovico Fantoni [called in different letters "avvocato," "abbate," and "conte"]. 129 largely autograph letters, with occasional passages in cipher, addressed to Fantoni primarily in Vienna, Madrid, Paris and Venice, 1698–1709[?]. At end bound in "Copia di lettera a Montauti," 1698 and "Relazione della morte . . . [di] Gran' Principe Ferdinando di Toscana," 1713. *Italy, 1698–1713.*

Paper. 172 ff. Various sizes (in vol. 24.5 x 18 cm.) With remains of seals. Contemp. vellum.

Ms. Lea 392 (Fr.)°

HISTOIRE DE L'HERESIE depuis l'an 1374 jusqu'en l'année 1631. *France, post 1631.*

Paper. 277 pp. 25 x 18 cm. Contemp. vellum. Contemp. unidentified bookplate.

Ms. Lea 393 (Ital.)°

ALVISE FOSCARI, patriarch of Venice. Ms. copy of one printed, and 3 ms. edicts: 10 June, 1743; 16 June, 1744; 10 March, 1747; 4 Jan., 1752 in volume consisting largely of printed broadsides. *Venice [etc.], 1626–1774* (date of entire coll., printed and mss.)

Paper. 1 v. 30 x 21.5 cm. Contemp. boards.—Prov.: Henry C. Lea.—Shelved as KK5.7.

Ms. Lea 394 (Ital.)°

CARLO REZZONICO, Cardinal. Pastoral letters, edicts, etc., collection of broadsides and tracts, largely printed, but incl. ms. copies (Indulgenza plenaria, 6 June, 1744; Pastoral letters, 14 July, 1744; 9 Feb., 1746; 20 Feb., 1746; 13 Feb., 1748; 1754). *Padua, 1743–58*, (date of entire coll., printed and mss.)

Paper. Collection bound in 2 vols. 30 x 21 cm. Contemp. boards.—Prov.: Henry C. Lea. Shelved as KK5.10–11.

Ms. Lea 395 (Ital.)°

SANTI VERONESE, Cardinal. Collection of tracts and broadsides, printed and manuscript, incl. in ms.: Predica (acc. to ms. table of contents "originale di mano propria dell' autore"), 8 ff.; Dissertatio de optione (copy), 38 ff.; Ex registro ducalium in cancelleria civitatis

Padovensis, 6 ff. (2 ff. blank); various pastoral letters; copy of a letter by Card. Rezzonico. *Padua, 1733–66* (date of entire coll., printed and mss.)

Paper. Collection bound in 2 vols. 30 x 21.5 cm. Contemp. boards.—Prov.: Henry C. Lea.—Shelved as KK5.21–22.

Ms. Lea 396 (Ital., etc.)°

ARCHIVIO MONTAUTI. Miscellaneous collection of letters, political dispatches, accounts, translations of reports, etc., incl. letters by and to Antonio Francesco Montauti, together ca. 150 items, boxed. *Various places*, the great majority written *between 1690 and 1710.*

Paper. Various sizes. Cf. Lea mss. 30–2, 198.

Ms. Lea 397 (Ital., etc.)°

VILLAFIORITA. Archives of the Dukes of Villafiorita, Princes of Aragon, collection of original documents, copies, and a few printed items. *Nos. 1–16:* BURGIO FAMILY (Dukes of Villafiorita since 1712). Copies of wills, 1417–1730. Dowry contracts, 1442–1831. Privileges from the Naselli and Morso, 1460–1589 (incl. vellum doc. for Aloisio Saccano of Casalnuovo, 1460; Nicola Campolo, 1459; Giovanni di Lamberto receiving rights to Limbrici, 1500; Pietro Fernando Saccano, 1515; Geronimo Campolo, 1548, etc.). Admission of Geronimo Burgio as doctor of law, Rome, 1661 (4 ff.). Copies of grants, 1676–1848. Inventories incl. copy of 1510 doc., 1722–1870. Appointment of the Prince of Aragon as "capitan de justicia" of Palermo by Emperor Charles VI, 1763 (6 ff.). Will of Pietro Giacomo Burgio, 1777. Business records, 18th cent. Lettere di manutenzione for Niccolò Burgio, 1803–4. Various 19th-cent. docs. (incl. suit against Antonio Montalbano di Ribera and Girolamo Turano).—*No. 17:* FRANCESCO DE BELVIS, castellano di Pantelleria. Will, Valencia, 1487 (property of Pantelleria sold to Luigi Requesens in 1492).—*No. 18* (bundle): CARRETTO FAMILY (conti di Recalmuto). Genealogy, certificates of baptism and death, marriage contracts, inventories, wills, etc., 1503–1764.—*Nos. 19–22:* GALLETTI FAMILY. 4 docs. concerning property of Vittoria Nicoletta, prioress of Santa Maria della Pietà, Palermo, 1766. Letters, business papers, wills, etc., 1791–1847. Inventories of the estate of Baldassare Naselli-Galletti, Prince of Aragon, and Marianna, 1863–72 (with a few earlier supporting docs.). Succession of Marianna with statement of creditors, 1871–2. *No. 23:* MARIANNA GRIFEO (or GRAFFEO), countess of Monte S. Angelo. Guardianship records, 1826–7.—*Nos. 24–9:* MORSO FAMILY. Wills, 1386–1735. Wills, privileges and grants (many concerning the land and castle of Gibellina), 1486–1728. Inventories, 1492–1736. Genealogy and family records (incl. marriage contracts, donations, etc.), 1528–1741. Privileges granted to Geronimo Morso, 1685–99. Historical account, 1485–1782, written ca. 1800 (10 ff., last 2 blank).—*Nos. 30–53:*

NASELLI FAMILY. Review of privileges to Lodovico de Caprera (or Cabrera), count of Mohac, and his heirs, 1351–1461, from the registers of Sicily, compiled in 1544 under Emperor Charles V (ca. 60 ff.). Privilege for the county of Mohac to Pericono de Nasello and heirs, 1479. Privileges concerning Caprera, 1497. Privileges for Mohac, 1558–9. Privilege to Beatrice de Nasellis, 1586. Documents concerning privileges and transfers of property granted by Frederick (1375, 19th-cent. copy) and Alphons, Kings of Aragon (incl. the transfer of Mohac from Bernardo Giov. Caprera to Pericono de Nasellis, 1456 < 24 ff., last 6 blank>, etc.) and Ferdinand, viceroy of Sicily (concerning Gibellina, 1485). Grant of King Alphons to Pericono de Nasellis alienating the rights of Antonio de Dionisio, 1446–7. Marriage contracts., etc., 1499–1809. Baldassare de Nasellis, Extension of taxes, 1504–59. Wills and business papers, 1517–1924. Privileges, 1519–1812. Inventories, 1551–1863 (incl. furnishings of the Palazzo di Gibellina, 18th cent.). Business papers, 1553–1821 (incl. those on sulphur mines). Record of donations, 1561–1739. Records relating to guardianships, 1561–1815 (incl. extensive inventory of 1586). Privileges and investitures, 1599–1812. Death certificates, 1709–1872. Luigi Naselli, Proceedings against vassals, 1661, and petition regarding debts by Giovanni Ant. Gelosús. Notes, letters, letter book, 1715–1858. Records concerning the canons of Comiso, 1719–1880's. Grant of gold cross of the Order of St. John of Jerusalem, 1733, to Baldassare de Nasellis. Investitures to the county of Comiso, 1812. Legal papers (incl. suit against Baldassare Naselli), 1819–1905. Act of emancipation of negro slave, 1820. Legal papers concerning properties (Palermo region, Spiro, Martorana), 19th cent. to 1904.—*Nos. 54–62:* REQUESENS FAMILY. Concession to Pantelleria, 1336–1852. Evidence of service to the Spanish throne (ca. 1400, 17th-cent. copy, 82 ff., some blank). Copies of documents pertaining to services rendered to the crown (incl. papers issued by Emperor Charles V, Queen Joane, etc., genealogy), 1463–1611 (98 ff.). Documents relating to Pantelleria (incl. material relating to the town of Marsala), 1469–19th cent. Genealogy and family papers, 18th cent.—*Nos. 63–5:* VENTIMIGLIA FAMILY. Francesco de Ventimiglia, Lord of Buscome, Will of 1386, reissued 1422. Grant by Martin, King of Aragon, to Guilelmo for the hamlet of Buscome, 1408. Vincenzo Ventimiglia appointed treasurer, 1587.—*No. 66* (vol.): NOTIZIE DELLE FAMIGLIE DE VIO, Ezquerre, de Yerma and Herrera and RELAZIONE de' servigi [!] degli Antenati, etc., 1730 (190 pp.).—*Nos. 67–77:* RECALMUTO. Documents relating to Recalmuto (involving the Villafiorita, Pantelleria, the prince of Palagonia, Burgo, the families Grillo, Naselli, etc.), 1558–1928.—*Nos. 78–9:* RIVERA (or RIBERA). Disputes over leases and rents, 1828–70.—*Nos. 80–91:* MISCELLANEOUS. Investitures and concessions relating to various Sicilian territories and families, 1340–1603 (incl. Castello, terra di Auda [?], Gasparo Montaperto, G. M. de Saccano, Lucio

Bonanno, etc.). Wills, 1498–1597 (incl. Petro Caetano, Cipriano Spinola, Antonio Platamone, Petro de Montaperto, Giovanni d'Aragona, Oliva d'Aragona, Bernardino Lanfranchi, etc.). Second series of wills, 1600–39. Documents relating to San Domenico in Palermo, 1597–1708. Tribunal in Messina, 1704–1833. Kingdom of the Two Sicilies, Raggioni, che assistone al publico banco per non permettersi in esso ignorazione di grani . . . , 1773–4 (52 ff.), and 5 other bundles.

Vellum and paper. 34 boxes, 18 bundles and a few bound volumes. Various sizes.—Printed items in the collection are described separately.

Ms. Lea 398 (Lat., etc.)°

SAMMINIATI ARCHIVE. 254 documents, mostly "rotulae" of varying length, originals and contemporary notarized copies, (nos. 1–2, 4–10, 12–15, 33, 44 and 108 photostats), incl. purchase contracts, trials, civil suits, leases, wills, benefices, investitures, etc. Localities mentioned incl., besides Florence and San Miniato, Prato, Vico, Lucca, Pisa, Pistoia, Siena; among families involved are the Benivieni, Bonaccorsi, Brunelleschi, Capponi, Corsini, Gabrielli, Medici, Riccomanni, Rucellai and Salviati; several documents concern the Ospedale di S. Giacomo di Altopascio. *Italy, [ca. 1200] 1247–1832.*

Vellum. Arranged in boxes: I, nos, 1–17, 1220–1314; II A, nos. 18–27, 1323–55; II B, nos. 28–33, 1362–78; III A, nos. 34–42, 1383–96; III B, nos. 43–51, 1400–4; IV A, nos. 52–61, 1407–14; IV B, nos. 62–70, 1414–19; V A, nos. 71–81, 1419–20; V B, nos. 82–92, 1420; VI A, nos. 93–103, 1420–1; VI B, nos. 104–14, 1422; VII A, nos. 115–28, 1422–31; VII B, nos. 129–41, 1432–56; VIII A, nos. 142–9, 1456–65; VIII B, nos. 150–60, 1467–85; IX, nos. 161–79, 1485–1516; X A, nos, 180–9, 1516–59; X B, nos. 190–8, 1570–1608; XI A, nos. 199–209, 1608–40; XI B, nos. 210–20, 1651–83; XII A, nos. 221–31, 1687–1723; XII B, nos. 232–45, 1724–86; XIII, nos. 246–53, 1791–1832, and 6 undated documents, of which 4 fall between the years 1200 and 1400.—The collection is accompanied by a typewritten catalogue (inventario, filed following Ms. Lea 398, box XIII) with genealogy of the "Casa Samminiati," indexes of "Famiglie illustri" (42), "Località," "Arte e metieri" (e.g. gunsmiths, textile trade, physicians, merchants), "Chiese, ordini religiosi," etc., "Istituti," and brief analysis of all documents.

Ms. Lea 399 (Ital.)°

GUADAGNI ARCHIVE. 1. NERI GUADAGNI. Dispacci di Sig. Marchese Neri Guadagni, inviato straord. di Toscana alla Corte Cesarea dal 1708 al 1717, scritti alla Segreteria di Stato, 4 vols.—2. TUSCANY, Segreteria di Stato. Dispacci . . . 1705–17, scritti al Sig. March. Neri Guadagni [etc.] Vol. 1: In occasione della missione . . . per far la condoglienza della morte dell' Imp. Leopoldo, e rallegrarsi dell' asunzione al trono dell' Imp. Giuseppe (mostly by Francesco Panciatichi) . . . . Riposti (incl. orig. letters of Cosimo III), 1705.—Vol. 2: Instruzione; document appointing Guadagni ambassador, and dispatches to

Guadagni (mostly by Panciatichi; some in cipher), 1708–11.—Vol. 3: Dispatches, 1712–3.—Vol. 4: Idem, 1714.—Vol. 5: Idem, 1715–7.— 3. COSIMO III, Grand Duke of Tuscany. Lettere . . . scritte dal Ser. Cosimo 3° . . . al Sig. March. Neri Guadagni, 1708–17 (some in cipher), 2 vols.—4. INFORMAZIONE della corte di Vienna e suo ministero lasciata dal S. Sen. Presidente Antinori al Sig. March. Guadagni.—Notizie diverse . . . dal Sig. Cav. Antinori (Prince Eugene, Court of Barcelona, siege of Portolungo, etc.).—Scritture lasciate dal Sign. Sen. Pres. Antinori, 1713 (incl. Memorial of March. Rinuccini from Frankfurt and the electoral college, Niccolò Amerighi, 1712, etc.). —Copia delle lettere credenziali.—5. ANNA, Electress Palatinate (daughter of Cosimo III). Lettere al Sig. March. Neri Guadagni, 1708–17, 3 vols.—6. LETTERE di diversi principi al Sig. March. Guadagni (mostly from members of the family of Cosimo III, 1708–20).— 7. MISCELLANEA di diverse relazioni (all printed), 1709–15. *Various places, 1705–20.*

Paper. 17 vols. (2° and 4°). Contemp. boards.

Ms. Lea 400 (Ital.)°

PIUS IV, Pope. Instruttioni al Vescovo Zaccaria Delfino mandato all' Imperatore Ferdinando . . . , 1560. *Italy, 17th cent.*

Paper. 10 ff. (last blank), numbered in a contemp. hand pp. 31–50. 27 x 20 cm. Boards.

Ms. Lea 401 (Ital.)°

PAUL III, Pope. Instruttioni diverse (mainly relating to Germany). 11 ambassadorial instructions for legations to Emperor Charles V, his brother Ferdinand, King Sigismund I of Poland, and the Council of Trent, 1534–48. *Italy, 17th cent.*

Paper. 132 ff. (last blank), numbered 23–178 in a contemp. hand (ff.29–30, 45–6, 53–4, 71–2, 95–6, 113–4, 138–40, 153–4, 161–2, 170–2, between instructions, probably blank, missing; f.83 omitted in numbering). 30 x 21 cm. Boards.

Ms. Lea 402 (Lat.)°

MISCELLANEA STORICA DI GUASTALLA. Collection of records in Latin and Italian, all but one in original or contemporary copies, many notarized, referring to controversy among members of the Torelli family over the rights to Guastalla (Reggio nell' Emilia) and sale to Ferrante Gonzaga, 1539–61. Contents: *Vol. I*, ff.1–19, Description and evaluation of the property of Guastalla for Renato Trivulzio in controversy with the Counts Torelli, 1492.—Ff.20–56, Examination of witnesses in the suit of Marcantonio Torelli against Paolo Torelli and his mother, Damigella di Giovanni Trivulzio, 1525.—Ff.60–3, Deposition in behalf of Paolo and his mother concerning the will of Francesco Torelli, Paolo's father, 1521.—Ff.67–78, Testimony in behalf of Marcantonio Torelli, in Mantua, 1525.—Ff.81–107, Further testimony, 1525.—

Ff.115–376, Summary of the case, 1531.—*Vol. II*, ff.3–110; Further testimony in behalf of Marcantonio Torelli against Paolo Torelli, 1531. —Ff.114–238, IDEM, 1531.—Ff.240–2, Judgment in favor of Marcantonio Torelli, by Alexander Amonius, "doctor et ducalis senator," Mantua, 1532.—Ff. 244–5, Judgment for Marcantonio, Milan, 1532–3 (defective).—Ff.247–51, Notarized copy of similar judgment, 1532, with appended docs., 1515–34.—F.267, Petition of Paolo Torelli to Pope Clement VII [?].—Ff.269–70, Petition to Charles V concerning purchase of Guastalla by Ferrante Gonzaga.—F.271, Petition to Charles V by Marcantonio Torelli.—F.273, Submission of the controversy to Charles V.—*Vol. III*, ff.1–15, Sale of property at Guastalla by Torelli family to Redulfo [Rodolfo?] Gonzaga, 1538.—F.17, License for sale of Guastalla to Ferrante Gonzaga by Charles V, 1539, with seal, signed R. Quadrius.—Ff.18–34, Copy of sales agreement of 1539 between Lodovica Torelli and Ferrante Gonzaga, copied in 1725.—Ff.36–41, Sales agreement between Marcantonio Torelli and Ferrante Gonzaga, 1546, on vellum.—Ff.42–59, Further sales agreements, 1561, before Giov. Batt. Landriani by various members of Torelli family.—Ff.60–86, Statements favoring claims of Marcantonio Torelli by Nicolao Alliprandi, the second with seal, undated (ca. 1531).—Ff.89–180, Similar testimonies by Carlo Malatesta, Geronimo de Medici, etc. *Italy, 1492–1725.*

Paper and 6 ff. vellum. 3 v. (376, 273, 182 ff.) Various sizes in 3 folio vols. With notarial signets and few seals. H/calf.—Cf. Ms. Lea 181.

Judgment for Marcantonio Torelli. Lea 402, f.44r (detail).

Edgar F. Smith Collection Manuscripts

Ms. E. F. Smith 1 (Ger.)

SPLENDOR SOLIS, oder Sonnen Glantz, tailt sich inn siben Tractat, durch welches beschrieben wirt die künstlich Würckhung des verborgnen Stains der alten Weisen. *Germany, second half 16th cent.*

Vellum. 41 ff. (numb. in contemp. hand 1–34 and 35–40, with unnumb. f. between ff.34 and 35). 30.5 x 20 cm. Spaces for illustrations left blank throughout; subjects indicated in contemp. writing.—Contemp. vellum.

Ms. E. F. Smith 2 (Ger.)

FEUERWERKBUCH. Feuer Buech, durch Eurem gelertten Kriegs Verstenndigen mit grossem Vleis auss villen probrertten [sic] Kunsten . . . zusamen gezogen. *Germany, 1584.*

Paper. 235 ff. 31 x 20.5 cm. With numerous colored illus. Contemp. vellum.— Style of illustrations resembles Berlin, Staatsb.ms.germ.qu.1188, cf. W. Hassenstein, ed., *Das Feuerwerkbuch von 1420*, (Munich, 1941), p. 121.

Ms. E. F. Smith 3 (Lat.)

ALCHEMICAL MISCELLANY. 1. ROGER BACON. Tractatus trium verborum [or] Epistolae tres ad Johannem Parisiensem, ff.1r–10r. —2. MORIENUS ROMANUS (apocryphal). Questiones inter Kalid regem et Morienum philosophum, ff.10r–13r.—3. GEBER. Summa perfectionis, ff.13v–42v.—4. AVICENNA. De anima, ff.42v–50r.—5. Index, f.50r–v. *England?, first half 15th cent.*

Paper. 50 ff. (last 4 ff. damaged, with loss of text). 30 x 21 cm. H/morocco.— Prov.: Hamon Styleman—le Strange, 1871; Falconer Madan (autograph note on fly-leaf), 1892; W. M. Voynich.

Ms. E. F. Smith 4 (Eng.)

ALCHEMICAL MISCELLANY. 1. GEORGE RIPLEY. The marrow of alchemy (dated in *expl.* 1476), ff.1r–10r.—2. IDEM. George Ripley unto King Edward IV (in verse), ff.10v–12v.—3. IDEM. Twelve gates (or The compound of alchemy; in verse), ff.13r–30v.—4. IDEM. Note of our fires, without the knowledge whereof our mastery is not performed, ff.31r–32v.—5. IDEM. Various recipes, ff.33r–34v.—6. IDEM. A partial abridgement of all the writings of George Ripley, ff.35r–36v.— 7. RAYMUNDUS LULLUS. An accurtation (incl. "Alia [sic] modus et forma distillationis;" "Another manner of practising accurtation"), ff.34v–40v.—8. Another special work of the basilisk, ff.40v–41r.— 9. RAYMUNDUS LULLUS. Accurtation (and "A very strong vinegar;" "A work in mineral stone," etc.), ff.41v–42r.—10. GUIDO DE MONTANOR. Sayings, f.42v.—11. THE DREAM OF GEORGE RIPLEY (tr. by Edward Cradocke), ff.42v–43v.—12. GEORGE RIPLEY. A secret; The vision; Recapitulatio, ff.43r–44v.—13. GEBER.

The testament, ff.44v–47r.—14. THE MIRROR of alchemy, ff.47r–51r.
—15. PEARCE, the Black Monk. Two poems, ff.51v–52r.—16. THE
CALENDAR of principles, ff.52r–53v.—17. COMPENDIOUS AB-
STRACT of alchemy, drawn out of Latin (Liber multipheris; on a per-
fect elixir), ff.54r–57r.—18. GEORGE RIPLEY. Concordance between
Raymond [Raymundus Lullus] and Guido [de Montanor], ff.57r–58r.—
19. THE LAWS of philosophers, ff.58v–59r.—20. JOHANN ISAAC
HOLLANDUS. Discussion of problems, in form of a dialogue (his
"Tractatus duo chemici"?), ff.59v–61v.—21. A GENERAL RULE for
all men that intend to be philosophers, f.61v.—22. THE MOST
SHORTEST AND THE MOST LIGHTEST WAY . . . that can be
done in this art of science, f.62r–v.—23. THE PSALTER OF PHILOS-
OPHERS, ff.63r–70r.—24. RAYMUNDUS LULLUS. Accurtation,
ff.70r–74r.—25. THE PRACTICE OF THE PHILOSOPHERS (incl.
notes attributed to Raymundus Lullus), ff.74r–75v.—26. PEARCE, the
Black Monk. Upon the elixir (verse), ff.76r–77v.—27. THE PHILOS-
OPHERS STONE, f.77v.—28. ARNALDUS DE VILLANOVA.
Treatise of the virtues of rosemary (?), f.78r–v.—29. GEORGE
RIPLEY. Notable lessons chosen . . . from the book of Guido (de
Montanor), ff.79r–80v.—30. BY THE GRACE OF GOD, poem of 21
lines (begins: Out of darkness I will lead you), followed by commentary,
f.80v.—31. ARNALDUS DE VILLANOVA. Epistola . . . ad papam,
ff.81r–83v.—32. CONSTANTINUS AFRICANUS. Stella complexi-
onis is the father of truth (from chapt.55 of Raymundus Lullus'
"Testamentum"), f.84r.—33. WILLIAM DE CENES (or Comes,
Genes?). Answers to questions posed by the Archbishop of Rheims,
ff.84v–91v.—34. MERLIN. Allegory containing perfectly the most pro-
found secret of the philosophers stone, ff.94r–95r. *England, ca. 1600*, supposedly in the hand of Henry Percy, 9th Earl of Northumberland.

Paper. 95 ff. (ff.92–93 blank). 34 x 22 cm. Contemp. vellum. Monogram
H B on front cover.—The poetry in this ms. corresponds in part with texts which
were published in E. Ashmole's *Theatrum chemicum brittannicum*, (London, 1652),
however with variants. The concordance follows: ms.4, no.2—Ashmole,
pp.109–16; no.3—Ashmole, pp.121–93; no.15—Ashmole, pp.428–29, 434;
no.26—Ashmole, pp.269–74 (with considerable differences).

Ms. E. F. Smith 5 (Lat.)

ALCHEMICAL MISCELLANY (fragment, incomplete at beginning),
containing among others "Auri potabilis descriptio" (f.2v); "Cur[r]us
triumphalis Basilii Valentini" (extracts from his *Triumph Wagen*, f.3r,
etc.); Paracelsus' "De separatione elementorum" (f.10r–v); "De quinta
essentia" (f.10v); "De elexiris" (f.12r); "Liber de vita longa" (f.13r);

Ad. E. F. Smith 4, no. 33: On William of Sens see John R. Williams in *Haskins
Anniversary Essays*, p. 384.

"De mercurio" (f.17r); "De antimonio" (f.18v); "De sulfure" (f.27v); "De aquis mineralibus" (f.29r), etc. *Italy, 17th cent.*

Paper. 35 ff. 28 x 18 cm. Contemp. boards.

Ms. E. F. Smith 6 (Fr.)

[KUNSTBUECHLEIN]. Collection of various recipes and prescriptions for the preparation of colors, soap, perfumes, how to illuminate, engrave, dye, make marbled paper, mirrors, preserve wine and oils, construct a study lamp, etc. *France, 16th cent.*

Paper. 65 ff. 17.5 x 11 cm. Drawing of study lamp (p.51). Vellum.

Ms. E. F. Smith 7 (Fr.)

PIERRE JEAN FABRE. Abregé de la chimie ou l'on voit la nature des vegetaux, animaux, et mineraux entièrement découverte avec un traité de la medicine generale . . . dedié à Monsieur Duc d'Orléans. [An extract.] *France, 17th cent.*

Paper. 1 f., 33 pp. (31-33 blank), 4 blank ff. 24 x 17.5 cm. Portfolio.—Paris, Bibl. nat. *Cat.*, XLIX, col.199 lists a work with similar title, Paris, P. Billaine, 1638,—cf. also Ferguson's *Bibliotheca chemica*, (Glasgow, 1906), I, pp.259-60.— "A Paris chez Pierre Blaise" on title. No such edition in Bibl.nat. or *Bibliotheca chemica.*

Ms. E. F. Smith 8 (Lat.)

DE ARTE CABALISTICA, seu de magisterio magno philosophorum, 62 pp. *inc.:* Dividitur hoc magisterium in quatuor partes; quarum prima consistit in praeparatione dissolventis.—*With* EXPLICATIO FIGURAE HERMETICAE a Khunrahdo [sic; Heinrich (?) Khunrath, 1560-1605] designatae, signed Mercurii Trismegistae suae philosophiae amator fidelis, 71 ff. *Germany?, 17th cent.;* date 1564 at end spurious.

Paper. 2 blank ff., 31 ff., irregularly numb. pp.1-62, 1 blank f., folded drawing, 71 (instead of 72) ff., wrongly numb. pp.1-160. 17.5 x 12 cm. Folded pen-and-ink drawing (after Khunrath). Contemp. red morocco.

Ms. E. F. Smith 9 (Ital. and Lat.)

GIOVANNI DA NOLA. Ricettario. (Collection of remedies against a great variety of ills, sometimes indicating source of information, e.g. Conte de Altavilla, Conte de Urbino, Raynoldo de Villa Nova, etc.) The beginning (f.1) missing, *expl.:* Ad venerabilem patrem [?] fratrem Joannes de Nola, scriptoris presentis Ricettarii Distichon: Obsecro suscipias hec vultu ac fronte serena/ Que Bernardinus scripsit ab asse tuus. *Italy, ca. 1530.*

Paper. 30 ff. (numb. pp.3-62; pp.1-2 lacking). 15 x 11.5 cm. Contemp. vellum (using 13th-cent. ms. fragment).—Upper inner margin badly stained, destroying small section of text.

Ms. E. F. Smith 10 (Ital.)

SCIELTA DELLE PRATICHE piu degne dell'una et l'altra medicina, divisa in III parte, nelle quali si tratta non solo delle medine [sic] interne, ma anco delle esterne et della qualità de forni, vasi, et fuochi, che per estrahere acque, olii, varie essenze et tinture. *Italy, first half 17th cent.*

Paper. 7 ff. (first 3 blank), 521 pp., 1 f., 50 pp. 30 x 20.5 cm. With 43 pen-and-ink drawings of furnaces, chemical instruments and experiments (approx. 5 x 13 cm. each). Contemp. vellum.—Owner's property stamp "Rec Pector," on title. Signet at end, eagle with inscription: Per rinovar mi al fuoco mi consumo.— Paper browned and weakened throughout by oxidation.

Ms. E. F. Smith 11 (Eng.)

JACQUES DE NUYSEMENT. Treatises of the true salt, the philosophers secrett, and of the generall spiritt of the world. *England, second half 17th cent.*

Paper. 6 ff., 141 pp. 19.5 x 15 cm. Contemp. sheepskin.—Translated from the first French edition "Printed in Paris . . . MDCXXI." The English title of the printed editions, 1657 and 1658, translated by Robert Turner, as described in Ferguson's *Bibliotheca chemica*, II, p. 148, is quite different.

Ms. E. F. Smith 12 (Ger.)

CHRISTIAN ERNEST KLEINFELD. Kurze Beschreibung von Verfertigung einer Essentia dulcis, nebst zwei von ihr entsprungenden Medicamenten, nehmlich: des schwarzen Pulvers und des sogenanten Balsami mineralis, ff.1–32.—*With* 10 ff., prescriptions in Latin and German and 1f. with notes in English (move into house, 13 South 4th St. [Philadelphia?], 1814), 121 ff. of prayers, etc. in German, and 3 ff. of accounts (1812 etc.) in English. *Germany?, late 18th cent.*

Paper. 134 ff. and some blank ff. 16.5 x 9.5 cm. Contemp. vellum.—It appears likely that this ms. was brought from Germany to the colonies by an unnamed immigrant.—C. E. Kleinfeld could not be identified in Ferguson's *Bibliotheca chemica;* Duveen's *Bibliotheca alchemica et chemica;* Poggendorff, *Allgemeine deutsche Biographie*, etc.

Ms. E. F. Smith 13 (Lat.)

ALCHEMICAL MISCELLANY. 1 MINERA PHILOSOPHORUM; brevis libellus incogniti autoris, ff.1r–19v.—2. Opusculum secundum RADIUS AB UMBRA, sive Restrictus theoricus, ff.20r–46v. —3. DE ARTE CHYMICA, et eius princeps, ff.47r–59r.—4. BERNHARDUS TREVISANUS [Trevirensis in ms.]. De lapide philosophorum, ff.60r–66r.—5. ELEGANTIA de opere philosophico, ff.66v–68r.—6. JOHANN ISAAC HOLLANDUS. Excerpts, ff.68r–71r.—

7. [OLIVERUS DE OLIVERIIS]. In tractatu primo Oliverii de Oliveriis in cap. 13, ff.71r–73r.—8. [PANTALEON]. In bifolio metalico dicitur . . . , ff.73v–83r.—9. [GEBER]. Ex aphorismis Gebri, ff.83r–97r.—10. [IDEM]. Expositio librorum Gebri et Raimundi Lullii . . . incerto autore, ff.97v–104v.—11. EXPOSITIO ALCHEMIAE GEBRI [title of explicit; caption:] In dialogo primo Da[=e]mogorgonis et Gebri, ff.105r–152v; 165r–167v.—12. DE SUBLIMATIONE MERCURII and other short extracts from Geber, Oliverus de Oliveriis, etc., ff.152v–158v.—13. JOHN BELYE. Tractatus, ff.158v–165r.—14. Extract from DIALOGUS Demogorgonis et Raimundi de Ligno, and John Dauston, ff.167r–169r.—15. DELLA SFERZA degl'alchimisti, ff.169r–181r.—16. DE FERMENTO et multiplicatione, ff.181r–192r.—17. PRACTICA, ff.192v–196v.—18. INDEX rerum notabilium, ff.197r–212v. *Italy, ca. 1700.*

Paper. 212 ff. 18.5 x 11.5 cm. Contemp. vellum.—Collection similar in content to the Ginaeceum chimicum, cf. Ferguson's *Bibliotheca chemica*, I, p.318.

Ms. E. F. Smith 14 (Eng.)

JOSEPH BLACK. [Lectures on chemistry.] Notes written by a student. *Edinburgh, ca. 1800.*

Paper. 6 vols. 22 x 18 cm. Cloth.—Prov.: Presented by James[?] Hill to the Society of Apothecaries [London?], 1832.

Ms. E. F. Smith 15 (Fr.)

TRAITÉS ALCHÉMIQUES. 1. BERNARDUS TREVISANUS. Reponce [!] à Thomas de Bolougne, pp.1–48.—2. ECHELLE DES PHILOSOPHES (Scala philosophorum), pp.49–111.—3. OEUVRES DES FEMMES et jeu des enfants (Opus mulierum), pp.112–142.—4. ROSAIRE DES FILOSOPHES (Rosarium philosophorum), pp.142–306.—5. ARNALDUS DE VILLANOVA. Rosaires de filosophes, pp.307–375.—6. IDEM. Nouvelle lumière, pp.376–389.—7. IDEM. La fleur des fleurs, pp.390–407.—8. IDEM. Epistre . . . scrite au Roy de Naples au sujet de l'alchymie, pp.407–412.—9. ROGER BACON. Livre . . . au sujet de l'admirable puissance de l'art et de la nature, pp.413–447. *France, 18th cent.*

Paper. 2 ff., 447 pp., 5 blank ff. 28.5 x 23 cm. Contemp. calf (badly damaged).—Prov.: "Ex libris manuscriptis Dr. Adami Clerici (Adam Clark) 1825."

Ms. E. F. Smith 16 (Lat., Ital., Fr.)

UNIVERSALIS ALCHYMIAE COMPENDIUM. Collection begins with section from Franciscus Onuphrius Marsciano's *Clavis arcis her-*

metis; it contains extracts from Jean Jacquet Manget's *Bibliotheca chemica* and other sources and covers a considerable area of the corpus of alchemical literature. *Italy, 18th cent.*

Paper. 9 ff. (ff.1, 8–9 blank), 122 pp., 2 blank ff., 28 pp., 2 blank ff., 26 pp., 3 blank ff., 11 pp., 5 blank ff., 10 pp., 5 blank ff., 5 pp., 3 blank ff., 12 pp., 6 blank ff., 27 pp., 2 blank ff., 10 pp., 5 blank ff., 35 pp., 6 blank ff., 62 pp., 5 blank ff., 30 pp., 1 blank f., 27 pp., 2 blank ff., 36 pp., 6 blank ff., 23, 6 pp., 3 blank ff., 4 pp., 2 blank ff. 31 x 20.5 cm. Few drawings, some tipped in. Contemp. boards.—Prov.: "Il presente volume proviene della bibl. del Cav. Rossi" (18th cent.); Godefr. Rivius (Rivio?), 1845.

Ms. E. F. Smith 17 (Ital.)

HERMES TRISMEGISTUS. Opera . . . della generatione del lapide, con l'espositione di Moise, Primate Hebreo, tradotta dal latino. *Italy, first half 18th cent.*

Paper. 34 ff. 29 x 22 cm. Figures of chem. apparatus. H/leather.—"L'original di questo si trova nella . . . libraria dell'Ser. Imperator Federico Terzo."

Ms. E. F. Smith 18 (Ger.)

LORENZ F. F. CRELL. Versuch über die Zerlegung der Borax Säure oder des Sedativsalzes, pp.1–21.—IDEM. Fernere Versuche über die Zerlegung der Borax Säure, pp.23–52. (With occasional corrections, in the author's hand?) *Germany, ca. 1799.*

Paper. 52 pp., 1 blank f. 22.5 x 18.5 cm. Portfolio.—According to the dealer's description the "Versuche" were printed in the *Chemische Annalen*, 1799, and an English translation in the *Philosophical Transactions* of the same year. The "Fernere Versuche" may have remained unpublished.

Ms. E. F. Smith 19 (Eng.)

LECTURES ON SCIENTIFIC SUBJECTS. 1. Arithmetic, ff.8–16.—2. Weights and measures, ff.20–26.—3. Geometria, ff.30–44.—4. Stereometria, ff.48–51.—5. Of the globes, ff.56–65.—6. Trigonometry, ff.67–72.—7. The description and use of some instruments, ff.74–88.—8. Dyalling, ff.88–126.—9. Astronomia, ff.128–140.—10. Cursus chymiae, ff.144–172. *England, ca. 1700.*

Paper. 200 ff. (ff.1–7, 17–19, 27–29, 45–47, 52–55, 66, 73, 84, 89–90, 127, 141–143, 173–200 blank). 33 x 23 cm. Illus. Contemp. gilt morocco.—Number of loose ff. tipped in, incl. one with name "Michael Askell" and date 1693, and 2 ff. "Medical and chymical characters explained."

Ms. E. F. Smith 20 (Ger.)

SECRETA des Doct.ʳ Krug. (231 preparations described.) *Germany, 18th cent.*

Paper. 165 ff. 20 x 15.5 cm. Paper, in portfolio.—Prov.: Gustav Wahrendorf, Eisleben, 1910.—"Doctor Krug" could not be identified in Ferguson's *Bibliotheca chemica;* Duveen's *Bibliotheca alchemica et chemica;* Poggendorff; Hirsch; etc.

Ms. E. F. Smith 21 (Ger.)

ABACOURT. Der dritte Theil zur Aurea Catena [Homeri, attributed to Anton Joseph Kitchweger in Ferguson's *Bibliotheca chemica,* I, pp. 469-70] von dem Herrn Baron d'Abacourt, welcher noch nicht im Druck zu haben ist. *Austria or Southern Germany, ca. 1750.*

Paper. 2 blank, 56 ff. (text), 1 blank, 4 ff. (appendix), 4 ff. (index), 6 blank ff. 20 x 17 cm. Contemp. boards.—"Abacourt" could not be identified in the *Gesamtkatalog der preussischen* [deutschen] *Bibliotheken; Catalogue générale* of the Bibliothèque nationale; *General Catalogue of Printed Books* of the British Museum; Ferguson's *Bibliotheca chemica;* Duveen's *Bibliotheca alchemica et chemica;* Michaud; Hoefer; Quérard; Holzmann-Bohatta; etc.

Ms. E. F. Smith 22 (Eng.)

ALEXANDER VAN SUCHTEN. Of the great mysterie of antimonie, ff.6r-160v (translated directly from the German ed. of Michael Toxites, Strassburg, 1570).—*With* BENEDICTUS FIGULUS. The golden and blessed Pandora of the great mysteries in nature holding forth the revelation of . . . Hermes Tresmegistus, interpreted by Theophrastus Paracelsus. Whereunto is annexed the elucidation of it, of . . . Alexander van Suchten. *England, 17th cent.*

Paper. 296 ff. (ff.1-4, 161-164, 293-296 blank). 19 x 15 cm. Contemp. calf, rebacked (fragment from Bible in English pasted inside of binding).—Prov.: Edmund Teynton (18th cent.); Thomas Winthrop, New London; Charles M. Taintor (Teyntor), 1868; I. R. Breuchaud, 1902.—Described in full, as ms.75, in W. T. Wilson, Catalogue of Latin and Vernacular Alchemical Manuscripts in the United States and Canada, *Osiris,* VI, pp.634-638, with detailed contents.—Letter from Mass. Hist. Soc. indicates that this ms. may be in the handwriting of John Winthrop, Jr. (1606-1676).

Ms. E. F. Smith 23 (Fr.)

LOUIS DESBOIS DE ROCHEFORT. Extrait des Leçons de matière medicale. *Paris, 1785.*

Paper. 92 ff. 21 x 16.5 cm. Contemp. calf.

Ms. E. F. Smith 24 (Ger.)

ALCHEMICAL TREATISE (title [author?], and names of substances in cipher; see reprod. of title); "Explicatio verborum," "Signa chymicorum," and "Unguentum contra venicas manuum" (with other recipes; in Rhaeto-Roman) at end. *Switzerland?, 1737.*

Paper. 68 ff., last 3 blank. 17 x 12.5 cm. Illus. Contemp. sheepskin.

(*Ms. Smith 24*)

Ms. E. F. Smith 25 (Fr.)

JEAN COCHET. Experience de physique, partie I [–II]. *Paris?*, 1746.

Paper. 2 blank ff., 308, 152 pp., 3 ff. (last blank). 17 x 11 cm. Contemp.calf.—Prov.: Guill. Nic. Davolle; Ad. F. Bandelier; Charles Albert Browne.—Partial contents: Les efforts des fluides et solides; sur les fermentations; sur la dissolution des métaux; sur les phosphores; sur l'electricité.

Ms. E. F. Smith 26 (Lat.)

JOHANN JACOB HORN. Disputatio medico-chymica de bismutho (ms. copy [?] of printed edition, Erfurt, Kindleben, of disputation held by Horn as a cand. med. at Freiberg, Aug. 1–2, 1697, Ludwig Jacob Friedrich presiding; a few ms. corrections in text. Autograph?). *Germany (Freiberg?), ca. 1697.*

Paper. 25 ff. (bound following H. Khunrath, *Magnesia catholica philos.*, 1599). 13.5 x 9 cm. Contemp. vellum.—Prov.: M. de Waldersee, Danish-Norwegian Counsellor and ambassador to the diet in Regensburg.—Described in detail as ms. 74 by W. J. Wilson in "Catalogue of Alchemical Manuscripts in the United States and Canada," *Osiris*, VI, pp. 631–33. Ms.26 is shelved as 540.1/K527.

Ms. E. F. Smith 27 (Eng.)

[PRIESTLEY FAMILY PAPERS]. 1. Diary of Joseph Priestley (merchant, cousin of Joseph Priestley, chemist), Jan. 7, 1759–Nov. 1, 1759. "Part of a diary of my dear father, Joseph Priestley," f.20v.— 2. Diary of Phebe (daughter of Joseph Priestley, merchant), Aug. 24, 1772–Dec. 12, 1772. *England, 1759–1772* (copied in a later hand?).

Paper. 2 blank ff., 40 ff. text, 1 blank f. 23 x 19 cm. Unbound.—Incomplete at beginning; missing text of diary in Ms. 28.

Ms. E. F. Smith 28 (Eng.)

[PRIESTLEY FAMILY PAPERS]. Same as ms. 27, part 1 (abbreviated), covering Jan. 1, 1759–Jan. 9, 1759. (Copy in calligraphic hand.) *England, ca. 1800?*

Paper. 6 ff. 24 x 19 cm. Unbound.

Ms. E. F. Smith 29 (Eng.)

[PRIESTLEY FAMILY PAPERS]. Memoirs of the Priestley family by Jonathan Priestley (1633–1705) and his grandson Nathaniel Priestley (1699–1781). "The present Mr. Joseph Priestley of Whitwindow lent his father's ms. to Mr. John Milnes[?] of Wakefield, who procured a transcript to be made of it, and of this transcript, the present is a faithful copy—Joseph Hunter—York—June 22, 1808" (p.34). Followed by genealogy of Heywood family. *England, late 18th cent.* [or 1808?].

Paper. 34 pp., 2 ff., 7 blank ff. 19.5 x 16.5 cm. Unbound.

Ms. E. F. Smith 30 (Eng.)

[PRIESTLEY FAMILY PAPERS]. Article on White Windows (Priestley homestead) "from Watsons History of Halifax—page 298" (ff.1–2), preceded by label (leather) "White Windows," used as bookplate, followed by three printed armorial bookplates of Priestley family (pasted on f.7v, one without name and legend "Fear God," two of

George Priestley and legend "Time Deum") and a drawing of the Priestley arms, with directions for coloring (f.8r). *England, late 18th cent.*

Paper. 8 ff. (ff.3-7 blank). 23.5 x 19 cm. Paper cover.

Ms. E. F. Smith 31 (Lat.)

THEODOR KERCKRING. Commentarius in Currum triumphalem antimonii Basilii Valentini, à se latinitate donatum. Amstelodami, sumptibus Andreae Frisii, 1671. *Amsterdam, 1671.*

Paper. 1 f., 288 pp., 11 ff. (last blank). 15 x 10.5 cm. Pen-and-ink drawn title (first prel. f.), signed "Romijn de Hoeghe fecit 1671," title vignette, 5 illus. of chemical apparatus, presumably all by the same artist. These may be the original drawings for the printed edition, Amsterdam, 1671. Cloth.—Most references, incl. Ferguson's *Bibliotheca chemica*, I, p.78, mention only an edition of 1685. The British Museum lists an edition of 1671 under "Valentinus, Basilius," without details.

Ms. E. F. Smith 32 (Fr.)

DE LA FAYE. La médicine universelle avec les regles et l'ordre à observer pour la manipulation. . . . Par M. Chamberland Delafay, avocat au Parlament de Paris. (Text and title in different hands; the title may not actually belong to the text which is largely alchemical). *France, Sept. 1767.*

Paper. 4 ff., pp.3-133. 17.5 x 12.5 cm. Cloth.—Prov.: Henry Seybert Library of Modern Spiritualism.—Author identical with George de la Faye (1699-1781)?

Ms. E. F. Smith 33 (Ger.)

JOHANN CHRISTOPH VON HARTMANN. Compendium der gantzen hermetischen Philosophie. . . . Ein geheimes Manuscript aus der Verlassenschaft Herrn Johann . . . Hartmann . . . , in welchem alle Geheimnisse der hermetischen Scientz und Universal-Tinctur theoretisch und practisch . . . beschrieben und erkläret sind. *Germany, 18th cent.*

Paper. 2 vols. (v. I: 2 ff., 85 pp.—II: 2 ff. <first blank>, 79 pp.) 19 x 12 cm. Contemp. paper cover.

Ms. E. F. Smith 34 (Eng.)

PRAELECTIONES PHYSICAE. 1. LECTURES of (a) Natural philosophy (ff.1-8); (b) Mechanical principles (ff.9-14); (c) Mechanical powers (ff.15-17); (d) The balance and the lever (ff.18-30); The first [-third] law of nature (ff.31-50), ff.1-50.—2. HYDROSTATICKS (incl. Proof that there is a great deal of air in the blood; Description of the air pump which Mr. Boyle made; Experiments on the air pump; Of barometers, thermometers, and hydrometers), ff.50–97.—3. CATOPTRICKS, ff.98–103.—4. DIPTRICKS, ff.104–129.—5. Sir Isaac Newtons colours, ff.129–132.—6. A description of the condensing engine, ff.133–134.—[In a later hand]: 7. ELECTRICAL MACHINE, ff.136–138.—8. AEOLUS HARP, ff.139–140.—9. CURIOUS AND ENTERTAINING EXPERIMENTS (The magic bottle; The enchanted mirrors; The wonderful phantoms [laterna magica]; [Dr. Franklin's] Clock; A very pretty fountain from Mr. Boyle), ff.141–152. *England, 18th cent.* (in three different hands).

Paper. 152 ff. (f.152 tipped in), all but the last f. with text on rectos only. 18.5 x 14.5 cm. Few diagr. and illus. in text, full-page illus. on f.135v, 146v, 148v and 149v. Cloth.

Ms. E. F. Smith 35 (Eng.)

UNIVERSITY OF EDINBURGH LECTURE NOTES. 1. [THOMAS CHARLES] HOPE. History of chemistry, followed by sections on metals (p.25); water (p.187); coloring matter (p.236); fermentation (p.248); animals (p.258); fluids (p. 267).—2. [ANDREW] DUNCAN. Lectures on the institutions of medicine (225 pp.; dated 1796).—3. [IDEM?]. Medical jurisprudence (20 pp.; dated Feb. 4, 1797).—4. [IDEM?]. Materia medica (14 pp.; dated Feb.[?] 6, 1797).—5. [DANIEL] RUTHERFORD. Origin of botany (68 pp., dated May 2, 1797). *Scotland, 1796–1797.*

Paper. 12 blank ff., 280 pp., 4 blank ff., 225 pp., 20 pp., 2 blank ff., 14 pp., 3 blank ff., 68 pp. 19.5 x 12 cm. Contemp. h/calf.

Ms. E. F. Smith 36 (Fr.)°

FRENCH MISCELLANY. 1. *Relating to history of chemistry:* a. ESSAYS ET AFFINAGES d'or et d'argent avec la manière de retirer successivement des eaues-fortes, l'argent et le cuivre après avoir fait le départ de l'or, et des tables pour l'alliages de l'or et de l'argent sur le pied de la refonte faite en France en 1726, pp.65–113.—b. PLUSIEURS RECETTES de très beaux vernis, vinaigres des quatre voleurs et autres; depart et affinage des métaux, etc. (with final section on medical prescriptions), also called RECETTES et secrets, pp.181–325.—2. *Literary:* a. J. B. J. WILLART DE GRÉCOURT. Philotanus, pp.1–50.—b. FRANÇOIS MARIE AROUET VOLTAIRE. Epitre à Uranie, pp.51–57.—c. POÉSIES DIVERSES faites à Bruxelles dans l'année 1756, pp. 117–179. *France, 1757.*

Paper. 15, 325 pp. (pp.58–64, 114–116 blank). 24 x 18 cm. Full page illus. of a furnace (p.67). Contemp. h/vellum.—Bibliothek Otto Rothschild, Berlin.

Ms. E. F. Smith 37 (Fr.)°

BASILIUS VALENTINUS. 1. Révélation et déclaration de Frère Bazile Valentin . . . contenant les plus curieux mistère[s] des teintures essentielles des septs métaux, et les vertus médicinales dicelles. (This title precedes the "chapitre premier" on ff.1–2, written in one of 4 or more somewhat different hands; the *inc.* of the text on f.1 reads: De la première vacine. . . . Pour faire voir. . . . The main text of this ms. begins on f.3, "chapitre premier," *inc.:* De l'esprit ou teinture du mercure. Plusieurs pourons trouver estrange. This part seems to end on p.65 and is followed by:—2. Plusieurs particulier[s] tant au blanc qu'au rouges [sic] tirez du mesme autheurs [sic], pp.65 ff.; Révélations de la parole caché par la sagesse des anciens ou la généalogie de la mère du mercure des philosophes, pp.105 ff.; Various recipes <one in cypher>; brief quotations from the Bible; Table des matières <up to p.203> and two alchemical entries). *France?*, *early 18th cent.* (cf. date 1709 on p. 196).

Paper. 2 ff., 217 pp., 12 ff. (numb. throughout ff.10–132 in one of several hands). 22 x 18 cm. H/leather.—Entry on last f.: "Quartier D[or F]auril."

Ms. E. F. Smith 38 (Lat.)°

BEDA VENERABILIS. De divinatione mortis, et vitae Petrosyris, ad Necepsum, regem Aegypti epistola (prec. by biogr. note), ff.3r–6v.—*With* ANTONIUS POSEVINUS. [Extract] Ex apparatu Antonii Posevini, S. J., tomo I, de Beda, ff.7r–8r.—IDEM. In verbo Cesar Baronius tom. I, pag. 281 [on numbers], ff.8r–11v.—ATHANASIUS KIRCHER. [Extract] Ex lib. 2, parte 4, pag. 386: De magnete, f.12r. *Italy*, *17th cent.*

Boards. 12 ff. 22.5 x 16 cm. With folded astrol. plate (between ff.11 and 12). In folder.

Ms. E. F. Smith 39 (Lat.)°

VIRIDARIUM REGALE (begins with "Operationes divini Raymundi Lulli," continues with "De medendis omnibus morbis"; among the sections are De tabaco (with illus. of pipes); De chymia (illus. of apparatus); Natura tincturarum, etc. *Italy*, *1676.*

Paper. 676 pp. 29 x 21.5 cm. Illus. (a few full-page). Contemp. calf.

Ms. E. F. Smith 40 (Ital.)°

RACCOLTA di celebri arcani chimici da diversi famosi filosophi date in luce et esperimentati. (Begins with chapter on "lapis philosphorum" and continues with astrological, alchemical and pharmaceutical sections, e.g. Sole di Fra Giorgio d'Armenia; sole in mercurio; lavoro mercuriale; oglio d'antimonio; sale di vitriolo; purificatione di mercurio; ad morbum gallicum). *Italy, 16th cent.*

Paper. 5 ff. (first blank), 165 pp. (text ends on p. 154). 19.5 x 14 cm. Astronomical and chemical symbols on prel. f.3. Contemp. h/vellum.—Prov.: Otto Orren Fisher.

Ms. E. F. Smith 41 (Fr.)°
IATRO-CHEMICAL and ALCHEMICAL COMPENDIUM describing a great variety of preparations and operations, e.g. concerned with "mercure d'antimoine," remedies against cancer, the plague, diseases of the eye, venereal diseases, etc., "aqua philosophorum," "clavis artis" (dated 1579, cf. p.375), calcination, amalgamation, etc. Many sources of information are indicated, among them a Henry von Stram (p.30); Wasseron (p.32 and *passim*); Rudellius Scurbergensis (i.e. Rüdel?, p.139); Raymundus Lullus (p.193); Hollerus (i.e. Blaise H. Holler?, p. 246); Camillus a Camillis (i.e. Hannibal C. Camillus?, p.291); Casanone (p.416).—(Most of the sources could not be identified in the more obvious reference works like C. G. Jöcher, *Allg. Gel. Lex.;* J. Young, *Bibl. chem.; Biogr. Lex. d. hervorrag. Ärzte;* Michaud and Höfer). A few sections in Latin. *France, first half 17th cent.*

Paper. 470 pp., 2 pp. (numb. 531–32)+1 f. (in a different hand); 4 ff. of smaller size laid in at end. 31.5 x 21.5 cm. Drawings of vessels used in distilling, etc. H/vellum.

Ms. E. F. Smith 42 (Fr.)°
LIVRE DE RAISON; recettes de medecine et d'alchemie; vers latins et français, etc. (Title added in later hand; ff.1–4 consist of account entries for the year 1660, followed by pharmaceutical and alchemical recipes in French, Latin and a few Italian, ff.5–24).—*With* Accounts, recipes and poetry, beginning at opposite end of vol., ff.II–XXIV (incl. Lat. poem "Si tibi suspecta est uxor dubiique pudoris/non habeas pulcros famulos pulcrosque sodales;" "Dies in mensibus infelices ex Roberto Flud[d];" "Pour le roy [Louis XIV] en l'année 1687 lors de son entrée à Paris"; "Pour M. le Duc de Verneil le jour de son entrée à Carcasonne"). *France, 17th cent.*

Paper. 92 ff. (ff.43–68, 79–80 and 92 blank). 20 x 25 cm. Contemp. vellum. Written in several hands, the main part in peculiar French.

Note: The E. F. Smith Collection contains a considerable number of letters (many autograph) by chemists. Most of these belong to the period after 1800, but some are earlier. None are included in this Catalogue. Inquiries about letters by chemists should be addressed to the Curator or the Custodian of the Edgar Fahs Smith Collection, University of Pennsylvania, Philadelphia 19104, Pennsylvania.

Veterinary Library Manuscript

Ms. Vet. Libr. 1 (Ger.)°

[HORSEMANSHIP]. The main text, dealing with all aspects of horsemanship (dated 1612 on f.364v), is interspersed by various texts in a different hand (ff.10r–31v, on military science; geography of Bohemia; on nobility; remedies against diseases of horses, etc.—Ff.334r–46v, "Symbola" of emperors of the Holy Roman Empire; Remedies.—Ff.365r–92v, Remedies). *Germany or Bohemia, first half 17th cent.*

Paper. 392 ff. 30 x 19.5 cm. Boards.—Prov.: Fairman Rogers. Classified as VR 798/H782.

Fine dell'Opera

(*Ms. Ital. 35*)

Addenda et Corrigenda

The editors have added these corrections after the publication of Dr. Benton's article (see Introduction). Users of the catalogue are urged to bring errors to the attention of the University of Pennsylvania Libraries (Edit., Ms. cat., University of Pennsylvania Libraries, Philadelphia, Pa. 19104).

Ad. Lat. 7: The unpublished Petrarch text has been published by Professor Guido Martellotti, "La Collatio inter Scipionem, Alexandrum, Hanibalem et Pyrrum; Un Inedito del Petrarca nella Biblioteca della University of Pennsylvania," *Classical, Mediaeval and Renaissance Studies in Honor of Berthold Louis Ullman*, Rome, 1964, vol. II, 145–68.

Lea 99, line 1: ALAMANNI DE MEDICI *read* ALAMANNO MEDICI.

Lea 254, lines 4–5: Giovanbattista Medici and Vincenzo de Ricci, and Francesco and Lorenzo Medici *read* Giovanbattista Michelozzi and Vincenzo de Ricci, and Francesco and Lorenzo Michelozzi.

Lea 265, line 2: Mongali *read* Mungai.

Lea 296, line 1: Medici household? *read* Gondi family.

Lea 297, line 2: Medici household? *read* Gondi family.

Lea 304, line 1: and *read* DI.

Lea 325, line 1: GIULIANO GONDI *read* FEDERICO DI GIULIANO GONDI.

Lea 326, line 1: LODOVICO *read* LORENZO.

Lea 340, line 1: BERNARDO [?] MUGNAIO *read* PIPPO DI BERNARDO MUGNAIO.

Lea 343, line 1: PECCORI *read* PESCIONI.

Lea 344, line 1: PARRINO and MARCO SECRANI [or Seccrani] *read* CARLO DE MEDICI.

Lea 347, line 1: DAVANZATI *read* BASAGNI.

Lea 348, line 1: VINCENZO CRISTOFANO *read* FRANCESCO BASAGNI.

Lea 349, line 1: GIRALDI *read* GERARDI.

Lea 350, line 1: GIONI *read* LIONI.

Lea 351, line 1: Nicolo Marmelli *read* Niccolo Mannelli.

Lea 355, line 2: Frangioni *read* Franciotti.

INDEX

Abacourt	Smith 21	Alberti, Leon Battista	Lat. 7
Abano, Petrus de	Eng. 24	Albertus, son of Nicolaus de Fontanella	
Abbondanti, Antonio	Ital. 129		Lat. 157
Aberdeen	Lat. 133	Albertus Magnus	Lat. 4, 180.—Lea 19
Abrégé chronologique de l'histoire de la		Albigensian Crusade	Lea 45
maison royale de Savoie	Fr. 69	Albizzi, Bartholommeo	Lat, 92, 122
Abrégé . . . du Sainct Concile de Trente		Albizzi, Francesco	Lea 96
	Fr. 102	Albrecht, Duke of Austria	Ger. 48
Académie française	Fr. 100	Albrecht, Duke of Bavaria	Ger. 35
Acatius, Ferdinandus	Lat. 25	Albrecht von Eyb	Ger. 6
Accademia degli Alterati	Ital. 33	Alcala, Universidad	
Accademia degli Innominati	Ital. 56		Span. 39, 40, 42, 44–5, 48
Accademia dei Ravvivati	Ital. 174	Alcala de Henares, Colegio mayor	
Accademici Indiavolati	Ital. 102		Span. 45
Acciaioli, Adovardo	Lea 261	*Alchemical Miscellany*	Smith 3–5, 13
Acciaioli, Angelo	Lea 28	*Alchemical Treatise*	Smith 24
Acciaioli, Benedetto	Lea 28	*Alcune regole per decidere le questioni*	
Acciaioli, Carlo	Lea 281		Lea 183
Acciaioli, Giovanni	Lea 28	Aldingh, Hinrik	Ger. 57
Acciaioli, Lorenzo	Lea 28	Aldini, Giovanni	Lea 363
Acciaioli, Margarita	Lea 28	Aldobrandino, Brunetto d'	Ital. 76
Acciaioli, Niccolò	Lea 28	Alençon	Fr. 93
Acciaioli, Simone di Lione	Lea 28	Alexander III, Pope	Ital. 47
Acciaiolo, Neri di Jacopo	Lea 28	Alexander V, Pope	Lat. 189
Accolti, Francesco	Lea 298	Alexander VI, Pope	Lat. 190.—Lea 82
Accountbook	Ger. 2	Alexander VII, Pope	Ital. 44, 139, 184
Adam, author of *Summula*	Lat. 164	Alexander VIII, Pope	Fr. 61
Adam, son of Teutio	Lea 27	Alexander de Saxoferrato	Ital. 32
Adimari, Leonardo di Paolo	Ital. 49	Alexander de Villa Dei	Lat. 45
Admont, Benedictine monastery		Alexander the Great	
	Lat. 25, 31, 77		Lat. 7, 44, 198.—Ger. 6
Adorno, Antonio	Lea 371	Alexandria, Egypt	Eng. 21
Adrien de le Borve	Fr. 97	Alexandria, Italy	Lea 53
Advielle, Victor	Fr. 10	Alexius, St.	Ger. 4.—Ital. 106
Aegidius de Fuscariis	Lat. 182	Alguacil, Manuel Lopez	Lea 150
Aelsen Library	Lat. 191	Aliffée, Conte d'	Lea 154
Aesop	Ger. 55	Aliotti, Lodovico	Lea 28
Affarusiis, Antonius de	Lea 122	Alleaume, René	Fr. 93
Agnes de Claustris	Lat. 106	Alliprandi, Nicolao	Lea 402
Agon-Gobillet, trial	Fr. 93	Almansor	Lat. 52
Agostini, Lorenzo d'	Lea 40	Almeriens	Span. 23
Agricola, Julius	Ital. 159	Alonso de Santo Thomas	Lea 130
Aivoldi, Nuncio apostolico	Lea 360	*Alphabetical Dictionary*	Lat. 126
Alamanni, Ludovico	Lea 274	*Alphabetum malarum mulierum*	Lat. 43
Alamanno, Jacopo d'	Lea 226	Alphons, King of Aragon	
Alanus de Insulis	Lat. 26		Lat. 139.—Lea 397
Alassio	Lea 370	Alphons X, King of Castile	Span. 14
Alba, Duke of (17th cent.)	Lea 171	Altamira, Margarita	Lea 371
Alban, St.	Lea 4	Altavilla, Conte de	Smith 9
Albana, Chiara Maria	Ital. 195	Altenpreising	Ger. 59
Albani, Annibale	Lea 362	Altenstadt	Lea 378
Albani, Antonio	Ital. 54	Altieri, Paluzzo	Lea 46
Albani Library	Ital. 86	Altmanshausen, Erasmus	Lat. 77
Albania	Ital. 64	Altopascio, Ospedale di S. Giacomo	
Albarez, Alonso	Span. 7		Lea 398
Albero del ben e del male	Ital. 126	Altoviti, Casa	Ital. 155–6
Albertano de Brescia	Lat. 107	*Altro miraculo*	Ital. 48
Alberti, Giovanni Battista	Ital. 105	Amadeus, Duke of Savoy	Lea 56

[247]

Amadori, Andrea	Lea, 304, 310, 312	Anselm, St.	Lat. 84.—Eng. 1
Amadori, Andrea di Lorenzo		Anselm, Carthusian	Lat. 79
	Lea 303, 305-9, 313-4	Ansermin	Lat. 106
Amadori, Andrea di Lorenzo di		Antinori, Tuscan senator	Lea 399
Francesco, *Addenda et corr.*	Lea 304	Antinori, Alessandro	
Amadori, Bartolomeo	Lea 311		Lea 227, 281-3, 287
Amadori, Francesco	Lea 316	Antinori, Alessandro di Nicolo	
Amadori, Francesco di Andrea	Lea 315		Lea 220, 226
Amadori, Lorenzo di Francesco		Antinori, Lorenzo	Lea 283
	Lea 304, 310	Antoine de Paule	Fr. 86
Amadori, Niccolò	Lea 316-9	Antoine, Sire de Craon	Fr. 84
Amarchios, Iosephos	Ital. 114	Antonelli, Antonio	Ital. 158
Amaury de Serrac	Lea 367	Antonello de Petruciia	Lea 192
Ambasciata del cielo	Ital. 38	Antonellus de S. Severino	Lea 192
Ambrose, St.	Lat. 63	Antoninus Florentinus, St.	
Amelius, St.	Ital. 71.—Lea 45		Ital. 30, 39.—Lea 18
America	Ital. 164.—Span. 49	Antonio de Dionisio	Lea 397
America Meridional	Lea 190	Antonius	Lea 19
American Congregational Assoc.		Antwerp	Eng. 21.—Flemish 2
	Eng. 19	Apollonius	Ital. 71
American Philosophical Society	Lea 371	*Aqua philosophica*	Lea 19
Amerighi, Niccolò	Lea 399	Aragon	Span. 5.—Lea 397
Amicus, St.	Lea 45	Aratinus de Pectinaciis	Lea 53
Amonius, Alexander	Lea 402	Arator	Ger. 60
Amor dei	Eng. 8	Archer, Michell	Eng. 4
Amsdorff, Nicolaus	Ger. 37	Archinto, Carlo	Ital. 197
Anabaptists	Ger. 45	*Archivio Montauti*	Lea 396
Anaya, Diego de	Span. 8	Arciero, Anello	Lea 158
Anaya, Pedro de	Span. 9	Arcisate	Ital. 127
Anchelberg, Conrad von	Lea 28	Arcos, Duke of	Span. 4, 27
Ancini, Antonio	Lat. 162	Ardenne	Lea 197
Ancona	Lea 107, 261, 373	Aretino, Carlo	Lat. 7
Andalusia	Span. 14	Aretino, Francesco	Ital. 78
Anders, Christian Friedrich	Lat. 183	Aretino, Pietro	Fr. 100.—Ital. 5
Andorff (Antwerp?)	Ger. 28	Argyropoulos, Joannes	Lat. 12-3
Andrade, Felix Duarde de	Lea 371	Ariosto, Lodovico	Ital. 151
Andrea de Petra	Lat. 64	*Aristoteles und Phyllis*	Ger. 4
Andreae, Johannes	Lat. 113	Aristotle Lat. 12-5, 17-9, 22-5, 27-31,	
Andreas, Bp. of Cracow	Lea 384	43, 49-50, 59, 63, 65-8, 70-1, 75-80,	
Andreas de Escobar	Lat. 118	87-8, 98, 100-2, 129, 134, 155, 163,	
Andreas de Lunigiana	Ital. 30	170-2, 175, 191, 193, 197.—Fr. 100.—	
Andreas Parisinus	Lat. 46		Ger. 4.—Ital. 4, 11, 31
Andria, Duke of	Ital. 179	Arivabenus, Petrus	Lat. 177
Anfang und Ende des verderblichen		Arles	Fr. 80
Baurenkriegs	Ger. 51	Armand, F.	Fr. 95
Angelinus Johanutti	Lea 67	Arndt, professor	Ger. 40
Angelo, Card. of Santa Croce de		Arnold, Johann	Lat. 100
Gerusalemme	Lea 66	Arnulfus Canonicus	Lat. 82
Angelus Carletus de Clavasio	Lat. 157	Arrianus	Lat. 198
Angeriano, Girolamo	Lat. 38	Arrighi, Arrigo	Lea 353
Anguissola, Carlo	Lea 46	Arrighini, Giovanni de Filippo	Ital. 152
Anguissola, Filippo Maria	Ital. 143	Arrigucci, Andrea di Filippo	Lea 321
Angulo, Juan Ximenez de	Span. 15	Arrigucci, Donato	Lea 320
Angulo, Lorenzo	Span. 39	Arrise, Francesco Baptista de	Lea 371
Aniello, Tommaso	Span. 4	Arroya	Span. 11
Anna, Electress Palatinate	Lea 399	*Arte della lana*	Lea 231
Anna Caterina, cantatrice	Ital. 155	*Artes dictaminis*	Lea 3
Anna Maria Luisa di Toscana	Ital. 174	*Artes mulierum*	Lat. 180
Anne of Brittany, Queen of France		*Articuli propter quos prohibetur . . .*	
	Fr. 66, 85	*communio*	Lea 152
Annecy	Lat. 106	Artinbau, Garau	Lea 371
Ansanus, St.	Ital. 73	Artois	Fr. 40

[248]

Arvanitidi, G. J.	Fr. 102		Balduin of Flanders	Lea 5
Ascetic Miscellany	Lat. 90		Ballati, Adriano	Ital. 174
Ascoli, Card.	Lea 154		Ballel, Joaquin	Lea 371
Ascoli, Cecco d'	Lea 173		Ballesden	Lat. 179
Ashburner, Walter	Ital. 24.—Lea 12		Bambacati, Abbot	Lea 77
Asiago	Lea 365		Bandelier, Ad. F.	Smith 25
Askell, Michael	Smith 19		Bandinelli, Giulio	Ital. 174
Aspra	Lat. 144		Bandinelli, Ottavio	Ital. 174
Assise del alta corte del Regno de Hierusalem			Bandini, Francesco	Lea 276, 278
	Lea 9		Bangi, Aycha	Lat. 119
Assizes of Romania	Lea 5		Banzi Library	Lea 208
Assumptio B. Virginis	Lat. 158		Baralt, R. M.	Span. 30
Astrology	Ital. 86		Barbar, Joanna	Lea 66
Astronomical Fragments	Lat. 62		Barbaro, Francesco	Lat. 7
Attila	Lea 13		Barbera y Manresa, Marques de	
Aubais, Marquis d'	Lea 48			Lat. 146
Aubusson, Georges d'	Ital. 117		Barberini, Antonio	Ital. 33
Auctoritates de decreto	Lat. 116		Barberino, Carlo da	Lea 219
Auctoritates scriptorum de . . . viciis peccatorum	Lat. 158		Barberino, Francesco da	Ital. 177.—Lea 219
Auda	Lea 397		Barcelona	Ger. 29.—Lea 371, 399
Auersperg, Prince Karl	Fr. 55		Barcelona, Inquisition	Lea 203
Auferius, Stephanus	Lea 141		Barcelona, Universidad	Span. 38, 48
Auger, Michel	Fr. 93		Bari	Lea 384
August II, King of Poland	Fr. 37, 67		Barleo, Gaspare	Ital. 204
August, Elector of Saxony	Ger. 44		Barnston, H. Charles	Lea 116
Augustin de la Florida	Lea 371		Baroncelli, Gianfranco	Lea 278
Augustine, St.	Lat. 36, 41, 63, 122.— Ger. 54.—Lea 1, 24		Baronius, Cesar	Smith 38
			Barsa, Wolfgangus Theodosius	Lea 125
Augustinians	Lat. 8, 11, 189.—Lea 51		Bartholomaeus Albicius Pisanus	
Augustino, Antonio	Ital. 132			Lat. 92, 122
Augustinus de Ancona	Lat. 92		Bartholomaeus de Bregantiis, Vicentinus	Lat. 91
Augustinus de Leonissa	Lat. 130			
Augustinus Vannutii	Lea 60		Bartholomaeus, of Trent	Lea 98
Auld, J.	Ital. 168, 172		Bartholomaeus Oxoniensis	Lea 24
Aulet, Joan	Lea 371		Bartolini, Deodato	Lea 182
Aurispa, Joannes	Lat. 7		Bartolomeo di Bartolomeo da San Miniato	Lea 97
Ausonius	Lat. 81			
Austria	Fr. 55		Bartolomeo of Messana	Lat. 43
Auxerre, Guillaume d'	Lat. 60		Basadona, Giovanni Francesco	Ital. 14
Avellaneda, Juan de	Lea 375		Basagni, Francesco, *Addenda et corr.*	
Avertimenti politici	Ital. 184			Lea 347–8
Avicenna	Smith 3		Basil of Caesarea, St.	Lat. 34, 83
Avignon	Lat. 131, 154		*Basilisk*	Smith 4
Avignonese Papacy	Lea 6		Basilius Valentinus	Smith 5, 31, 37
Avisos para confessores	Lat. 150		Basire family	Fr. 93
Avversità notabilissima di Papa Paolo IV	Lea 154		Basle, Council	Lat. 64, 130, 196
			Bassetti, Apollonio	Lea 198
Axzaedo, Monte de	Span. 24		Bateman	Span. 37
			Batie Roland, Seigniory	Fr. 92
			Bauhinus, Caspar	Lat. 133
Backer, H. de	Flemish 3		Bauter, Samuel	Eng. 8
Bacon, Roger	Lat. 4.—Smith 3, 15		Bavaria	Ger. 34–5, 46
Badoer, Federico	Ital. 84, 146		Bayard, Jean	Fr. 72
Baffry, Monsieur	Fr. 94		Beatus, St.	Ital. 82
Bagad, Ganberto Fabricio	Span. 5		Beauchamp, Marquis de	Fr. 58
Baïf, Jean Antoine de	Fr. 5		Beauvain	Fr. 93
Balangero	Lea 56		Beauvilliers, Duc de	Fr. 71
Balbi, Jacobus	Lat. 177		Beccadelli, Antonio	Lat. 7
Balbi, Piero	Lat. 177		Bechstein Collection	Lat. 183
Baldo, Giovanni di	Lea 222		Bede, Venerable	Lea 362.—Smith 38
Baldovinetti, Antonio	Lea 284		Beer, John T.	Lat. 50

Bellato, Ambrosio	Lea 360
Belli italici	Ital. 188
Bellieure, de	Fr. 98
Belluno	Ital. 204
Belvis, Francesco de	Lea 397
Belye, John	Smith 13
Bembo, Pietro	Ital. 37, 151, 204
Benedict of Nursia, St.	Lat. 36
Benedict XIII, Pope	Lea 362
Benedictines	Lat. 36.—Ital. 87
Benedictiones et exorcismi	Lea 146
Benedictiones ornamentorum ecclesiae	Lat. 108
Benivieni family	Lea 398
Benoit de St. Maure	Fr. 24
Benserade, Isaac de	Fr. 63, 100
Bentivoglio, Guido	Ital. 67
Benvenuto de Rambaldis	Lat. 81
Benzoni, Carlo di Simone	Lea 222
Bequille	Fr. 57
Beraldus, Antonius	Lat. 173
Berardus, Bernardus	Lat. 88
Berengarius	Lat. 118
Berengarius, Raimundus	Lea 88
Bergamo	Ital. 6, 134, 195.—Lea 360
Bernard, Samuel	Fr. 8
Bernard of Siena	Lat. 158
Bernardinus, notary	Ital. 93
Bernardinus, scribe	Smith 9
Bernardis, Florio de	Lea 360
Bernardo, Card. of St. Sabina	Lea 66
Bernardus [of Bescaran]	Span. 26
Bernardus Paschualis	Lea 88
Bernardus Raymundi	Lat. 114
Bernardus Trevisanus	Smith 13, 15
Bernhard, St.	Lat. 61, 92, 122.—Fr. 12.—Ital. 75.—Lea 360
Bernhard, Bp. of Passau	Ger. 48
Berni, Francesco	Ital. 181
Berry, Jehan, Duc de	Lea 197
Bersi, L. M.	Lat. 19
Bersuire, Pierre	Lat. 131
Bertelli, Giovanni	Lea 239, 289
Bertin, Aymé	Fr. 50
Bertran de Tarride	Lea 197
Beslaut, Nicolas	Fr. 93
Bettini, Giovanbattista	Lea 231-2, 277
Bettini, Luigi	Lea 231
Biagio, Oddo di	Lea 373
Bibiena	Lea 284
Bible	Lat. 20-1, 84, 89, 196.—Smith 37
Bible. O.T. Apocrypha. Maccabees.	Lat. 81
Bible. O.T. Psalter	Dutch 1.—Eng. 1, 29.—Ital. 125, 183
Bible. N.T.	Eng. 6
Bible. N.T. Apocrypha. Gospel of Nicodemus.	Ital. 197
Bible. N.T. Gospels. Matthew.	Lat. 84
Bibliophile Handbook	Lat. 123
Biblioteca San Francesco	Ital. 183
Biblioteca, bibliotheca, etc. (*see* under place or name)	
Bichi, Nuncio in Portugal	Lea 362
Bidon, René	Fr. 93
Bidoro d'Antonio	Ital. 93
Bilicich, Stephanus	Lea 62
Billy, Jacques	Ital. 176
Biron family	Fr. 62
Bischazza, Alberto	Lea 10
Der Bischoff zue Cöllen	Ger. 8
Black, Joseph	Smith 14
Blackburne, Gilbert Ireland	Eng. 1
Blainville	Fr. 93
Blancandin	Fr. 22
Blarer, Jacob Christian	Ger. 38
Blatt, Dominicus	Lat. 175
Blondo, Joseph	Lea 154
Blot, Baron de Chauvigny	Fr. 63
Bocca, Silvio	Lea 183
Boccaccio, Giovanni	Fr. 9.—Ital. 12, 105, 125
Boccalini, Traiano	Ital. 134, 159
Boccanegra, Antonio	Lea 370
Böse, Johann Georg	Fr. 37, 67
Boethius	Lat. 129
Bohemia	Vet. 1
Boindin, Nicolas	Fr. 43
Boiville, François de	Fr. 93
Boldoni, Sigismundo	Ital. 134
Bologna	Lat. 156, 167.—Lea 208, 261
Bologna, Convento di S. Giacomo Maggiore	Lea 208
Bolzanio, Giampietro	Ital. 204
Bonaventura, St.	Lat. 122, 196.—Eng. 8.—Ital. 2
Boncompagni Library	Ital. 86, 206
Boncampagno	Lea 373
Bondi, Johannes	Lea 3
Bondumievo, Zaccaria	Lea 360
Bonea, Ithier	Lea 2
Boneri, Boniface	Lat. 106
Boni, Giovanni	Lea 280
Boni Homines, Alphonsus	Ger. 3
Boniface VIII, Pope	Lat. 114.—Ital. 66
Boniface IX, Pope	Lat. 189
Bonifacio, Marchese de Monferrato	Lea 5
Boninsignis, Joannes Cristophorus de	Lat. 137
Bonnano, Lucio	Lea 397
Bonnet, Honoré	Fr. 20
Bonnier de la Mosson	Fr. 63
Bonsens	Fr. 100
Bonvesinus, Marcus	Lea 18
Booklist	Ital. 151
Boot, Anselmus de	Lat. 133
Bordeaux, Confrérie de Sainte-Euladie et de Saint-Gênes	Fr. 65
Borghini, Vincenzo Maria	Ital. 92
Borgia family	Lea 196

Borgia, Cesare	Lat. 13		Brugueres, Michele	Ital. 43
Borgia, Francesco	Lea 127		Brunelleschi family	Lea 398
Borgo, Carlo	Lea 37		Bruni, Leonardo Aretino	Lat. 7, 15, 34
Boris, Bernat	Lea 371		Brunslock	Lat. 165
Borri, Francesco Giuseppe	Lea 124		Brussels	Fr. 44
Borromeo, Carlo, Card.			Brusserius, Philipus de Civitadei	Lea 55
	Ital. 141.—Lea 360		Buda	Ital. 43
Borsèle, Max. de	Fr. 81		Buel, Richard H.	Lea 144
Bosc, de	Fr. 100		Bürger, Gottfried August	Ger. 32
Boschereccio	Ital. 92		*Bullarium augustinianum*	Lea 51
Bosco Marengo	Lea 12		Bullinger, Heinrich	Ger. 22
Bouchet	Fr. 100		Buol-Schauenstein, K. R. von	Fr. 55
Bougis, Grégoire Charles de	Fr. 93		Buonaccorsi family	Lea 398
Boullay, Isaye	Fr. 93		Buonaccorsi, Bernardo	Lea 285
Bourbon, Bona	Lea 56		Buonaccorsi, Biagio	Lea 103
Bourbon, Louis de	Fr. 100		Buonaventuri, Pietro	Lea 77
Boxeda, Josef	Lea 371		Buoninsigne, Bartholomeo	Lat. 137
Boyle, Robert	Ital. 210.—Smith 34		Buonsostegni family	Lea 128
Bozzolini	Lea 351		Burchardus de Monte Sion	Lea 4, *note*
Bracchi, Francesco di Matteo	Lea 239		Burgio family	Lea 397
Bracchi, Matteo	Lea 289		Burgio, Geronimo	Lea 397
Braco, Petrus de	Lat. 121		Burgio, Niccolò	Lea 397
Bragadin family	Ital. 1		Burgio, Pietro Giacomo	Lea 397
Braganza, Duke of	Ital. 44, 184		Burgos	Span. 11, 23–5
Brahe, Tycho de	Lat. 162		Burgundy	Fr. 2
Brandano	Ital. 45.—Lea 173		Burr, Charles W.	Lat. 101–2.—Ital. 4
Brandis, Christopher	Lat. 17, 70–1, 76		Buscome	Lea 397
Brandolini	Ital. 120		Busdraghi, Matteo	Lea 383
Brandolini, Bernardo di Piero	Lea 227		Busdraghi, Nicolao	Lea 383
Brant, Geeraert	Fr. 100		Busdraghi, Piero	Lea 383
Brantwood, John Ruskin	Lea 49		Bustron, Florio	Lea 9
Breitinger, Johann Jacob	Ger. 52		Butlar, John	Eng. 8
Brescia	Lat. 156, 160.—Ital. 119		Butler, Arthur John	Ital. 114
Breslau	Lea 384		Buxheim, Carthusian monastery	
Bressanone, Carthusian monastery			Lat. 14, 27–8, 70, 76, 78–9, 118, 158.	
	Lat. 17, 41, 92			—Lea 152
Breuchaud, I. R.	Smith 22		*By the grace of God* (poem)	Smith 4
Breve ragguaglio	Fr. 67			
Breventano, Angelo	Lea 362			
Breventovsky	Fr. 37, 67			
Brevilogium de malis	Lea 152		Caberico, Dominico	Span. 6
Brevilogium de vana . . . oblectatione			Cabrera	Lea 397
	Lea 152		Cacciani, Giovanni Francesco	Ital. 195
Brevis descriptio anatomica	Lat. 133		Caen	Fr. 100.—Lea 197
Bricci	Lea 176		Caesar, Caius Julius	Lat. 7.—Ger. 54
Brigid, St.	Ger. 54.—Lea 362		Caetano, Petro	Lea 397
Brindisi	Ital. 201		Cagliari	Lat. 98
Brisebarre de Douai	Fr. 15		*Cahier de chansons*	Fr. 70
Brisighella, Giulio da	Ital. 134		Caietano, Tommaso de Vio (called)	
Brito, Guilelmus	Lat. 39			Lat. 150
Brittany	Fr. 71		Caillet, Louis François	Fr. 93
Brixen, Carthusian monastery			Caimus, Ad.	Lat. 73
	Lat. 17, 41, 92		Calamarius, Hyacintus	Lea 92
Brocardus Teutonicus	Lea 4		Calanus, Juvencus Coelius	Lea 13
Brockenstedes, Albrecht	Ger. 57		Calderón, Rodrigo	Lea 130
Brockett, John Trotter	Lea 148		Calderón de la Barca, Pedro	
Brondi, Maria Caterina	Lea 77			Span. 32–3
Brosinopiano	Ital. 142		Caldrinis, Caspar de	Lea 24
Brousses, Seigniory	Lea 2		*Calendar of Principles*	Smith 4
Brown, Rawdon	Lea 49		Calidi, Giacomo	Lea 183
Browne, Charles Albert	Smith 25		Call, E. A.	Ger. 45
Bruckemann, Bethmann	Ger. 57		Camaiano, Honofrio	Ital. 132

Cambiano, Com.	Ital. 143	Carrafa family Ital. 122, 179.—Lea 196	
Camerarius, Joachim	Lat. 198	Carrafa, Bp. of Aversa	Ital. 66
Camillus a Camillis	Smith 41	Carrafa, Carlo Ital. 144.—Lea 154	
Campanile, Giuseppe	Ital. 169	Carrafa, Decio	Ital. 122
Campano, Antonius	Lat. 137	Carranza y Miranda, Bartolomé de	
Campo/anpiero—Maldura Archive			Lea 120, 130, 141, 382
	Lat. 186	Carrara family	Lea 317
Campolo, Geronimo	Lea 397	Carrara, Francesco da	Ital. 36
Campolo, Nicola	Lea 397	Carrara, Marsilio da	Ital. 36
Canal, Bernardo	Lat. 148	Carretto family	Lea 397
Canalis, Hieronymus	Ital. 1	Carretto, Scipione del	Lea 370
Canals	Fr. 87	*Carta escrita a un cavallero de Cordova*	
Cananus, Julius	Ital. 132		Lea 190
Cançon en Agenais	Fr. 45–6	Cartagena, Gonzalo Peres de	Span. 11
Candia	Lea 360	Carteron, Jean	Lat. 106
Canisius, Petrus	Ital. 82	Carthusians	Lat. 99, 108
Canizarès, Joseph	Span. 35	Carvuni, Antonio	Ital. 162
Canon Law	Lea 389	Casado y Velas Chesa, Francesco	
Canon Law Miscellany	Lat. 42		Ital. 62
Canonice, Matteo Luigi	Lea 5	Casalis, Bartholomeus	Lea 205
Canovas del Castillo, A.	Lat. 3	Casalis, Leonardus	Lea 205
Canzonetti	Ital. 33	Casalnuovo	Lea 397
Canzoni siciliane	Ital. 114	Casanone	Smith 41
Capasso, Nicolo	Lea 164–6, 172	Caspar de Caldrinis	Lea 24
Cape of Good Hope	Eng. 22	Casso, Lodovico	Lea 336–9
Capell, Algernon	Eng. 5	Castagnolo	Lea 234
Capello, B.	Ital. 37	Castaldi, Antonio Ital. 160.—Lea 172	
Capitolo fratesco	Ital. 103	Castaldo, Giuseppe	Ital. 65
Capitula et conditiones pacis inter . . .		Castelfranco, Santo Stefano	Lea 312
Clementem VII et Carolum V	Lea 14	Castell y Ravella, Pablo	Lea 371
Capitulaciones de la vida . . . de		Castelli, Bastiano	Lea 289
D. Francisco de Quevedo y Villegas		Castelli, Giovanni	Lea 289
	Lea 130	Castello	Lea 64, 69
Capitulationi	Ital. 192	Castello del Vivaro	Lea 92
Cappello, Bianca, Grand Duchess of		Castelnau-de-Lévis	Lat. 178
Tuscany	Lea 77	Castile	Lea 374
Capponi family	Lea 398	Castillione, Joannes Jacobus	Lat. 38
Capponi, Filippo	Lea 273	Castino	Lea 54
Capponi-Medici	Lea 261–2	Casto, Lodovico	Lea 336–9
Caprera, Bernardo Giovanni	Lea 397	Castres	Lat. 110
Caprera, Lodovico de	Lea 397	Catapani, Scipio	Lea 384
Capua, Thomas de	Lea 3, 16	Catherine of Bologna, St.	Ital. 2
Capuchins	Lat. 42	Catherine of Siena, St.	
Caracciolo, Roberto	Lea 28		Lat. 179.—Ger. 4.—Ital. 73
Caradoc, John Hobart, 2nd Baron		Cattanei family	Lat. 97
Howden	Span. 3	Cattani, Alberto	Lat. 146
Caravita, Domenico	Ital. 65	Cavalcanti, Antonio	Lea 284
Carbi	Lat. 144	Cavalcanti, Giovanni	Lea 78
Carcasonne	Smith 42	Cavalcanti, Mainardo	Lea 283
Cardelinis, Julius de	Lat. 5	Cavalcanti, Tommaso	Lea 279–80
Cardenas, Inigo de	Lea 387	Cavalli family	Ital. 58
Carder D. de Monte, Valentin de		Cei, Francesco	Lea 104
	Span. 30	Celio, Roberto	Lat. 136
Cardines, Leonardo di	Lea 154	Cenci, Bernardino	Ital. 112
Cardona, Violante	Lea 154	Centino	Lea 154
Carmignola, Francesco	Ital. 36	Centurioni, Georgeta	Lat. 97
Carmina Amaltheorum	Lea 360	Cerda, Juan de la	Lea 190
Carminas, Francesco	Lea 150	Cérésier	Fr. 74
Carmine alla Beata Vergine Maria	Ital. 9	Ceriziers, René de	Eng. 26
Carnatic Region, India	Fr. 88	Cermisoni, Antonio	Lat. 7
Carnesecchi, Amerigo	Lea 231	Certosa del Galuzzo	Lea 28
Carosi, Bartolomeo Ital. 45.—Lea 173		Ceruti, Giovanni Antonio	Lea 360

Cervera	Span. 7, 48
Cervera, Universidad	Lea 371
Cesaria, Giuliano	Ital. 132
Cesarini, Giuliano, Prince	Lea 72
Cesis-Savelli, Francesco	Ital. 35
Chabanais	Lea 2
Chalcidius	Lat. 13
Chambellay	Lea 202
Chandon de Briailles, Henri	Ital. 17
Chanson de parade	Fr. 36
Chanson d'un inconnu	Fr. 36
Chansonnier	Fr. 15
Chansons historiques et gaillardes	Fr. 63
Chappaz de la Prat, Comte	Fr. 87
Charante	Lea 2
Charles IV, German Emperor	Lea 28
Charles V, German Emperor	Lat. 167.—Ger. 28-9, 54.—Ital. 84, 144.—Lea 14, 138, 141, 360, 397, 401-2
Charles VI, German Emperor	Lea 397
Charles II, King of England	Fr. 100
Charles VI, King of France	Lat. 110.—Span. 34
Charles VII, King of France	Fr. 91.—Lea 367
Charles VIII, King of France	Lat. 52
Charles III, King of Jerusalem	Fr. 83
Charles II, King of Spain	Lea 108, 382
Charles III, King of Spain	Span. 40, 42.—Lea 135
Charles IV, King of Spain	Span. 43.—Lea 135
Charles le Hardy	Fr. 44
Charles le Témeraire, Duke of Burgundy	Fr. 84
Charlestown	Lea 371
Chartier, Alain	Fr. 21
Charvin Aîné	Fr. 2
Chasson, J.	Lat. 106
Chastellain, Georges	Fr. 44
Chastro, Dieghode	Lea 223
Chatanus, Albertus	Lat. 146
Chatoney, E.	Fr. 30
Cheney, Edward	Lea 49
Chépy, Nicolas de	Fr. 103
Cherbonnier, Nicolas	Fr. 93
Chesnel, François	Fr. 93
Chessetto, Bartolomeo & Tomaso Cholni	Ital. 12
Chevaliers de l'Aigle	Lea 136
Chevreau, Urbain	Fr. 43
Chevrel, Nicolas	Fr. 93
Chiaramonte, Scipione	Ital. 204
Chiesa, Sebastiano	Ital. 154
Chigi, Agostino	Ital. 174
Chioccarelli, Bartolomeo	Lea 199-200
Chirac	Lea 2
Chiracus de Fulginio	Lat. 16
Chirardazzi, Cherubino	Lea 208
Chorier, Nicolas	Lat. 186
Christophorus, St.	Ital. 75
Christophorus, son of Antonius de Luca	Lat. 157
Chronicle	Lat. 169
Chronique versifiée	Fr. 11
Churruca, Joannes de	Lea 20
Cicchi, Baptista	Lea 67
Cicero, Gabriele	Ital. 162
Cicero, Marcus Tullius	Lat. 7, 125, 163.—Ger. 56
Cistercians	Lat. 120
Civaleri, Pietro	Lea 12
Civitella, Joannes Paulus	Ital. 39
Claret, Annibal	Fr. 50
Clarke, Adam	Eng. 5.—Smith 15
Clark[e], Samuel?	Lat. 192
Claudianus, Claudius	Ital. 61
Clement I, Pope	Lea 141
Clement V, Pope	Lat. 189
Clement VII, Pope	Lat. 173.—Lea 14, 366, 402
Clement VIII, Pope	Lat. 149.—Ital. 46, 99.—Lea 14, 59, 63, 360
Clement IX, Pope	Lea 355
Clement X, Pope	Ital. 123
Clement XI, Pope	Ital. 43
Clement XII, Pope	Ital. 45.—Lea 79, 362
Clementines	Lat. 95, 111, 113
Cleomedes	Lat. 13
Closa, Ramón	Lea 371
Clouet, Julien	Fr. 93
Cobenzl, Ludwig	Fr. 55
Cobenzl, Philipp	Fr. 55
Cochet, Jean	Smith 25
Codex Justiniani	Lat. 42, 73
Coimbra, Inquisition	Lea 206
Colbert, Jean Baptiste	Fr. 90, 100
Coleman, Catherine and Thomas	Lat. 20
Colis, Joannes Antonio de	Ital. 52
Colla, Saverio de	Ital. 190
Collecta decreti	Lat. 92
Collectanea opusculorum eruditorum	Lea 360
Collectio diversorum decretorum	Lea 137
Collection of Poems	Ital. 15
Colleoni, Bartolomeo	Ital. 152
Colloquium regis Salomonis cum Marcolpho	Ger. 55
Cologne	Ger. 7-9, 45
Cologne, Congress (1673)	Ital. 123
Colombani, Antonio Peregrino	Lea 385
Colonna, Card.	Ital. 63
Colonna, Guido de	Lat. 47
Colonna, Marc Antonio	Ital. 132
Colonna, Vincenzo	Lea 44
Colwell Library	Eng. 21
Comazzi, Gioan Battista	Ital. 140
Combetti, Giuseppe	Lea 54
Comedia dels pastorets	Span. 20
Comedia el mas feliz cautivero	Span. 21
Comete, Phederiche	Lea 371

[253]

Commazzi, Giambattista	Ital. 140	Corrispondenza delle monete	Lea 360
Commentarium florum pontificum	Lat. 174	Corró de Munt	Lea 88–9
Commentum super predictionem Rabani		Corsini family	Lea 398
Anglici	Lat. 174	Corsini, Bartolomeo	Ital. 20
Comminatoria dell' interdetto	Lea 356	Corte, Cesare	Ital. 134
Como	Lea 118	Coscia, Niccolò	Lea 79
Compassio B. Mariae	Lat. 122	Cosent, J. Fr.	Eng. 28
Compendio dell' aritmetica	Ital. 206	Cosimo II de Medici, Grand Duke of	
Compendio della vita della . . . Suor Maria		Tuscany Ital. 33.—Lea 210–1,	
Caterina Brondi	Lea 77	231, 251–2, 259, 264, 369	
Compendio di sfera	Ital. 189	Cosimo III de Medici, Grand Duke	
Compendious Abstract of Alchemy	Smith 4	of Tuscany	Lea 30–2, 198, 399
Compendium historiae ecclesiasticae	Lea 131	Cosmographies	Lat. 13
Compromissum super statu Bari	Lea 384	Costa, Giovanni Andrea	Lea 370
Computus ecclesiasticus	Lat. 118	Cotxet, Francesco	Lea 371
Conanici, Matteo Luigi	Fr. 83	Coulanges, Phillipe Emmanuel de	
Conclave fatto per la sede vacante di Papa			Fr. 61, 63
Alessandro VIII	Ital. 150	Courax, de	Fr. 100
Concubinatum clericorum	Lea 376	Cousin, censor	Fr. 98
Condé, Henri II, de Bourbon	Ital. 67	Coutainville	Fr. 93
Congiura di Lorenzo de' Medici	Lea 77	Cracow	Lea 384
Conradus de Brundelsheim	Ger. 41	Cradocke, Edward	Smith 4
Conradus de Soltau	Lat. 10	Crell, Lorenz F. F.	Smith 18
Conseil au Roy François Ier	Fr. 18	Crequi, Maréchal de	Fr. 100
Constance	Ger. 22	Crestomazia di poeti italiani del Cinquecento	
Constance, Council	Lat. 92		Ital. 37
Constantia, daughter of Hyronima		Crete	Lea 83
	Lea 204	Crisse	Lea 202
Constantinople	Eng. 21.—Lea 5	Cristina di Lorena, Grandduchess of	
Constantinus Africanus	Smith 4	Tuscany	Ital. 128
Consultas y resoluciones sobre . . . la		Cristofano, Vincenzo	Lea 348
ynquisición	Lea 117	Crofts, Thomas	Ital. 165
Contarini	Ital. 120	Crotto, Luigi	Lat. 7
Contarini, Alvise di Niccolò		Crusius, Martin	Greek 1
	Ital. 44, 184	Cuenca, San Pablo	Lea 156
Contarini, Francesco	Lea 41	Cumanus, Rafael	Lat. 146
Contarini, Gaspare	Lat. 104	Cunningham, Alexander	Lat. 102
Contarini, Lorenzo	Ital. 146	Cura novitiorum	Lat. 122
Conti, Paolo Antonio	Lea 198	Curia Romana (see Papacy)	
Conventio inter rectores ospitalis civitatis		Curtius, Lancinus	Lat. 7
Placentie	Lea 126	Cybo, Alderanus	Lea 75
Conventus Sanctae Mariae super		Cynthius, Laurentius	Lea 42
Taburrum	Lat. 171	Cyprus	Ital. 85
Copernicus, Nicolaus	Lat. 162	Cyriax, Johann	Ger. 39
Copia della dichiarazione	Lea 362	Cyrillus, St.	Lat. 174
Copia schedula	Ger. 39		
Coppula, Francisco	Lea 192		
Cordova, Ramón de	Span. 16		
Cordova, Raphael de	Lea 190	Daillon, Comtes du Lude	Fr. 49
Cordova, Inquisition	Lea 380–1	Dalberg, K. T. A. M. von	Fr. 55
Cordt, Count	Ger. 57	Dalle Laste, Natale	Ital. 88
Corfu	Ital. 89	Dalmatia	Ital. 60, 64, 132
Cornaro, Giorgio	Ital. 6	Dandalus Ylardensis	Lat. 174
Corneille, Pierre	Fr. 100	Daniello, B.	Ital. 37
Cornelius (S.J.)	Lat. 23	Dante Alighieri	Ital. 175
Corner, Giovanni	Ital. 110	Danube	Lea 360
Cornico, R.	Ital. 104	Dardier, Imbert	Fr. 80
Corona Beatae Mariae Virginis	Ital. 90	Dason, Balthasar	Ger. 23
Corona Domini	Ital. 90	Dati, Gregorio	Lea 104
Coronelli, Vincenzo	Lea 360	Dati (see also Deti)	
Coronelli, Vincenzo Maria	Lea 186	Daubeney, Amelia	Lea 116
Corrispondenza Acciaioli	Lea 28	Dauphiné	Fr. 92

[254]

Dauston, John	Smith 13
Davanzati, Francesco	Lea 347
Davanzati, Mariotto	Ital. 125
Davenant, John	Eng. 5
Davila, Enrico	Ital. 204
Davila, Enrico Caterino	Lea 90
Davolle, Guill. Nic.	Smith 25
De arte bene moriendi	Lat. 90
De arte cabalistica	Smith 8
De arte chymica	Smith 13
De assumptione maiore	Lat. 158
De Bry, Johann Theodor	Lat. 188
De casibus conscientiae	Lea 59
De casibus reservatis	Lea 59
Dechamp, Cl.	Lat. 172
Declaratio . . . arboris consanguinitatis	Lea 152
De coitu	Lat. 180
De conciliis	Lea 131
De confessione	Lat. 55, 103.—Lea 17
De decem preceptis	Lat. 118
Dedi (*see* Deti)	
Deedes, Curt	Eng. 19
Defensa de España	Span. 17
De fermento et multiplicatione	Smith 13
De fide catholica	Lat. 196
De Franchi, Giovanni	Ital. 135
De haeresibus	Lea 131
De horis canonicis	Lea 24
De imposturis	Lea 145
De jure canonico	Lea 131
De la Barde	Lea 2
De la Barre	Fr. 70
De la Baume, Mme.	Fr. 100
De la Cerda, Juan	Lea 190
De la Faye	Smith 32
De Langobardorum origine	Lea 362
De la philosophie	Fr. 79
Delaplanches	Fr. 1
De la Quint	Lat. 66
De la Reynie	Fr. 90
De la Tour d'Auvergne, Henri	Fr. 100
Delfino, Giovanni	Ital. 193
Delfino, Zaccaria	Lea 400
Delignières, J. A. J.	Fr. 10
Della Casa, Giovanni	Ital. 37
Della congiura di Bagiamonte Tiepolo	Lea 360
Della Fonte, Jacopo	Lea 277, 281
Della Rovere family	Ital. 196.—Lea 196
Della Rovere, Vittoria	Ital. 174
Della sferza degl' alchimisti	Smith 13
Della Torre, Giovanni Battista	Ital. 72
Del pecchato del parlar disonesto	Ital. 106
Del pecchato de vani	Ital. 106
Del regno di Francia	Ital. 149
Del Rio, Martin Antoine	Ger. 60
Demante, Pierre	Fr. 93
De Marinis, T.	Ital. 16
De meditationibus Beati Augusti	Lat. 122
De mensibus anni	Lat. 118
De mensuris	Lat. 133
De meretrice	Lat. 180
Demetrio	Ital. 117
Demogorgo	Smith 13
Demon jeiunandi	Lat. 158
Demosthenes	Ital. 109
De musica	Lat. 36
De partibus mulierum	Lat. 133
De privilegiis cisterciensibus	Lea 131
De pugna spirituali	Lat. 55
De quatuor humoribus	Lat. 133
De Santo Joanne Heremita	Ital. 71
Desbois de Rochefort, Louis	Smith 23
Descartes, René	Lat. 162.—Fr. 100.—Ital. 210
Deschamps, Eustache	Fr. 15
Descriptio feminarum malarum	Lat. 61
Description historique de toutes les cérémonies . . . à Rome	Fr. 68
Descrizzione della Germania	Ital. 133
De septem peccatis mortalibus	Lat. 187
Desposorio entre el cassar y la iubentud	Lea 130
De sublimatione mercurii	Smith 13
De summi pontificis auctoritate	Lea 61
De supremo regno	Ital. 139
Desvignes	Fr. 8
Deti, textile firm	Lea 332
Deti, Antonio di Taddeo	Lea 310
Deti, Giovanantonio	Lea 287
Deti, Giovanbattista	Lea 287, 327–31, 346
Deti, Giovanmaria	Lea 327–31, 346
Detti (*see* Deti)	
De una controversia bellicosa tra li Anconitani	Lea 373
De Vio, Tommaso	Lat. 150
De virtutibus et vitiis variis	Lat. 196
De vi signorum	Lat. 118
De vitiis	Lat. 48, 55, 61
Dialogo fra il confessore del imperatore ed un gesuita	Lea 362
Dialogue des morts	Fr. 36
Dialogus in miseros . . . alchymistas	Lea 19
Diaz, Froilan	Lea 179–80, 382
Diaz, Manuel	Lea 25
Dichiarazione agli elettori	Lea 362
Dichiarazione dell' Imperatore [Charles VI]	Lea 362
Dichiarazione dell' investitura del regno di Napoli	Lea 362
Dictionary	Ital. 84
Dictionary of Synonyms	Lat. 116
Didelot, Gerard	Lea 388
Diedo, Antonio	Ital. 89
Dietrichstein, Count	Ger. 19
Dietrichstein, F. J. J. N. von	Fr. 55
Dillingen	Lat. 18
Dinetus, Jacobus	Lat. 105
Dinus de Mugello	Lat. 113
Diogène, pseud.	Fr. 95
Diophantus	Ital. 176

Diplomatic Relations	Ital. 44, 184	Drury, Henry	Lea 1
Directorium divini officii	Lat. 120	Du Bellay, Joachim	Fr. 5
Discorsi familiari	Ital. 203	Dubos, J. B.	Ital. 147
Discorso academico	Lea 360	Duff, Jane Clerk	Lat. 133
Discorso delle cose concernenti le differenze		Duff, William	Lat. 133
	Lea 356	Du Hamel, Louis	Fr. 93
Discorso politico sopra la forza del denaro		Duncan, Andrew	Smith 35
	Ital. 139	Dunn, George	Lat. 15, 62
Discorso sopra la riforma	Ital. 132	*Duo dialogi de philosophia morali*	Lat. 40
Discorso sopra le scritture	Ital. 132	*Duodecim capita processus Card. Caroli*	
Discurso al sermón de zeniça	Lea 130	*Carafae*	Lea 154
Discurso apologetico de la inquisición		Dupin, Louis Ellies	Lea 148, *note*
	Lea 112	Durantus, Guillelmus	Lat. 108
Dispacci diplomatici di Toscana	Lea 198	Durazzo, Giuseppe	Ital. 162
Disputatio de quattuor intelligentiis		Durhame, J.	Eng. 15
	Lat. 197	*Dutch East and West Indies Company*	Fr. 47
Disputatio de virtute morali in communi			
	Lat. 197		
Disputatio in libros Aristotelis De anima		*Échelle des philosophes*	Smith 15
	Lat. 170	Ecija	Span. 14
Disputationes in decem libros [Ethicae]		Eck, Johannes	Ger. 22
Aristotelis	Lat. 197	*Ecò des montagnes*	Lea 362
Disputationes in Metaphysicam Aristotelis		Edet, Louis	Fr. 93
	Lat. 197	Edinburgh, University	Smith 35
Dissertationes jurisdictionales	Lea 166	Eduardo, Duke of Parma	Lea 360
Disticha Cornuti	Lat. 185	Edward IV, King of England	Smith 4
Distinctiones magistri super quattuor libros		Eenthius, Henricus	Lat. 100
sententiarum	Lat. 196	*Effetti della maleditione paterna*	Lea 154
Dits moraux des philosophes	Fr. 33	Egidius, St.	Ital. 93
Diverses mémoires	Fr. 98	Ehrhardt, Siegismund Justus	Ger. 60
Diviaco, Hieronimo	Ital. 6	Einsiedel, Heinrich von	Ger. 30
The Divine Politicks	Eng. 20	Einsius, Daniel	Ital. 204
Doazan, Jacob	Lea 148	*Elegantia de opere philosophico*	Smith 13
Dodici arthicholi della fede	Ital. 75	Elizabeth, St.	Lea 98
Dokeianos, Ioannes	Greek 1	Elizabeth, Queen of England	Eng. 4
Dolfini, Giovanni	Ital. 99	*Elogio del Card. Annibale Albani*	Lea 362
Domenico de Mairis	Ital. 30	Ely, William	Lat. 6
Domenicus, St.	Lea 362	*Embassy to the Curia*	Lea 355
Domingo	Lea 193	Embrun	Lea 362
Dominica septuagesima	Lat. 103	Enego	Lea 365
Domitilla, St.	Ital. 3, 75	Engadin	Lea 147
Don Carlos, of Spain	Lea 39, 362	England	Eng. 10.—Fr. 93, 100.—
Dona, Francesco	Ital. 47		Ger. 54.—Lea 6, 362
Donado, Marco	Ital. 36	*English Religious Poems*	Eng. 1
Donato, Antonio	Lea 359	Enjubault, Isaac	Fr. 93
Donato, Jacopo	Lea 28	Ennau	Ital. 186
Dongois, Nicolas	Lea 50	Enriquez, Juan Antonio	Lea 141
Doni, Agnolo	Lea 273	*Epistola contra Wiclefistas et Husitas*	Lat. 92
Doni, Giovanni d'Ottaviano	Lea 223	Epping, Johann	Ger. 23
Donnino family	Lea 128	Erasmus, Desiderius	Ital. 59
Donzelli, Giuseppe	Ital. 171	Erbs, Magdalena	Ger. 53
Dordoni, Trajano	Ital. 145	Erding	Ger. 59
Doria, Antonio	Ital. 132	*Ernea*	Ital. 200
Doria, Giovanni Andrea	Ital. 132, 196	Ernesti, Johann Christian Gottlieb	
Dortigues, Pierre	Fr. 98		Ger. 56
Douai	Fr. 42	Ernst, Bp. of Passau	Ger. 48
Doutes et questions sur le traité de Versailles		Ernst, Archduke of Austria	Lat. 149
	Fr. 89	Ertegne family	Fr. 64
Drenthe	Dutch 4	Escóbar, Jerónimo	Lea 203
Dresden	Ger. 29	Escobedo	Lea 150
Drichiarelli, V.	Ital. 8	Escouchy, Matthieu d'	Fr. 91
Dritto della S. Sede apostolica	Lea 362	Espinosa, Pedro de	Lea 156

Essays et affinages	Smith 36	Ferdinand I, King of Bohemia	Ger. 17
Essington Library	Ital. 19	Ferdinand II of Aragon, King of Spain	
Este, Giovanni d'	Lat. 119		Lea 377
Este, Leonello d'	Lat. 7	Ferdinand V, King of Spain	
Estrada y Naba, Bernardo Pablo de		Span. 9–10, 16.—Lea 141	
	Span. 49	Ferdinand VI, King of Spain	Lea 172
Estratto delle historie dell' Impero Ottomano		Ferdinand IV, King of the Two Sicilies	
	Ital. 207		Ital. 201
Ettolino, Francesco	Lea 274	Ferdinand, Archduke of Austria	Fr. 55
Eucharistia, St.	Ital. 29	Ferdinand II, Archduke of Austria	
Euclid	Ital. 55		Lea 63
Eufrasina, St.	Ital. 3	Ferdinand, Viceroy of Sicily	Lea 397
Eugene IV, Pope		Ferdinand II, Grand Duke of Tuscany	
Lat. 122, 139, 189.—Ital. 46		Ital. 33, 196.—Lea 65, 201, 391	
Eugene, Prince Ital. 43.—Lea 145, 399		Ferdinand, Prince of Wuerttemberg	
Eugenia, St.	Ital. 3		Fr. 55
Eulatte, Juan de	Span. 41	Feria, Duke of	Ital. 192
Euphrosia, St.	Ital. 71	Fernel, Jean	Lat. 133
Evangile de l'enfance	Fr. 41	Ferrante (Ferdinand I), of Naples	
Everett, James	Eng. 5		Ital. 152, 180
Ewald, Johann Joachim	Ger. 43	Ferrara	Lat. 156.—Lea 34
Examen du système des cours de Vienne Fr. 13		Ferrara, Capuchin monastery	Lat. 42
Excommunicatio	Lat. 108	Ferrara, S. Maria Angelorum	Ital. 209
Eximeno, Jacobus Benedictus	Lat. 190	Ferreira, Pedro A.	Lea 121
Exortatione et interrogatione in colloquio		Ferrini, Vincenzo	Lea 284
delli monaci	Lat. 108	Ferro, Antonius	Lat. 176
Explanation of the Tables of the Planets		Fetterolf, Edwin H.	Lat. 6
	Lea 144	*Feuerwerkbuch*	Smith 2
Explicatio figurae hermeticae	Smith 8	Fideli, Vincenzo	Ital. 143
Expositio alchemiae Gebri	Smith 13	Fiesole	Ital. 16
Expositione de lo patre nostro	Ital. 90	*Fifteenth Century Miscellany*	Lat. 36, 92
Eyb, Albrecht von	Ger. 6	Figulus, Benedictus	Smith 22
Ezquerre family	Lea 397	Filippo Maria, Duke of Milan	Lat. 7
		Filomarino, Card.	Ital. 168
		Finellus, Antonius Francescus	Lea 126
Fabre, Pierre Jean	Smith 7	Fini, Card.	Lea 362
Faenza	Ital. 191	Finkenstein, Karl von	Fr. 55
Fairbridge	Lat. 153	Fiore, Giovanni Tommaso di	Ital. 168
Falces, Ottavio	Ital. 201	Fiore, Joachim de	Lat. 174
Falconieri, Pacholo	Ital. 152	*Fioretti tracti della . . . Beatissima*	
Falieri, Marino	Ital. 36	*Lisabetta*	Ital. 75
Fantoni, Lodovico	Lea 391	Fisher, Otto Orren	Smith 40
Farnaby, Giles	Eng. 29	Fitch, W. S.	Eng. 19, *note*
Farnese family	Lea 196	Fitzpatrick, Ellia	Lat. 20
Farnese, Alessandro, Card.	Ital. 173	Fitzwalter, C.	Eng. 11
Farnese, Ranucci	Ital. 15	Flanders Flemish 3.—Fr. 97.—Ital. 67	
Farrell, William	Lat. 20	Flanders, Comtesse de	Lea 197
Fascoli, Alexandro	Ital. 61	Flatman, Thomas	Eng. 28
Faucher, Denis	Lat. 179	Flemming, H. H.	Fr. 37, 67
Favier, Jean Louis	Fr. 89, *note*	Florence	Lat. 169.—Eng. 21.—
Faz, Juan de	Span. 22	Ger. 28.— Ital. 132, 143, 152.—	
Feiss, Paul-Louis	Flemish 1	Lea 14, 28, 73, 76–8, 83–4, 86–7, 90,	
Felix V, Duke of Savoy	Lat. 139	95, 100, 102–4, 109–10, 119, 128, 261,	
Felton, John	Lat. 35	360, 398 (*see also* Gondi Archives)	
Feltre family	Ital. 196	Florence, Priorista	Ital. 49
Ferabos, Giovanni Andrea	Ital. 78	Florence, Ritiro della Quiete (*see* Gondi	
Ferdinand I, German Emperor		Archives)	
Lat. 195.—Lea 400–1		Florence, S. Lorenzo	Lea 280
Ferdinand II, German Emperor		Florence, S. Vincentio	Lea 386
	Ital. 192	Florence, Santa Maria del Fiore	
Ferdinand III, German Emperor			Lea 222–3, 225, 227
	Ital. 146		

[257]

Florence, Spedale di Santa Maria degli
  Innocenti   Lea 220, 227
Florence, Spedale di Santa Maria
  Nuova
        Lea 219, 222–3, 225–7, 277, 323
Florence, Universitas mercatorum
                                Lat. 136
Flores, Alonso de   Span. 4
Florida Blanca, Conde de   Lea 371
Fludd, Robert   Ger. 1.—Smith 42
Folsham, Johannes   Lat. 59
Fonseca Soares, Antonio da   Span. 19
Font, Pablo   Lea 371
Fontaine-Éttouppefour   Fr. 93
Fontanesius, Dionysius   Lea 363
Fontenay   Fr. 93
Fontio, Bartolomeo   Ital. 78
Fontoli, Gabriel   Span. 4
Forli   Lat. 144
Formae Romanae curiae   Lea 16
Fornari, Leonardo de   Lea 281
Forner, Juan Pablo   Span. 46
Foscari, Alvise   Lea 393
Foscari, Marco   Lea 83
Foscarini, Marco   Ital. 95
Foscolo, procuratore   Lea 360
Fosse, François de la   Fr. 5
Fosses, Arière de   Fr. 81
Foster, John   Lea 206
Foza   Lea 365
France   Fr. 3, 34, 55, 100, 103.—
      Ger. 52.—Ital. 23, 46, 100, 187.—
      Lea 6, 90, 362, 387 (*see also* names of
      sovereigns)
Franceschi, Giulio   Lea 251
Francesco da Pesaro   Lea 125
Francesco di Leone   Lat. 176
Francesco di San Giovanni, Prior
                                Ital. 93
Francesco Maria II, Duke of Urbino
                                Lea 359
Francesco Maria, Governor of Siena
                                Ital. 174
Franche-Comté   Lea 81
Francheville, Joseph du Fresne de
                                Ital. 140
Franciotti, Bartolomeo, *Addenda et corr.*
                                Lea 355
Franciotus, Georgius   Lea 51
Francis, St.   Lea 98
Francis I, King of France   Fr. 18
Franciscan Miscellany   Lat. 122
Franciscans, Avignon
                     Lat. 154.—Ital. 194
Franciscans, Metz   Lat. 93
Franciscans. *Ordo in missa*   Lat. 122
Franciscus, son of Gabriele de
     Pradonerio   Lat. 157
Franeker, Academy   Dutch 2
Frangioni, Bartolomeo   Lea 355
Frangipano, Cornelio   Lea 360
Frangnani   Lat. 69

Frank, Johannes   Lea 152
Frankfurt   Ger. 33.—Lea 399
Franklin, Benjamin Fr. 95.—Smith 34
Frascerepnico, T.   Ital. 51
Frater Georgius   Lat. 195
Frederick I Barbarossa, German
     Emperor   Ital. 47
Frederick III, German Emperor
                                Smith 17
Frederick, King of Aragon   Lea 397
Frederick II, King of Prussia
                     Ger. 43.—Ital. 140
Frederick August I, Elector of Saxony
                      Fr. 37, 67.—Lea 362
Frederick William I, King of Prussia
                                Ital. 188
French Legal Documents   Lea 197
French Miscellany   Smith 36
Frescobaldi, Luigi   Lea 77
Fresneau   Fr. 93
Fridolin, St.   Ital. 82
Friedrich, Ludwig Jacob   Smith 26
Frignano   Lea 364
Friuli   Lea 194
Froelich, Wilhelm   Lat. 134
Fronberg, St. Mary and Catherine
                                Lea 66
Fuchs, Christian   Lat. 61
Fugger, Count   Lea 376
Fuidoro, Innocenzio   Ital. 169
Fullá, Pedro   Lea 371
Fumagalli, Giuseppano   Ital. 79
Fundamentum puerorum   Lat. 118
Fusco, Pietro de   Lea 171
Fyrbas, Simon   Lat. 175

Gabineto de prencipi   Ital. 139
Gabriel de Jesu Maria de Cataluña
                                Lea 371
Gabriele, Trifone   Ital. 131
Gabrielli family   Lea 398
Gaetano, Tommaso de Vio (called)
                                Lat. 150
Gaillarde, Jane   Fr. 66
Gaita, Francisco   Ital. 162
Galeano, Giuseppe   Ital. 162
Galeazo   Ital. 120
Galilei, Galileo   Ital. 128, 210
Galiotti, Matteo   Lea 352
Galiotti, Niccolò   Lea 352
Galleazza dal Moglietto   Lea 360
Galletti family   Lea 397
Galletti, Gust. C.   Ital. 83
Gallio   Lea 365
Galvani, Vitaliano   Lat. 119
Gamaliel, Abaris   Lat. 192.—Fr. 95
Gambacorti, Pietro   Lea 28
Gambara   Ital. 108
Garabito, Pedro   Span. 8
Garcia, Pedro   Lea 108

[258]

Gardette	Lea 388
Garosi, Bartolomeo Ital. 45.—Lea 173	
Gassendi, Pierre	
Lat. 162.—Fr. 100.—Ital. 210	
Gaston, Duke of Orléans	Fr. 98
Gastone, Giovanni	Lea 198
Gaudet, Claude de	Fr. 72
Gaulli, Giulio	Ital. 167
Gay-Vernon, Léonard-Honoré	Fr. 74
Gayangos, Pascual de	Lea 20
Gayer, Constantin	Lat. 25
Geber Lat. 3.—Lea 19.—Smith 3, 4, 13	
Geber, Hanns	Ger. 51
Gedicht von einer stoltzen . . . Jungkfrauen	
	Ger. 8
Geigy-Hagenbach, Karl	Span. 50
Gelosús, Giovanni Ant.	Lea 397
General Rule for all Men	Smith 4
Genoa Lat. 97, 155, 169.—Eng. 21.—	
Fr. 59.—Ger. 28–9.—Ital. 167, 196.—	
Lea 114, 261, 356	
Gentile III, da Varrano	Lea 28
Gentili, Antonio Saverio	Ital. 144
Genzano	Lea 72
Geometriae compendium	Lat. 102
Georgius, Frater	Lat. 195
Gerardi, Alamanno di Giovanbattista,	
Addenda et corr.	Lea 349
Gerardin	Fr. 25
Géraud of Figeac	Lat. 173
Gerbel, Nicolaus	Lat. 198
German Poetry Collection	Ger. 32
Germany Fr. 61.—Ital. 44, 66–7, 129,	
146, 184.—Vet. 1 (*see also* names of	
sovereigns)	
Gerson, Johannes Lat. 36.—Lea 152	
Gervais, Jullien	Fr. 42
Gervais de Donchery	Lea 197
Ghilini, Girolamo	Ital. 134
Ghizzi, G.	Lat. 69
Giamboni, Bono	Ital. 31
Giambullari, Bernardo	Ital. 16
Giannone, Pietro Lea 168, 188–9, 207	
Giannotti, Donato	Lea 90
Gibbon, Mr.	Eng. 28
Gibellina	Lea 397
Gilbert, Bp. of Bath	Eng. 6
Gillet Collection	Span. 18–22
Ginaeceum chimicum	Smith 13
Ginori-Conti, Pietro	Lea 385–6
Gio, Georgius	Lat. 134
Gioni, Cosimo	Lea 350
Giorgi, Giorgio Ippolito	Ital. 180
Giorgini, Marolino	Ital .15
Giorgio d'Armenia	Smith 40
Giorgio, Marco	Lat. 177
Giotto, Niccodemo di	Lea 289
Giovanni da Nola	Smith 9
Giovanni d'Aragona	Lea 397
Giovanni di Lamberto	Lea 397
Giovanni di Leone	Lat. 176
Giovannucci, Ferdinando	Ital. 20
Giraldi, Alamanno di Giovanbattista	
	Lea 349
Giraldi, Francesco	Lea 251
Girardelli, Lorenzo	Ital. 134
Girardi, G.	Lat. 106
Giuffre, Vincenzo	Ital. 162
Giugni, Galbotto	Lea 14
Giuliari Library	Ital. 147
Giundatio, Fabritio	Ital. 27
Giuseppe, Mustio Estense	Lea 46
Giusti, Baron	Fr. 55
Giustiniani, Leonardo	Lat. 7
Giustiniano	Ital. 143
Glannafoglio, Monastery	Lea 182
Goa, Inquisition	Lea 206
Godo, Llorens	Lea 371
Göbel, Paul	Ger. 17
Goldner, Johannes	Lat. 92
Golio, Jacopo	Ital. 204
Gomberville, Marin Le Roy de Fr. 100	
Gondi Archives	Lea 212–355
Gondi family, *Addenda et corr.* Lea 296–7	
Gondi, Antonio	Lea 323
Gondi, Antonio Francesco di Lorenzo	
	Lea 324
Gondi, Bartolomeo	Lea 285
Gondi, Carlo	Lea 273
Gondi, Federico di Giuliano, *Addenda*	
et corr.	Lea 325
Gondi, Filippo	
Ital. 72.—Lea 276, 282, 323	
Gondi, Giuliano	Lea 325
Gondi, Lodovico di Mariotto Lea 326	
Gondi, Lorenzo di Mariotto	
Lea 323, *Addenda* Lea 326	
Gondi, Pagolo Giovanni	Lea 225
Gondi, Simone	Lea 322
Gongora y Argote, Louis de	Span. 37
Gontaut family	Fr. 62
Gontaut-Biron, Theodore de	Fr. 62
Gonzaga	Ital. 120
Gonzaga, Carlo	Ital. 83
Gonzaga, Federigo	Lea 28
Gonzaga, Ferdinando	Ital. 33
Gonzaga, Ferrante	Lea 402
Gonzaga, Rodolfo	Lea 402
Gorch, Antonio	Lea 371
Gori, Agusto	Ital. 174
Gori, Silvio	Ital. 174
Gottraw, Peter	Lat. 18
Gottsched, Johann Christoph	Ger. 43
Goveru, Juan	Lea 371
Grafoldarius, Petrus	Lat. 160
Grana, François	Lat. 173
Grandson, Oton de	Fr. 15
Grant, Charles Cathcart	Eng. 22
Grassi, Achille de	Ital. 132
Grassi, Giovanni	Lat. 146
Gratian, the Canonist	Lat. 42, 92
Graville, Anne de	Fr. 21
Gravina, Cesare	Ital. 162
Great Britain	Fr. 3

Great Britain, Privy Council	Eng. 19
Grecismus cornutus	Lat. 185
Grécourt, J. B. J. Willart de	Smith 36
Greek Orthodox Church	Gr. 3
Grégoire, Bp. of Blois	Lea 112
Gregoras, Nicephorus	Greek 1
Gregoriis, Gregorius de	Lat. 174
Gregorios of Constantinople	Greek 1
Gregoritsch, Elias	Ger. 49
Gregory I, Pope	Ger. 60
Gregory XI, Pope	Lea 6, 70
Gregory XIII, Pope	Ital. 62.—Lea 166
Gregory XV, Pope	Ital. 66
Gregory, de Chastellar	Lat. 106
Grenville, W. W.	Fr. 55
Gresset, Jean-Baptiste-Louis	Fr. 29
Grifeo, Marianna	Lea 397
Grillo family	Lea 397
Grillo, Angelo	Ital. 204
Grimaldi family	Lea 196
Grisoles	Fr. 87
Grisone, Federico	Ital. 151
Gritti, Andrea	Lat. 160
Groowe, D. D. R. H.	Eng. 28
Grouches, Nicolas de	Fr. 103
Gruber, Leopold	Ger. 6
Guadagni Archive	Lea 399
Guadagni, Neri	Lea 399
Guagni, Domenico	Ital. 130
Guagni, Domenico Emiliano	Ital. 130
Gualterio di Basilicapietra	Ital. 153
Gualtieri, Lorenzo	Ital. 21
Guarinus de Verona	Lat. 7
Guasconi, Pierantonio	Lea 345
Guastalla, Signori di	Lea 181, 402
Gueffier	Fr. 38
Guer, Abraham	Lea 175
Guernon, Jean	Fr. 93
Guerra, maestro	Lea 130
Guicciardini, Francesco	Lea 276
Guicciardini, Jacopo	Lea 278–82
Guicciardini, Jacopo di Piero	Lea 42
Guida, Jacobus de	Lea 8
Guidiccioni, G.	Ital. 37
Guido delle Colonne	Lat. 47
Guidone de Guidoni, Giovanni Battista	Lat. 53
Guilelmus de Mandagoto	Lat. 115.—Lea 116
Guilelmus de Monte Lauduno	Lat. 111.—Lea 21
Guilelmus Paraldus	Lat. 140
Guilelmus Parisiensis	Lea 22
Guilelmus Rothwellus	Lat. 32, 118
Guillaume d'Auxerre	Lat. 60
Guillaume de Belmont	Fr. 92
Guillaume de Estouteville, Cardinal	Lat. 189
Guillaume de Lorris	Fr. 1
Guillaume de Montlauzun	Lat. 113.—Lea 21
Guillaume de Salins	Lea 81
Guillaume, of Carreria	Lat. 106
Guillaume, of Figeac	Lat. 173
Guinigi, Fabbio	Lea 355
Guzzotti, Pietro	Ital. 96
Halberstadt, Monastery Unser Lieben Frauen	Ger. 57
Hall (Tyrol), Congregation Mariae Verkündigung	Lea 129
Haller, Berchtold	Ger. 22
Halter, Richard	Eng. 1
Hamburg	Eng. 21
Han, Ulrich	Lat. 37
Handwergs Büchlein	Ger. 24–5
Hannibal	Lat. 7
Hapsburg vineyards	Ger. 42
Harmsworth Trust Library	Eng. 2
Harnin, Antoinne de	Fr. 81
Hartmann, Johann Christoph von	Smith 33
Hauser, Hans	Lat. 153
Hébert, Conseiller	Fr. 40
Hébert, Paul François	Fr. 93
Heinrich IX, Duke of Brunswick	Ger. 37
Heinrich Moritz	Ger. 39
Heinrich von Langenstein	Lat. 4
Helianus, Ludovicus	Lat. 128
Henricus de Hassia	Lat. 36
Henry VIII, King of England	Ger. 28–9
Henry II, Duke of Guise	Ital. 96
Herbert, Peter von	Fr. 55
Hercolani, Philippus	Lea 44
Herman, Abp., Landtgraf zu Hessen	Ger. 50
Hermannus de Schildis (=de Alemannia)	Lat. 118
Hermes Trismegistus	Smith 17, 22
Herrera family	Lea 397
Hervault, Marquis d'	Fr. 100
Hesius, Ricardus	Lat. 74
Heuss, Johannes	Lat. 132
Heywood family	Smith 29
Hierardi, Vergilius	Lat. 108
Hildebert	Lat. 61
Hildegard, St.	Lea 362
Hill, James	Smith 14
Hillin, Conradus	Lat. 158
Hilton, Walter	Eng. 8
Hingston, James	Eng. 25
Hippocrates	Lea 360
Hirninger, Johannes	Lat. 27–8
Histoire de l'hérésie	Lea 392
Historia Beati Albani	Lea 4
Historia de Papa Alexandro III	Ital. 47
Historia de preliis	Lat. 44
Historia de transfiguratione	Lat. 99
Historia dei re di Portugallo	Ital. 132
Historia gestorum Alexandri pueri magni	Lat. 44

[260]

Historia naturalis	Lat. 162
Historical Miscellany	
	Lea 90, 130, 362
Hodson, Lawrence W.	Lat. 15
Hoe, Robert	Span. 3
Hoeghe, Romijn de	Smith 31
Holkot, Robert	Lat. 196
Hollandus, Johann Isaac	Smith 4, 13
Holler, Blaise H.	Smith 41
Homilies	Eng. 2
Honofrius, St.	Ital. 29
Honorius Sancti Jacobi	Lea 64
Hontalba, Pedro de	Lea 172
Hope, Thomas Charles	Smith 35
Hopkinson, Edward, Jr.	Eng. 29
Hopkinson, Oliver	Eng. 29
Horae	Lat. 6.—Flemish 1
Horatius Flaccus, Quintus	Fr. 5, 100
Horn, Johann Jacob	Smith 26
Horsemanship	Vet. 1
Houdar de la Motte, Antoine	Fr. 63
Hours	Lat. 6.—Flemish 1
Houssemain	Fr. 93
Hoym, L. G.	Fr. 37, 67
Huber, Johann	Lat. 17, 70–1, 76
Hugh of Montrelais	Lat. 91
Hugo de Sancto Victore	Lat. 122
Hugoneti, Stephanus	Lat. 95
Humphry, William	Eng. 20
Hungary	Lat. 195.—Ital. 46.—
	Span. 27.—Lea 74
Hunter, Joseph	Smith 29
Hurtado de Mendoza y Bobadilla, Francisco	Lea 134
Huss, Jan	Ger. 54
Hussites	Lat. 92, 158
Huygens, Constantin	Fr. 100
Hymne auf Maria	Ger. 4
Hymns and Prayers	Lat. 132
Iatro-Chemical and Alchemical Compendium	Smith 41
Illumineirr Buch	Ger. 5
Imperiali, Giuseppe Renato	
	Lea 96, 149
In Aristotelis libros De generatione	
	Lat. 170
Index privilegiorum [Poloniae]	Lea 384
Indulgences	Ital. 11
Infidélité punie	Fr. 57
Informatio . . . super conversione Sarracenorum	Lea 20
Informatione del successo di queste armate	
	Ital. 132
Informazione della corte di Vienna	Lea 399
Inghirami, Admiral	Lea 353
In libro monachorum de temporalibus contemnendis	Lea 4
Innocent III, Pope	Lat. 55, 90
Innocent IV, Pope	Lat. 174
Innocent V, Pope	Lat. 32
Innocent VI, Pope	Lea 6
Innocent VII, Pope	Lat. 93.—Lea 28
Innocent X, Pope	Ital. 62, 129
Innocent XII, Pope	Fr. 61.—
	Ital. 150.—Lea 98, 167, 169–70, 187
Innocentius, son of Antoninus Antonii	
	Lea 205
Inquisitio pro rebus magicalibus	Lea 360
Insinuazione fatta al Conte Filippi	Lea 362
Instruttioni e memoriali	Ital. 132
Iohannes Benedictus Paulus de Nursia	
	Ital. 29
Isaac of Syria	Ital. 2
Isabel of Aragon	Lea 384
Isabel of Bavaria, Queen of France	
	Fr. 12, 15
Isabel of Castile, Queen of Spain	
	Span. 9–10.—Lea 377
Isherwood, Mary	Eng. 18
Istoria de S. Euphrosia	Ital. 71
Istoria del sacco di Roma	Ital. 45
Istoria della Signora Bianca Cappello	
	Lea 77
Istorie tragiche	Lea 154
Itagre, Thomas	Lea 371
Italian Historical Miscellany	Ital. 132
Italian Miscellany	Ital. 13
Italian Religious Miscellany	Ital. 29
Italy	Fr. 61.—Ital. 43, 184
(*see also* individual republics and city states)	
Ivo of Chartres	Lat. 58
Jabir ibn Aflah	
	Lat. 3.—Smith 3–4, 13.—Lea 19
Jackson, John C.	Lat. 6
Jackson, Richard C.	Ital. 165
Jacobus, Bp. of Breslau	Lea 384
Jacobus, "comes palatinus"	Lat. 47
Jacobus Craccii	Lea 60
Jacobus de Tuderto	Lat. 122
Jacobus de Voragine	Ital. 209
Jacomo, Fra	Ital. 29
Jacopo d'Appiano	Lea 28
Jansenism	Fr. 5.—Lea 131
Jaques Lempereur	Lea 197
Jaromini, Jacomo	Lea 107
Jastrow, Morris	Ital. 1
Jauer, Nicolas Magni de	Lea 24, *note*
Jean d'Armagnac	Lea 367
Jean de Vernoils	Fr. 87
Jehan d'Anizy	Fr. 82
Jehan de Beaumont	Fr. 93
Jehan de Poitiers	Fr. 98
Jehan de St. Germain	Lea 197
Jehannot des Près	Fr. 85
Jerome, St.	Ital. 71
Jeronymus filius Ludovici de Favallibus	
	Lat. 157
Jerusalem	Lat. 156
Jesselin de Cassagnes	Lat. 113

Jesuits	Fr. 5, 36, 94.—Ital. 79, 202.—Lea 362, 371	Josephus Flavius	Lea 90
		Jovalta	Rhaeto-Rom. 1
Jevon, Isaac	Eng. 24	Jovius, Alexander	Lat. 88
Jews	Lea 159, 384	Juan Alfonso de Bene . . .	Span. 24
Joan I, Queen of Naples	Lea 66	*Jüngste Tag*	Ger. 51
Joan II, Queen of Naples	Ital. 25	Julianus Caesarinus	Lat. 64
Joan of Aragon, Queen of Sicily	Lea 377	Julius, St.	Ital. 106
		Julius III, Pope	Ital. 132, 141
Joannes, Abp. of Taranto	Lat. 64	Justinian Code	Lat. 42, 73
Joannes a Capistrano, St.	Lea 362		
Joannes Aloisius Tuscanus	Lat. 108		
Joannes Angeli de Crema	Lea 51	Kaehler, Johann Sigismund	Ger. 36
Joannes a Prato	Lat. 119	Kaiser, Peter	Ger. 27
Joannes Carazolus	Lea 192	Kalid, King	Smith 3
Joannes de Bologna	Lat. 82	Kalisch	Lea 384
Joannes de Caligariis	Lat. 157	Kant, Immanuel	Ger. 36
Joannes de Claromonte	Lat. 110	Karl Gustavus, King of Sweden	Fr. 100
Joannes de Grassis	Lat. 146		
Joannes de Polna	Lat. 26	*Katherinenlegende*	Ger. 4
Joannes de Rupescissa	Lea 19	Keller, Alexandre de	Fr. 20
Joannes de Sacrobosco	Lat. 191	Kemeden, Oltze	Ger. 57
Joannes de Segovia	Lat. 196	Kemp, Johannes	Lat. 164–5
Joannes de Tambaco	Lat. 36	Kendall, E. Otis	Eng. 23
Joannes Hispaniensis	Lat. 163	Ker, John Edgar	Lat. 16
Joannes Menchutii	Lea 60	Kerckring, Theodor	Smith 31
Joannes (*see also* Jean, Johann, John, etc.)		Kern, Georg	Lat. 76
		Kerssenbroch, Hermann à	Lea 191
Johan, Deacon	Ger. 57	Kestenholtz	Ger. 16
Johan de Verdu	Fr. 45	Khunrath, Heinrich	Smith 8
Johann Isaac Hollandus	Smith 4, 13	King, Henry	Eng. 29
Johann Maximilian, Freiherr von Preysing	Ger. 59	Kircher, Athanasius	Smith 38
		Kirchweger, Anton Joseph	Smith 21
Johann Wilhelm, Count Palatine	Lea 198	Kleinfeld, Christian Ernst	Smith 12
		Kloss, Georg	Ger. 14.—Lea 19
Johanna, dicta La Fromme	Lea 197	*Die Koenigin von Frankreich*	Ger. 4
Johannes, Frater	Lat. 108	Kolb, Frantz	Ger. 22
Johannes de Brauneck	Lat. 92	Kothen, Charles	Lat. 154
Johannes de Garlandia	Lat. 185	Kreidenmann, Friedrich Wilhelm	Ger. 60
Johannes Friburgensis	Lat. 118		
Johannes Parisiensis	Smith 3	Krembser, Franciscus	Lat. 23
Johannes, scribe, XIVth–XVth cent.	Lat. 118	Krug, Dr.	Smith 20
		Kunstbüchlein	Smith 6
Johannes, scribe, 1422	Lat. 164–5		
John, St.	Ital. 71		
John II, Pope	Lat. 63	La Bastide	Lat. 178
John XXII, Pope	Ital. 75.—Lea 6	La Baume-Leblanc, Louis César de	Fr. 4
John, Card. of S. Lorenzo in Damaso	Lea 66	La Beaume, Charles Joseph de	Lea 48
John II, King of Castile	Span. 34	Lachèvre, Frédéric	Fr. 29
John IV, King of Portugal	Lea 139	Lacroix, Paul	Fr. 29
John Cassian, St.	Lat. 122	Ladislaus, King of Naples	Ital. 25
John Chrysostom, St.	Lat. 83.—Ital. 117.—Lea 42	La Fillotière	Lea 202
		La Fizelière, A. de	Fr. 43
John de Burgh	Lea 23	La Fontaine, Jean de	Fr. 100
John of Jerusalem, St.	Lea 397	La Fosse, François de	Fr. 5
John (*see also* Jean, Joannes, etc.)		La Grange-Chancel, François Joseph	Fr. 48
Jolly, François	Fr. 93		
Jonston, Johann	Lat. 135	Laidi, Jacobus	Lat. 19
Jordanus, C. S.	Lea 57	Lakon, Andreas D. E.	Greek 1
Jordanus de Quedlinburg	Lat. 196	Lamanna, Girolamo	Ital. 162
Josef, Archduke of Hungary	Fr. 55	*Lamentation of St. Anselm*	Eng. 1
Joseph I, German Emperor	Lea 399	La Mesnière, Parish	Fr. 93

Lamoignon, C. F. de	Lea 6		Leggienda di Messere S. Gilio	Ital. 106
Lampsonio, Domenico	Ital. 204		Leggienda di S. Alesso	Ital. 106
Landriani, Giovanni Battista	Lea 402		Leghorn	Eng. 21.—Ital. 24
Landriani, Marsilio	Ital. 148		Legnaiolo, Francesco	Lea 223
Landrini, Antonio de	Ital. 153		Leguay, Jean Pierre	Fr. 93
Lanfranchi, Bernardino	Lea 397		Leibnitz, Gottfried Wilhelm	Lat. 192
Langenstein, Heinrich von	Lat. 4		Leidl, Johann Baptist	Ger. 59
Langevelt, Petrus S.	Lat. 191		Leinbauch, Georg	Lat. 100
Langevine	Lea 202		Leipzig	Ger. 29
Langlois, Françoise	Fr. 93		Lempereur, Jaques	Lea 197
Lantrecht van Zallant	Dutch 4		Leo I, Pope	Lea 42
Lanzi, Guido	Ital. 134		Leo XI, Pope	Ital. 33
Lapi, Francesco	Lea 284		Léon, Michel de	Lat. 154
La Porte, Richard de	Fr. 21		Leonardo y Argensola, Bartolomé	
La Porte, Robert de	Fr. 21			Span. 31
Lapuente	Span. 25		Leonardo y Argensola, Lupercio	
La Rochette, Pascal de	Fr. 64			Span. 29, 31
Laste, Natale della	Ital. 88		Leonarducci	Ital. 205
Latin Charters	Lea 66		Leoncinus, Paulus	Ital. 1
Latin-English Miscellany	Eng. 28		Leonissa, Augustinus de	Lat. 130
Latini, Brunetto	Ital. 165		Leopold I, German Emperor	
Latro, Ettore Capece	Ital. 98		Ital. 44, 184.—Lea 198, 399	
Laubardemont, Jean Martin	Lea 195		Leopold, Duke of Austria	Ger. 48
Laude	Ital. 73		Lesage, Joseph	Fr. 93
Laude del corpo di Christo	Ital. 73		Lesureul, François	Fr. 93
Laude del vano parlare	Ital. 73		Leszcynski, Stanislas	Lea 362
Laude del venardi santo	Ital. 73		*Lettera di una monaca*	Ital. 68
Laude di Santa Caterina da Siena	Ital. 73		*Lettere di diversi principi*	Lea 399
Laude di Santa Domitilla	Ital. 3		*Lettere inedite*	Ital. 204
Laude di Santo Ansano	Ital. 73		*Lettere scritte da donna di senno*	Ital. 41
Laude e gloria	Ital. 13		*Letters Historical and Gallant*	Eng. 25
Lauderdale, Duke of	Eng. 19		Levant	Ital. 60.—Lea 210
Laurent, Frère	Fr. 32		Lewis, James	Lea 137
Laurie, James	Flemish 1		Lezignac	Lea 2
La Vallière, Duc de	Fr. 4, 33		Libelli, Giaconto	Lea 46
Lavelli, Ottavio	Lea 360		*Liber fortunae*	Fr. 16
Lavicia, Guilelmus de	Lea 62		*Liber multipheris*	Smith 4
La Vigne, André de	Fr. 21		*Liber scintillarum*	Lat. 55
La Vigne, Mlle. de	Fr. 100		*Liber sextus . . . decretalium*	Lat. 42
Laws of Philosophers	Smith 4		*Libretto delli brevi*	Lea 125
Lazzeri, Luigi	Ital. 56		*Libro della disciplina*	Ital. 69
Lea, Henry C.	Lea 16, 18–26, 37–40,		*Libro della resurrectione*	Ital. 13
79, 82, 120, 130–1, 134–42, 144–51,			*Libro di S. Justo Paladino*	Ital. 28
153–60, 164–73, 175–80, 182–4, 187–			Liechtenstein Library	Ger. 60.—
92, 200, 358, 368, 374–5, 387, 393–5			Ital. 36.—Lea 44, 93, 123	
Lebrec, Vincent	Fr. 93		*Lied wie es in dem frenkischen Baurnkrieg*	
Le Brecq	Lea 388		*ergangen ist*	Ger. 51
Lebzeltern, Ludwig von	Fr. 55		Liège	Lea 47
Le Clerc, Michel	Fr. 100		Limbrici	Lea 397
Lectures on Scientific Subjects	Smith 19		Limoges	Fr. 74
Lefeller, Abbot	Lea 37		Limon-Hallewin, Baron	Fr. 55
Le Fèvre d'Ormesson, A.	Fr. 61		Limou	Lat. 110
Le Fran, greffier	Fr. 40		Lindie, John	Lat. 133
Le Franc	Fr. 36		Lingaud, Jean-Baptiste	Fr. 74
Legal Documents	Lat. 151		Lioni, Cosimo, *Addenda et corr.*	Lea 350
Legende des Hl. Alexius	Ger. 4		Lippi, Carlo	Ital. 21
Leggenda di Christofano	Ital. 75		Lippo, Pietro	Ital. 10
Leggenda di S. Bonaventura	Ital. 2		Lippomano, Aloysio	Lea 384
Leggenda di S. Orsina	Ital. 75		Lippomano, Girolamo	Lea 83
Leggende della gloriosa Vergine Maria			Lisbon, Inquisition	Lea 193, 206
	Lat. 103		*Lista das personas que has de ouuir . . .*	
Leggende di S. Domitilla	Ital. 75		*sentenças do auto . . . da fee*	Lea 193

[263]

Litaniae B. M. V.	Lat. 147
Liturgy	Lat. 147
Livius Patavinus, Titus	Lat. 7
Livorno	Eng. 21.—Ital. 24
Livre de raison	Smith 42
Livre des trois imposteurs	Lea 368
Lob der Hl. Katherina	Ger. 4
Lobers (France)	Lea 2
Lockhart, Dean	Lat. 7
Löffler, Heinrich	Lat. 100
Lollino, Luigi (also called Aloysius)	
	Ital. 204
Lombardina, Johanna	Ital. 142
Lombardini, Antonio	Ital. 142
Lombardy	Lat. 167.—Ital. 60
London	Eng. 21.—Fr. 100
London, St. Paul	Eng. 29
London, Society of Apothecaries	
	Smith 14
Longerioni	Lea 360
Longpra family	Fr. 64
Longueville, Duc de	Fr. 93
Lonray	Fr. 93
Lopez de Cordova	Span. 34
Lori, Andrea	Ital. 181
Lorraine, Chevalier de	Fr. 100
Lorraine, Compagnie de commerce	
	Fr. 54
Lorris, Guillaume de	Fr. 1
Loschi, Antonio	Lat. 7
Lotti, Simone	Lea 284
Loudun	Lea 195
Louis XI, King of France	Fr. 84
Louis XIV, King of France	
Fr. 5, 36, 38, 100.—Ital. 187.—	
Lea 360, 362.—Smith 42	
Louis XV, King of France	Fr. 51, 99
Louvain	Lat. 191
Louvain, Université	Fr. 3
Low Countries	Fr. 3, 47, 53
Lower, William	Eng. 26
Lucarellus, Cesar	Lea 72
Lucas y Lopez, Juan de	Span. 44
Lucca	Ital. 22.—Lea 398
Lucca, Confraternità della S. Croce	
	Lea 383
Lucca, Conventus Sancti Augustini	
	Lea 51
Lucchesi, Francesco Saverio	Ital. 20
Lucianus Samosatensis	Lat. 7
Lucidarius super Biblia	Ital. 71
Lucilius	Lat. 184
Ludovicus, (S. J.)	Lea 140
Ludovicus de Favallibus	Lat. 157
Ludovisio, Card.	Lea 85
Ludwig, Count Palatine	Ger. 48
Luke, Harry	Lea 9
Lull, Ramón	Lat. 5.—Lea 19.—
	Smith 4, 13, 39, 41
Lume, Hinrik, de Eldere	Ger. 57
Lupus, Abp. of Saragossa	Lat. 139
Lusiana	Lea 365

Luther, Martin	Lat. 167.—Ger. 51, 60
Luzarche Collection	Lat. 89
Lyell, J. P. R.	Lat. 32, 35, 48.—
	Fr. 9.—Lea 55
Lyons	Lea 261
Lyons, Académie	Fr. 50
Macanaz, Melchor de	Lea 177–8
Macauley, Francis Campbell	
Ital. 2–3, 12, 78, 84, 128, 175, 178.—	
	Span. 1, 28
Macciochi family	Ital. 166
Macciucca, Thomas Vargas	
	Lea 167, 187
Machaut, Guillaume de	Fr. 15
Macherani, Bartolo	Ital. 35
Machiavelli, Niccolò	Ital. 140.—Lea 84
MacKenzie, Henry	Eng. 14
Madan, Falconer	Eng. 19.—Smith 3
Madrid	Eng. 21.—Fr. 94.—Lea 374,
	391
Madrigale e canzoni	Ital. 57
Magalotti	Ital. 178
Magazin des modernes	Fr. 57
Magno, Pietro	Ital. 108
Mahaut d'Artois, Countess of	
Burgundy	Lea 81
Mahoma en Granada	Lea 375
Mahomet Kutabanda, King of Persia	
	Lea 15
Mainbourg	Lea 388
Malachia, St.	Lea 362
Malaga, Colegio Jesuita	Span. 41
Malatesta	Ital. 120
Malatesta, Carlo	Lea 402
Malatesta, Novello	Ital. 78
Malebranche, Nicolas	
	Fr. 78.—Ital. 210
Malespini, Lorenzo Giacomino	
	Ital. 182
Malogoscz, Societas Sanctae Annae	
	Lat. 138
Malta, Knights of	Lat. 177.—Lea 367
Malvicini, Albericus	Lea 204
Mancini, Franciscus	Lat. 123
Mandagot, Guillaume de	Lea 116
Manget, Jean Jacquet	Smith 16
Manifesta	Lea 360
Manifesto del re di Sardegna	Lea 362
Manifesto per la Republica di Venezia	
	Lea 360
Mannelli, Marco	Lea 275
Mannelli, Niccolo, *Addenda et corr.*	
	Lea 351
Mannucci, Andrea	Lea 284
Manolessi, Emiliano Maria	Lea 83
Manresa	Lat. 151
Mansi, Raffaelo	Lea 355
Mantua	Lat. 94.—Lea 360, 362, 402
Manuale d'aritmetica commerciale	Ital. 185
Manucci, Francesco	Lea 223

Manucci, Matteo	Lea 223		Matthew of Faventia	Lat. 1
Marais, René	Fr. 93		Matthieu, Pierre	Lea 39
Marcaldi, Francesco	Ital. 85		Maurique, Alonso	Lea 20
Marcel	Fr. 1		Mauromatti, Teodoro	Ital. 89
Marcello, Lorenzo	Lea 360		Maurus, St.	Lea 182
Marchand, Gaspard	Fr. 93		Mavrocordatos, Nicholas	Greek 2

Manucci, Matteo — Lea 223
Marais, René — Fr. 93
Marcaldi, Francesco — Ital. 85
Marcel — Fr. 1
Marcello, Lorenzo — Lea 360
Marchand, Gaspard — Fr. 93
Marchesa Castracani (comedia) — Ital. 94
Marco, Giulia de — Lea 158
Marcus de Venetiis — Lea 55
Mari, Giacinto de — Lea 171
Maria Theresa, German Empress — Fr. 3.—Lea 181
Mariana, Juan de — Lea 157
Marianic Sequence — Ger. 4
Mariano, Fra — Ital. 16
Marie de Verdun — Fr. 46
Marie Elisabeth, Archduchess — Lea 155
Marienburg — Lat. 121
Marini, Vicentius — Ital. 5
Marino, Gasparo — Lea 360
Mark de Rome — Fr. 14
Marmelli, Nicolo — Lea 351
Marot, Jean — Fr. 21, 66
Márquez, Antonio — Lea 151
Marsala — Lea 397
Marsciano, Franciscus Onuphrius — Smith 16
Marseille, Marie Anthoinette de — Fr. 93
Marsigli, Antonio — Lat. 19
Martegli, U. — Ital. 37
Martelli, Bartolomeo di Larione — Ital. 76
Martelli, Tommaso — Lea 279
Martialis, Marcus Valerius — Lat. 125
Martin V, Pope — Lat. 189
Martin, King of Aragon — Lea 371, 397
Martin Lopez de Cordova — Span. 34
Martinellus, Blasius — Lat. 141
Martinez, Bartholomeo — Lea 20
Martini, Giuseppe — Ital. 97, 105–6, 112, 114–7, 120, 181, 209.—Lea 74, 372–3.
Martinozzi, Benedetto — Ital. 77
Martinuzzi, George — Lat. 195
Martorana — Lea 397
Mary, Virgin — Lat. 158.—Ital. 3, 9, 13, 54, 70, 73, 90, 93, 106
Marzio, Marco — Lat. 189
Marzucchi — Ital. 206
Masaniello — Ital. 168–9, 171–2
Mascara de Mascaris — Lat. 119
Mascaro, Hiacinto — Lea 371
Mascaro, Joan — Lea 371
Mascherata de' principi — Lea 362
Mason, Charles — Eng. 22
Mathematics — Ital. 55
Mathi — Lea 56
Mathurin de Montalais — Lea 202
Matignon, François de — Fr. 93
Mattei, Mauro — Ital. 181
Matteo, son of Filippo Fori — Lea 204
Matthew of Cracow — Lat. 90

Matthew of Faventia — Lat. 1
Matthieu, Pierre — Lea 39
Maurique, Alonso — Lea 20
Mauromatti, Teodoro — Ital. 89
Maurus, St. — Lea 182
Mavrocordatos, Nicholas — Greek 2
Maximilian II, German Emperor — Ger. 26–7.—Lea 360
Mayans y Siscar, Gregorio — Lea 131
Mayansiana, Bibliotheca — Span. 29
Maydestone, Richard — Eng. 1
Mayenne, de — Fr. 98
Mayer, Johann Friederich — Lea 145
Mazarin, Giulio — Fr. 100
Mazzolla, Calisto — Ital. 63
Mechtild, St. — Ital. 91
Mecocci, Luca — Lea 297
Medical, Geometrical and Optical Treatises — Lat. 133
Medici family — Lea 84, 87, 128, 212–302, 385, 398–9
Medici Mint — Lea 252
Medici, Agostino de — Lea 285
Medici, Alamanno de — Lea 267, 271–2, 276, 279–80, 287
Medici, Alamanno di Bernardo de — Lea 99, 226
Medici, Alamanno di Bernardo di Alamanno, *Addenda et corr.* — Lea 99
Medici, Alessandro de — Lea 77
Medici, Andrea de — Lea 243, 245–47, 249–50, 255–8, 265, 295
Medici, Andrea di Carlo de — Lea 237
Medici, Anna de — Lea 399
Medici, Bivigliano de — Lea 298
Medici, Bivigliano d'Alamanno de — Lea 216, 302
Medici, Camillo di Carlo de — Lea 330
Medici, Carlo de — Lea 213–5, 217–220, 222–3, 225–9, 237–9, 245, 254, 272–89, 299, *Addenda et corr.* Lea 344
Medici, Carlo Bernardo Alamanni de — Lea 230
Medici, Carlo di Bernardo de — Lea 232, 236
Medici, Carlo di Ferdinando de — Lea 224, 278
Medici, Cosimo de — Lat. 7
Medici, Cosimo, Grand Dukes of Tuscany, *see under* Cosimo
Medici, Fabrizio di Luigi de — Lea 231, 233, 235, 240–2, 290, 293
Medici, Fernando Alamanni de — Lea 269
Medici, Francesca di Bivigliano de — Lea 300
Medici, Francesco de — Ital. 196.—Lea 30, 220, 254, 261, 285, 347
Medici, Francesco Maria de — Lea 198
Medici, Geronimo de — Lea 402
Medici, Giovanbattista de — Lea 254
Medici, Giuliano de — Lea 173, 220

Medici, Giulio de	Lat. 124	Mercurio	Ital. 139
Medici, Gregorio de	Lea 220	*Mercurius corporis*	Lea 19
Medici, Lorenzino de	Lea 77	Merles, Balthasard François de,	
Medici, Lorenzo de		Marquis de Beauchamp	Fr. 58
	Ital. 16.—Lea 77, 219, 254	Merles, François de	Lat. 86
Medici, Lucia de	Lea 205	Merlin	Smith 4
Medici, Lucrezia de	Ital. 16	Merode, Richard de	Fr. 81
Medici, Luigi de	Lea 222–3, 233–5, 240, 268	Merz, August	Ger. 51
		Mesmer, Hieronymus	Lat. 18
Medici, Luigi di Bivigliano de		Messina	Lea 261, 353, 397
	Lea 270, 301	Metastasio, Pietro	Ital. 79.—Lea 362
Medici, Luisa di Bivigliano de	Lea 234	*Metra moralium philosophorum*	Lea 4
Medici, Maria de	Ital. 33	Metz	Lat. 93.—Fr. 11
Medici, Mariotto de	Lea 219–20	Metz, Jesuit College	Ital. 117
Medici, Mariotto di Gregorio de		Meung, Jehan de	Fr. 1
	Lea 222–3, 225, 227	Meursius, Joannes	Lat. 186
Medici, Niccolò de		Meursius, Wilhelm	Ital. 204
	Lea 231, 233, 235, 240–1, 274–5	Meusnier, Marie Charlotte de	Fr. 73
Medici, Niccolò di Luigi de	Lea 291–2	Mexico, Inquisition	Lea 25, 160
Medici, Ottaviano de		Michael de Massa	Lat. 48
	Lea 219, 222, 273–6	Michelozzi, Giovanbattista, *Addenda et*	
Medici, Ottaviano Giuseppe de	Lea 87	*corr.*	Lea 254
Medici, Ottomano Alamanno de		Michelozzi, Lorenzo, *Addenda et corr.*	
	Lea 277		Lea 254
Medici, Pandolfo de	Lea 232	Michiel de Cambier	Lea 197
Medici, Raffaello de	Lea 132	Michiel, Francesco	Ital. 187
Medici, Tommaso de	Lea 275	Michieli, Gabriel	Lat. 166
Medici, Vincenzo de	Lea 211, 217, 237, 243–50, 253, 255–8, 260–1, 263, 294–5, 317, 352, 369	Middleton, Henry	Ital. 61
		Middleton, J. J.	Ital. 61
		Migliore family	Lea 128
Medici Farnese, Margarita de	Ital. 180	Milan	Lat. 156, 167, 169.—Ger. 22. —Ital. 152, 192, 197.—Lea 8, 261, 360
Medina, Gomez de	Span. 22		
Medina, Isabel de	Lea 379		
Meditatione della vita de Sancto Johanni		Milan, Collegium Braÿdense	Lat. 22
Baptista	Ital. 29	Milford, J.	Eng. 28
Meisterbuch	Ger. 31	Milledoni, Antonio	Ital. 26
Melanchthon, Philipp	Ger. 54	Millet, Jacques	Fr. 12
Melander, Placidius Aegidius	Lat. 80	Millotet, Marc-Antoine	Fr. 2
Melgar, Francisco del	Lea 130	Milnes, John	Smith 29
Melius, Antonius	Lea 51	Miltitz, Karl von	Fr. 37, 67
Melk, Monastery	Lea 3	*Minerva philosophorum*	Smith 13
Mello, Orontio	Lea 207	Miniato, Rafaello di	Lea 225, 278
Melzi, G.	Ital. 16	Mirabeau, Honoré Gabriel Riqueti	
Memmingen, St. Martin	Lea 152		Fr. 31
Mémoire d'une cruauté inouïe	Fr. 36	Mirabella	Ital. 27
Mémoire sur la province de Bretagne	Fr. 71	*Miracholo che facie la Vergine*	Ital. 106
Mémoire sur l'état politique des Païs Bas		*Miracholo chome una santa donna*	Ital. 106
	Fr. 3	*Miracholo . . . della Vergine Mara*	
Memorial ajustado del processo . . . de			Ital. 106
Antonio Pérez	Lea 150	*Miracholo di nostra donna*	Ital. 106
Memorial que dió en una academia		*Miracholo d'una reina*	Ital. 106
	Lea 130	*Miracholo et assenpro d'una . . . donna*	
Memoriale date dal S. Coll. de' Cardinali			Ital. 106
	Lea 362	*Miracholo et assenpro d'uno . . .*	
Memoriale presentato . . . alla Santità		*chavaliere*	Ital. 106
d'Alessandro Settimo	Ital. 44	*Miracoli de la Vergine Maria*	Ital. 13
Memoriale presentato dal Duca di Terra		*Miracoli e leggende*	Ital. 106
Nuova	Ital. 44, 184	Mirandola, Francesco	Lea 278
Menander	Span. 22	*Miroir des bonnes femmes*	Fr. 32
Mendoza, Diego Hurtado de	Span. 1	*Mirror of Alchemy*	Smith 4
Menneken, Arnold	Lat. 191	*Mirror to Lewde Men and Wymmen*	
Menzini, Benedetto	Ital. 202		Eng. 3

Miscellanea ad historiam Poloniae saec. XVI pertinentia	Lea 384
Miscellanea autographica ecclesiastica italiana	Lea 196
Miscellanea di diverse relazioni	Lea 399
Miscellanea storica di Guastalla	Lea 402
Modus absolvendi ab excommunicatione	Lat. 108
Modus disponendi se ad mortem	Lea 152
Moench von Heilsbronn	Ger. 41
Des Moenchs Not	Ger. 4
Moerbeke, Guilelmus de	Lat. 49
Mohacs	Lea 397
Molière, Jean Baptiste Poquelin	Fr. 29, 100
Molinari, Oratio	Ital. 142
Molinetto, Antonio	Lea 360
Molineux, Antoine	Lat. 33
Molino, Domenico	Ital. 204
Molza, Francesco Maria	Ital. 37, 181
La monarchia spagnola	Ital. 164
Moncada family	Lea 29
Moncada, Ferdinando de	Lea 29
Moncelese	Lat. 109
Monfort, Matheo	Lea 371
Mongali, Domenico di Giovanni	Lea 265
Moñino de Floridablanca, José	Lea 135
Monitorium	Lea 360
Montalais, Mathurin de	Lea 202
Montalbano di Ribera, Antonio	Lea 397
Montalvan, Alonso de	Span. 2
Montalvo, Antonio	Lea 315
Montanor, Guido de	Smith 4
Montaperto, Gasparo	Lea 397
Montaperto, Petro	Lea 397
Montausier, Duc de	Fr. 100
Montauti, Antonio Francesco	Lea 30–2, 198, 391, 396
Montedoglio	Lat. 53–4
Monte Lauduno, Guilelmus de	Lat. 111.—Lea 21
Monteleone, Dukes of	Ital. 98
Monte Mileto, Duca di	Lea 362
Monterubbiano	Lea 67
Montferrat, Charles de	Fr. 46
Montgomery, Thomas H.	Ital. 153
Montigny, François de	Fr. 93
Montlauzun, Guillaume de	Lea 21
Montmartin-en-Oranges	Fr. 93
Montoia, Ysabel de	Lea 160
Montreuil	Fr. 93
Morante, Marquis de	Lea 180
Moraschino, Michele	Ital. 162
Morbecque	Fr. 97
Morbio, Carlo	Ital. 134
Morbio Library	Lat. 104, 109.—Ital. 58, 79, 82, 134.—Lea 8, 94, 204–5, 362
Morel, René	Fr. 93
Morell, Anthonio	Lea 371
Morelli, Nicolaio di Lorenzo	Lea 351
Moresino, Giuseppe	Lea 360
Moret, Louis de	Fr. 73
Moretto, Giuseppe	Ital. 162
Morienus Romanus	Smith 3
Morin, Simon	Lea 358
Moritz, Duke of Saxony	Ger. 58
Morosini, Andrea	Ital. 204
Morosini, Donato	Ital. 204
Morosini, Niccolò	Ital. 100
Morovelli, Francisco de	Lea 130
Morro, Pietro	Ital. 47
Morso family	Lea 397
Morso, Geronimo	Lea 397
Morte del Duca Alessandro de' Medici	Lea 77
Morte di Cecco d'Ascoli	Lea 173
Morte di Giuliano de Medici	Lea 173
Morte di Vincenzio Serzelli	Lea 77
Moscow	Eng. 21
Most Shortest Way	Smith 4
Motivi delle risoluzioni del Re Louis XIV	Lea 362
Mouravit, Gustave	Fr. 43
Münster	Lea 191
Muggenthal, Eberhardus Adolphus a	Ger. 46
Mugnaio, Bernardo	Lea 340
Mugnaio, Pippo di Bernardo, *Addenda et corr.*	Lea 340
Munau	Fr. 36
Munby, A. N. L.	Lat. 143
Mungai, Domenico di Giovanni, *Addenda et corr.*	Lea 265
Muoni, Damiano	Lea 74
Murad III, Emperor of the Turks	Lea 15
Muraire	Fr. 33
Muronius, Hieronymus	Lat. 166
Murtza, Josef	Lea 371
Murtza, Raymundo	Lea 371
Myerstein, E. H. W.	Lat. 51
Mystère de la passion	Fr. 12
Mystic Miscellany	Ger. 41
Naevius	Lat. 184
Nafissa	Ital. 102
Nanni, Battista	Ital. 44, 183
Nanni, Francesco di Domenico	Lea 271
Nanteuil, M. N.	Flemish 2
Napier, Capt.	Lea 77
Naples	Eng. 21.—Ital. 46, 96, 98, 152, 160, 168–72.—Span. 4, 27.— Lea 164–71, 189, 192, 199–200, 207, 261–2, 353, 362
Naples, Inquisition	Lea 98, 187
Nardeo, Giovan Theseo	Ital. 10
Nardi, Jacopo	Lea 14, 87

Narratione del successo della morte della		*Novum Judaeorum crimen*	Lea 384
Duchessa Violante di Cardona	Lea 154	Nürnberg	
Nascimento della Vergine Maria	Ital. 70		Ger. 12–3, 51.—Lea 123, 378
Naselli family	Lea 397	Nuysement, Jacques de	Smith 11
Naselli, Beatrice	Lea 397		
Naselli, Luigi	Lea 397		
Naselli-Galletti, Baldassare	Lea 397	Obereit, Jakob Hermann	
Naselli-Galletti, Marianna	Lea 397		Lat. 192.—Fr. 95
Nasello, Pericono de	Lea 397	Ockham, William of	Lat. 1
Nassau, Louis, Count of	Ital. 186	Oddo di Biagio	Lea 373
Naudé, Gabriel	Ital. 34	Oecolampadius, Joannes	Ger. 60
Navagero, Bernardo	Lea 83	*Oeuvres des femmes*	Smith 15
Navarro, Antonio	Lea 203	Oliva d'Aragona	Lea 397
Naxament del niño Jesus	Span. 18	Olivares, Duke	Lea 130
Necepsus, King of Egypt	Smith 38	Olivariis, Guillelmus Gilaberti de	
La Nenciotta	Ital. 199		Lea 89
Nény, Patrice-Mac	Fr. 3	Oliveriis, Oliverus de	Smith 13
Nepi	Lea 127	Olózaga, Salustiano de	Span. 3
Neri, Pompeo	Lea 86	Olschki, L. S.	Fr. 15
Nerli, Filippo	Lea 76	Ombrera, Maria	Lea 371
Nerli, Jacopo	Ital. 130	*Opéra comique*	Fr. 57
Netherlands	Fr. 100	*Optica*	Lat. 133
Neue Zeitung	Ger. 8, 28–9	*Opus mulierum*	Smith 15
Neufville, Nicolas de	Fr. 26, 98	*Opus universale*	Lea 19
Neuilly-le-Bisson	Fr. 93	*Oraisons*	Fr. 81
Neustadt a. d. Orla	Ger. 25	*Oratio ad Carolum V*	Lea 360
Newton, Isaac	Lat. 192.—Fr. 95	*Oratione*	Ital. 73
Niccolò Niccoli	Lat. 7	*Oratione della Vergine Maria*	Ital. 73
Nicelli, Paolo	Lat. 152	Orchi, Carlo	Ital. 134
Nicholas IV, Pope	Lat. 122	*Ordre de la Nef*	Fr. 83
Nicholas V, Pope	Lat. 189	*Ordre du Navire*	Fr. 83
Nicholo di Jacopo	Ital. 93	*Ordtnung des Brüchtenverhörs*	Ger. 45
Nicolas, Cardinal Deacon	Lea 366	*Origine e descendenza della casa de Medici*	
Nicolaus de Dinkelsbühl	Lat. 36, 92		Lea 84
Nicolaus Magni de Jauer		Orlandi, Antonio	Ital. 42
	Lea 24, and 24 *note*	Orlandi, Gisberto	Ital. 42
Nicolaus von Wyle	Ger. 6	Orlandi, Giuseppe	Ital. 42
Nidardo, Juan Everardo	Lea 142, 156	Orléans, Duc d'	Smith 7
Noailles family	Fr. 62	Orléans, Henri d'	Fr. 93
Noircourt	Fr. 5	Ormesson, André François d'	Fr. 61
Nola, Giovanni da	Smith 9	Orne	Fr. 93
Nolli, Rodrigo	Lea 171	Orosius	Lat. 63
Noot	Lea 371	Orsina, St.	Ital. 75
Nores, Giasone	Ital. 131	Orsini, Card.	Ital. 46
Nores, Pietro di	Lea 40	Orsini, Bertoldo degli	Lea 28
North, Frederick, Earl of Guilford		Orsini, Rinaldo degli	Lea 28
Fr. 79.—Ital. 19, 133.—Lea 71, 96, 372		Orsino, Fulvio	Ital. 204
		Orsome	Fr. 84
Northumberland, 9th Earl of	Smith 4	Osequerra, Andrés	Lea 117
Nostiz, C. W. G. von	Lat. 134–5	*Osservazione dell' imperatore*	Lea 362
Nostiz, C. W. L. B. von	Lat. 134	Otho, Johann	Ger. 34
Nostrodamus, Michael	Lea 362	Otto III, German Emperor	Lea 27
Nota de capi principali	Lea 384	Otto of Freising	Lea 55
Notabilia de vitiis	Lat. 61	Ottoboni, Card.	Lea 75, 194
Notabilia varia	Lat. 118	Overijssell	Dutch 4
Notabilis specialis	Lat. 122	Ovidius Naso, Publius	Fr. 100
Notamento per la restitutione . . . *di Bari*			
	Lea 384		
Notarial Handbook	Lat. 82	Padavia, Marc Antonio	Ital. 14
Notitia delle ragioni	Lea 362	Padua	Lat. 108.—Lea 394–5
Notizie delle famiglie de Vio, Ezquerre, de Terma . . .	Lea 397	Padua, S. Agostino	Lat. 10

[268]

Padua, S. Luca	Lat. 119
Page, William	Lat. 33
Pages	Lea 371
Pagnoni, Ernesto	Lat. 90
Pagula, William	Lat. 33
Palagonia	Lea 397
Palamos, Count of	Lea 377
Palermo	Lea 261, 353, 397
Palermo, S. Domenico	Lea 397
Palermo, S. Maria della Pietà	Lea 397
Palestine	Lea 4, 55
Pallavicino, Ferrante	Ital. 208
Palude, Petrus de	Lea 45
Panagathus, L.	Lat. 167
Pancera, Francesco	Lat. 108
Panciatichi, Francesco	Lea 198, 399
Pandolfini, Alessandra	Lea 340
Pandoni, Petrus	Lat. 46
Panin, Count	Fr. 55
Panteleon	Smith 13
Pantelleria	Lea 397
Panza, J. Casimir	Lat. 171
Papacoda, Giovanni Lorenzo	Lea 384
Papacy	Fr. 68.—Ital. 141, 148.— Lea 355 *(see also* names of individual popes)
Papal States	Lat. 144
Papeles varios	Lea 141
Pappe, F. F.	Lea 368
Paracelsus, Theophrastus	Smith 5, 22
Paradiso, Paul	Fr. 21
Paradixo, Gabriello	Ital. 11
Paraldus, Guilelmus	Lat. 140
Pare, Joan Baptista	Lea 371
Paris	Fr. 90.—Lea 391
Paris, Chambre des comptes	Fr. 25
Paris, Parlement	Fr. 28, 73.—Smith 32
Parma	Lea 101, 360
Parma, Duke of	Ital. 153
Parole dévote	Lat. 108
Parrini, Pietro	Lea 239, 289
Parthenios, Patriarch of Jerusalem	Greek 2
Pascal family	Fr. 64
Pascal, Jean	Fr. 64
Pasquillas in aulicos colonienses	Ger. 7
Passau	Ger. 48
Passerat, Jean	Lat. 184
Passio Jesu Christi	Lat. 196
Passion de notre sauveur Jesus Christ	Fr. 41
Passione del nostro Signor	Ital. 13, 97, 161
Passione e resurrezione di Christo	Ital. 70
Pastore, Rafaello	Ital. 59
Pastorius family	Ger. 54
Pastorius, Dorothea Esther	Ger. 54
Pastorius, Melchior Adam	Ger. 54–5
Patavini, Francesco	Lea 296
Patetta, Federico	Lea 51
Patkul, J. R.	Fr. 37, 67
Paul, St.	Eng. 29
Paul III, Pope	Ital. 141.—Lea 107, 401
Paul IV, Pope	Ital. 144.—Lea 40, 154, 387
Paul V, Pope	Ital. 46.—Lea 356, 360
Pauli, Joannes	Lat. 191
Paulus de Liazariis	Lat. 113
Paulus de Nursia	Ital. 29
Paulus Pergulensis	Lat. 16
Pavard, Jacques	Fr. 93
Pavia	Lat. 146
Pawilhar	Lea 47
Paxiente, Antonio Manuel	Span. 17
Payne, Richard	Lea 371
Pearce, the Black Monk	Smith 4
Peccati mortali	Ital. 76
Peccori, Guglielmo	Lea 343
Pedraça, Alonso de	Lea 156
Pegasi, Francisco	Lat. 108
Pego, Jacobus de	Lea 8
Peignot, Gabriel	Fr. 98
Pelafol	Fr. 92
Pelayre, Miguel	Lea 371
Pèlerinage de damoiselle sapience	Fr. 10
Pelisson-Fontaine, Paul	Fr. 100
Pellotus, scribe	Lat. 122
Penn, William	Ger. 54
Penna, Albertus	Lea 205
Pennaforte, Raymondus de	Lat. 89, 164, 196
Pennsylvania	Fr. 95
Penrose, Boies II	Lea 55
Percitio dell'anima	Ital. 75
Percy, Henry, 9th Earl of Northumberland	Smith 4
Peregrinus de Santo Vito	Lea 4
Peregrinus Polonus	Lat. 158
Pérez, Antonio	Lea 150–1, 153
Perpetual Card	Lat. 144
Perrin, Elisabeth Thérèse	Fr. 93
Perto, Sebastiano	Lea 118
Perugia	Ital. 42
Perugia, Inquisition	Lea 60
Perugia, S. Lorenzo	Lea 43
Perutiles quedam observationes	Lat. 133
Pescara Papers	Ital. 124
Pesciettus, Jacobus Maria	Lat. 155
Pescioni, Guglielmo, *Addenda et corr.*	Lea 343
Peter the Great, Russian Emperor	Fr. 100
Petit du Noyer, Anne Marguerite	Eng. 25
Petrarca, Francesco	Lat. 7, 43.—Ital. 7, 73, 151
Petroni, Riccardo	Ital. 105
Petrus Bertrandus	Span. 26
Petrus, cardinalis Firasonensis	Lat. 108
Petrus Damianus	Lat. 107
Petrus de Abano	Eng. 24
Petrus de Braco	Lat. 121
Petrus de Copertone	Fr. 45

[269]

Petrus de Monastero	Lea 194
Petrus de Palude	Lea 45
Petrus de Riga	Lat. 112
Petrus de Tussignano	Lat. 52
Petrus de Vincentia	Lat. 93
Petrus Johannes Olivi	Lat. 122
Petrus Lombardus	Lat. 2, 32, 196.—Lea 24
Peyrat	Fr. 87
Pfeffel, Gottlieb Konrad	Ger. 32
Pfeffingen	Ger. 38
Pfeuffer, Georg	Lea 22
Phalaris	Ital. 78
Philadelphia	Fr. 95
Philip II, King of Spain	Ital. 144.—Span. 2, 15.—Lea 39–40, 83, 106, 138, 141, 387
Philip III, King of Spain	Span. 30.—Lea 153, 369
Philip IV, King of Spain	Ital. 178.—Span. 30–8.—Lea 130
Philip V, King of Spain	Ital. 43.—Span. 39.—Lea 362
Philippe, Duke of Burgundy	Fr. 44
Philipus Brusserius	Lea 55
Phillipps, Thomas	Lat. 15, 45, 58, 63, 83.—Fr. 14, 38, 49.—Ger. 14.—Ital. 67, 89, 133, 146.—Lea 10, 23, 62, 71, 83, 96, 111, 113, 115, 361, 390
Philo Judaeus	Lat. 13
Philosophers Stone	Smith 4
Philosophus perpulcer	Lea 19
Phontio, Bartholomeo	Ital. 78
Photius, St.	Ger. 60
Piacenza	Lat. 145.—Ital. 145, 153.—Lea 126, 204–5, 317–8
Pianto de la Vergine Maria	Ital. 13
Pibrac family	Fr. 62
Piccolomini, Antonio	Ital. 174
Piccolomini, Francesco	Ital. 174
Piccolomini, Giovanni Tedeschini	Lat. 124
Piccolomini, Nerius Gabrielli di	Lea 70
Piccolomini Papers	Lea 71
Pichon, Jérome	Fr. 21
Pietro Damiani, St.	Lat. 107
Pietro da Prata	Lea 28
Pietro di Toledo	Ital. 160
Pignatelli, Antonio, Card.	Ital. 150
Pilichdorf, Petrus de	Lea 22
Pin	Lat. 106
Piña, Antonio	Lea 371
Pinerolo	Ital. 107
Pinzonibus, Venturinus de	Lat. 177
Pio, Giovan' Battista	Ital. 85
Pisa	Ital. 101.—Lea 262, 353, 398
Piscicello, Hettore	Ital. 10
Pistoia (salina)	Lea 221
Pistorien, F.	Ital. 129
Pitti, Anastasio di Buonacorso	Lea 219–20, 222–3, 226
Pitti, Antonio	Lea 220
Pitti, Antonio di Giovanni	Lea 223
Pitti, Buonacorso	Lea 225
Pitti, Giovanni	Lea 219–20
Pius II, Pope	Lat. 93.—Ger. 6
Pius IV, Pope	Ital. 132, 141.—Lea 400
Pius V, Pope	Lea 360
Pius VI, Pope	Ital. 79
Plan, Hans Heinrich	Rhaeto-Rom. 1
Planas, Pablo	Lea 371
Platamone, Antonio	Lea 397
Platea, Johannes Franciscus de	Lea 10
Plato	Lat. 13
Plusieurs recettes	Smith 36
Plymouth	Eng. 22
Poccobelli	Lea 360
Poema sopra le guerre dall' anno 1733	Ital. 188
Poenitentiale	Lat. 55
Poesie varie	Ital. 43
Poésies diverses . . . 1756	Smith 36
Poetical Miscellany	Ital. 17
Poetry Miscellany	Fr. 94
Poggio Bracciolini	Lat. 7
Poland	Fr. 13, 37, 67.—Ital. 43, 46, 154, 164.—Lea 362, 384
Polich, Martinus	Lat. 52
Pollicey undt Landtsordtnung	Ger. 45
Polna, Johannes de	Lat. 26
Pommereu, intendant	Fr. 71
Pompeius Magnus, Cn.	Lat. 7
Pompignan	Fr. 87
Pongracz, Georgius	Lat. 127
Pons, Maria	Lea 371
Ponticus Virunius, Ludovicus	Lea 13, *note*
Ponze de Leon, Luiggi	Ital. 197
Porcacchi, Thommaso	Lat. 108
Portellet de Senas, Rainant	Fr. 80
Portia, Prince	Ital. 139
Portolano	Ital. 104
Portolungo	Lea 399
Portugal	Ital. 44, 132, 184
Portugal, Inquisition	Lea 121, 139
Portuguese Fortune Book	Port. 1
Possevino, Antonio	Ital. 204.—Smith 38
Potoski, Primate	Lea 362
Poulin, George	Fr. 20
Poullais, Nicolas	Fr. 93
Poveda Domistico	Span. 43
Poznań (Posen)	Lea 384
Pozzabonelli, Girolamo	Ital. 198
Pozzabonelli, Giuseppe	Ital. 198
Practica	Smith 13
Practica magni philosophi	Lea 19
Practice of the Philosophers	Smith 4
Pradel, Mlle.	Fr. 100
Pradenico, Petrus	Lea 360
Prades	Lat. 110
Praelectiones physicae	Smith 34
Prague, University	Lat. 92
Pratica deli devoti	Ital. 91

Prato	Lea 28, 398	Rabanus Anglicus	Lat. 174
Prayer Book	Ger. 53	Rabelais, François	Fr. 5
Preambula communicationis	Lat. 118	Rabutin, Michel-Celse-Roger de,	
Premierfait, Laurens de	Fr. 9	Comte de Bussy	Fr. 63
Previté-Orton, C. W.	Lat. 143	*Raccolta d'alcuni avvertimenti . . . di*	
Prevostin of Cremona	Lat. 62	*Mons. Landriani*	Ital. 148
Preysing, von	Ger. 59	*Raccolta di celebri arcani chimici*	
Pribeck	Ger. 49		Smith 40
Priestley Family Papers	Smith 27–30	*Racconto del grave delitto del Centino*	
Priestley, George	Smith 30		Lea 154
Priestley, Jonathan	Smith 29	*Racconto della sollevatione di Napoli*	
Priestley, Joseph	Smith 27, 29		Ital. 172
Priestley, Nathaniel	Smith 29	Racier, Père	Fr. 87
Priestley, Phebe	Smith 27	*Radius ab umbra*	Smith 13
Prinz, Nicolaus	Lea 159	Raesfelt, Lambert	Ger. 45
Prioli, Laurentio	Ital. 19	*Raggioni state presentate ad instanza del Re*	
Prodhomme, Jacques	Fr. 93	*di Portogallo*	Ital. 44
Profetia ex Ioanne Luxembourg	Lea 362	Raginaldus Colli Rubei	Lea 197
Profezia di S. Brigita	Lea 362	Ragona, Jacobus	Lea 13
Profezie del pazzo	Lea 362	Raimundus *see* Raymondus	
Prohibitio de proprietate tenenda	Lea 24	Rambaldis, Benvenuto de	Lat. 81
Prophecy	Lat. 124	Ramon dela Faga	Fr. 45
Prophetia anonymi	Lat. 156	Ramoneda, Esteban	Lea 371
Prophicey . . . auf das 1400 Jar	Ger. 19	Ranchin, Jacques de	Fr. 100
Provence	Fr. 35	Randall, Mrs.	Eng. 9
Provence, Parlement	Fr. 98	Ranshofen, St. Pancratius	Lat. 140
Provinciale secundum provincias	Lea 11	Rasaille	Lea 388
Prudentius	Lat. 99.—Ger. 60	Rasponi, Cesare, Card.	Ital. 100
Prussia	Fr. 3, 55	Rasser, Rudolfus	Lat. 41
Psalter	Lat. 154	Ratisbon, Schottenabtei St. Jakob	
Psalter of Philosophers	Smith 4		Ger. 23
Psalterium	Dutch 1	Rauscher, Romanus	Lat. 77
Pscherer, Lorentz	Lea 378	Ravenoldus, Johannes Petrus	Lat. 166
Pubius, Ludovicus Jacobus	Lea 363	Ravigny	Fr. 93
Pusol, Miguel	Lea 371	Raymon de Villa Nova	Fr. 80
Pyrrhus	Lat. 7	Raymondus de Ligno	Smith 13
Pyrrus de Baulio	Lea 192	Raymondus de Sabunde	Lea 7
		Raymondus Lullus	
		Lat. 5.—Lea 19.—Smith 4, 13, 39, 41	
		Raymundus de Pennaforte	
			Lat. 89, 164, 196
Quadrius, R.	Lea 402	Razumovski, Andreas	Fr. 55
Quaestio utrum hoc possit scire	Lea 152	Recalmuto	Lea 397
Quaestiones de accidentibus anime rationalis		Recaneto, Antonius	Lea 51
	Lat. 56	*Recettes et secrets*	Smith 36
Quaestiones de ente possibili	Lat. 170	*Rechts Ordnung*	Ger. 45
Quaestiones duo	Lat. 103	*Recueil de poësie*	Fr. 27, 29, 100–1
Quaestiones pulchre de contritione	Lat. 196	Reddan, James H.	Lat. 69
Quaratesi, Vincenzo	Lea 354	*Reformatio jurisdictionis . . . Curiae*	
Quartier Dauril	Smith 37	*coloniensis*	Ger. 45
Quawden, Francis	Eng. 1	Regensperger, Johannes	Lea 22
Querini, Leonardo	Lea 360	*Registrum historiarum Evangeliorum*	
Quesada, Fernando de	Span. 10		Lea 152
Questio	Lat. 118	Regnault, Claude	Fr. 54
Quevedo y Villegas, Francisco de		*Regole generali del S. Officio*	Lea 149
	Lea 130	*Regulae iuris*	Lat. 42, 113
Quinault, Philippe	Fr. 100	Reif, G. N.	Fr. 30
Quindecim signa	Lat. 55	Reims	Lat. 194
Quintana	Span. 25	Reinartz, Bertram	Ger. 33
Quinziano, Guilio	Ital. 7	Reinecke, Conrad Viet	Ger. 18
Quirini, Girolamo	Ital. 143	*Relación de lo acaecido en España*	Lea 142
Quiroga, Card.	Lea 120	*Relación de los reos*	Lea 193
Quirot, Pierre	Fr. 34		

[271]

Relation des affaires de Provence	Fr. 98	Ricci, Vincenzo de	Lea 254
Relatione de Firenza	Lea 119	Riccomanni family	Lea 398
Relatione . . . della forma de negotiare con Swizzeri	Ital. 143	Richelieu, Card. Fr. 100–1.—Ital. 204.—Lea 195	
		Richi, Giovanni	Lea 28
Relatione della giustitia fatta di Onofrio Santacroce	Lea 154	Ridolfi, Tommaso	Lea 342
		Riegel, Jacob	Lat. 6
Relatione delle potenze e forze delli principi d'Italia	Ital. 44, 184	Rieux, Gabriel Bernard de	Fr. 38
		Riflessi e discorsi politici	Ital. 139
Relatione dell'institutione . . . dei cavalieri di Rodi	Ital. 143	*Riflessioni politiche sopra Tacito*	Ital. 139
		Rigondandolo, Doge of Venice	Lea 5
Relatione di Roma	Ital. 44, 183	Rijnland, Heemraad	Dutch 3
Relatione di stato de Milano	Lea 360	*Rime burlesche*	Ital. 181
Relatione di tutta la provincia di Dalmatia	Ital. 132	*Rime di Timante Frascerepnico*	Ital. 51
		Rime varie del secolo XVII	Lea 360
Relazione dei tribunali di Roma	Lea 183	Rinaldo di Falente	Lea 233
Relazione de' servigi degli Antenati	Lea 397	Rinuccini, Alessandro	Lea 77
Religious Poem	Ital. 29	Rinuccini, March.	Lea 399
Religious Tracts	Ital. 2	Ripas	Lat. 148
Religious Verse Miscellany	Ital. 73	Ripley, George	Smith 4
Remedia pro casibus contingentibus	Lat. 92	Risaliti, Francesco di Stefano di	Lea 236, 332–5
Renaissance Miscellany	Lat. 7, 34		
Renato, Giuseppe	Lea 362	*Ristretto circa li delitti . . . à giudicarsi nel S. Officio*	Lea 149
Renger, Albrecht	Ger. 51		
Renier, Thomas	Fr. 93	*Ristretto dell' atto di confederazione*	Lea 362
Rennert, Hugo Albert	Span. 30, 32–5, 37	*Rituale praedicatorum*	Lat. 9
		Rivagorza, Conde de	Lea 141
Renselaer	Fr. 100	Riva Palacio, General	Lea 25
Renson, A.	Flemish 2	Rivera	Lea 397
Repnin, N. V.	Fr. 55	Rivius, Godefr.	Smith 16
Réponse . . . à . . . l'Archiduchesse Marie Elisabeth	Lea 155	Rizzo, Andrea	Ital. 162
		Roano	Lea 365
Requesens family	Lea 397	Robert, monk of the XVth cent.	Fr. 10
Requesens, Luigi	Lea 397	Robert, Antoine	Fr. 46
Requesenus, Johannes	Lea 371	Roberts, Lewis	Eng. 21
Responsio synodalis	Lat. 64	Robusti, Ansermus	Lea 53
Responsiones . . . praelatorum Poloniae]	Lea 384	Rocabertino, Guillermus de	Lea 371
		Rocabruna, Jayme	Lea 371
Ressano, Cesare	Ital. 107	Rocco, D.	Ital. 104
Ressano, Giov. Paolo	Ital. 107	Rocha, Rafael	Lea 371
Ressano, Horatio	Ital. 107	Roda y Arrieta, Manuel	Lea 131
Resurrexione di Christo	Ital. 70	Rodriguez, Sebastian	Lea 25
Reyff, George Nicolas	Fr. 30	Rodriguez, Ysabel	Lea 25
Rezay, Guillaume Bernard de	Fr. 73	Rogers, Fairman	Vet. 1
Rezzonico, Carlo	Lea 394	Rohault, Jacques	Fr. 100
Rhodes	Fr. 50	Roland (bastion)	Fr. 92
Ribera	Lea 397	Rolandus de Monte	Lea 45
Ribera, Juan de	Lea 203	Rolet, Antoine	Lat. 106
Ricardo e Cattilla	Ital. 84	Rolewinck, Werner	Lat. 85
Ricasoli family	Lea 280	Rolle, Richard	Eng. 1, 8
Ricasoli, Bernardo	Lea 285	Roma, Julio, Card.	Ital. 134
Ricasoli, Elbrardo di	Lea 283	*Roman de Troie*	Fr. 24
Ricasoli, Lorenzo	Lea 317	Romanellus Egidii	Lea 60
Ricasoli, Vincenzo	Lea 317	Romania	Lea 5
Riccardi, Bernardo	Lea 261	Rombouts family	Fr. 44
Riccardi, Jacopo	Lea 251	Rome Lat. 7.—Eng. 21.—Ital. 44–5, 99, 167, 183, 195.—Lea 38, 83, 201, 261–2, 384	
Riccardi, Lorenzo	Lea 317		
Ricchieri, Lodovico Celio	Ital. 204		
Ricci, Aurelio	Ital. 122	Rome, Biblioteca corsiniana	Ital. 20
Ricci, Bartolomeo	Lea 239	Rome, Inquisition Lea 111, 113, 115, 158, 167–71, 184, 206–7	
Ricci, Federigo de	Lea 274, 351		
Ricci, P.	Lat. 162	Rome, S. Maria di Loreto	Ital. 40

[272]

Romena, capt.	Lea 369	Saccano, Pietro Fernando	Lea 397
Romena, Compagnia della gloriosa		Sacchetti, Giulio	Ital. 178
Vergine Maria	Ital. 93	*Sacramental Handbook*	Lat. 118
Roncourt	Lea 388	Sacrobosco, Johannes de	Lat. 191
Ronsard, Pierre de	Fr. 5	Sagredo, Niccolò	Lea 360
Rorincus, Antonius	Lat. 179	St. Denis, Louis de	Fr. 93
Ros de Medrano, Diego Castello		Saint Dié	Lea 388
	Lea 130	Saint Gall	Rhaeto-Rom. 1
Rosaire des filosophes	Smith 15	Saint-Gelais, Adrien de	Fr. 21
Rosanus, Philippus	Lat. 171	Saint Jean de Jerusalem (order)	Fr. 86
Rosarium philosophorum	Smith 15	St. John, James Augustus	Lat. 21
Rosengarten, J. G.	Ger. 54–5	Saint-Michel, (knights)	Fr. 17
Rosenheim Collection	Lea 373	Saint Remy	Fr. 97
Ross, T. Edward	Lat. 20–1.—Eng. 6	Saint Sernin	Lat. 178
Rossano	Lea 384	Saint Severus, Bp. of	Lea 63
Rosselli, Leone	Ital. 162	Saint Vaast, Abbey	Fr. 40
Rossi, Cav.	Smith 16	Saint-Vallier	Fr. 98
Rossi, Niccolò	Ital. 20	Sainte Croix	Lat. 178
Rossi, Patritio de	Ital. 62	Sainte Geoire	Fr. 64, 72
Rossi, Pino de	Ital. 125	Salamanca	Span. 8
Rothenburg	Ger. 51	Salamanca, Notre Dame de Pilar	
Rothesay, Stuart de	Lea 134		Greek 1
Rothschild, Otto	Smith 36	Salamanca, Universidad	
Rothwellus, Guilelmus	Lat. 32, 118		Span. 39–40, 42–3, 46, 48
Rottenburgische Cronica	Ger. 51	Salazar, Ignazio de	Span. 22
Rottweil	Ger. 22	Salazar de Mendoza, Pedro de	
Rotzo	Lea 365		Lea 120, 130
Rouen, Augustinian Hermits	Lat. 189	Salbany, Miguel	Lea 371
Rouen, Parlement	Fr. 93	Salelles	Lat. 110
Rousseau, Jean-Jacques	Fr. 95	Sallustius Crispus, C.	Lat. 125
Roussel, D.	Lat. 66	Salmati, Pietro	Lea 275
Roussel, Pierre	Fr. 93	*Salmista di David*	Ital. 183
Rovigo	Lat. 166, 176.—Ital. 113	Salsa, Marquis de	Ital. 25.—Lea 199
Royaumont, St. Mary, Monastery		Salutati, Coluccio	Lea 373
	Lat. 39	Salva, Biblioteca	Span. 31
Rozé, Alexis	Fr. 93	Salvaterra	Lat. 155
Rucellai family	Lea 398	Salvatori, Andrea	Ital. 33
Rucellai, Carlo	Lea 275	Salvetti, Francesco	Lea 261
Rucellai, Francesco		Salviati family	Lea 398
	Lea 273–4, 276, 279–83, 285	Salviati, Filippo	Lea 282
Rucellai, Francesco di Girolamo		Salviati, Giannozzo	Ital. 16
	Lea 219	Salviati, Guerardo	Lea 227
Rucellai, Giovanni	Lea 283	Salviati, Piero d'Alamanno	Lea 227
Rucellai, Girolamo	Lea 277	Salvini, Anton Maria	Ital. 165
Rucellai, Giuletto	Lea 278, 282–3	*Samminiati Archive*	Lea 398
Rucellai, Giuletto Francesco	Lea 277	Samuel, Rabbi	Ger. 3
Rucellai, Mariotto	Lea 283, 287	Sanctus Nicholas, Monastery	Lea 62
Rucellai, Pandolfo	Lea 279	Sandelli, Martino	Ital. 204
Rudellius Scurbergensis	Smith 41	Sanderson, N.	Eng. 23
Rudianus	Lea 19, *note*	Sanfelice, Giuseppe	
Rudolf II, German Emperor	Lea 356		Ital. 129.—Lea 188
Rupescissa, Joannes de	Lat. 19	Sangallo, Antonio da	Ital. 196
Russia	Fr. 55.—Ital. 164	Sanini, Joannes	Ital. 1
Rutherford, Daniel	Smith 35	Sanlecque, Louis	Fr. 52
Ruvo, Conte de	Ital. 179	San Marino	Ital. 34
		San Miniato	Lea 398
		San Miniato, Bartolomeo da	Lea 97
Sabatini, Battista	Lea 287	Sanonus, Jacobus	Ital. 119
Sabini, Antonio	Ital. 147	Sans, Jayme	Lea 371
Sabunde, Raymondus de	Lea 7	Sansonius, Fulvius	Lea 127
Saccano, Aloisio	Lea 397	Sansovino, Francesco	Ital. 151
Saccano, G. M. de	Lea 397	San Spirito, near Reggio	Lat. 157

Santacroce, Costanza	Lea 154	Seguer, Gili	Lea 371
Santacroce, L.	Ital. 46, 141	*Seifrit*	Ger. 6
Santacroce, Onofrio	Lea 154	Seneca, Lucius Annaeus	
Santacroce, Paolo	Lea 154		Lat. 51, 129, 181
Santa Maria di Loreto	Ital. 40	Senna, Servio	Ital. 188
Santa Maria super Taburrum, Convent		*Sentenza d'un clarissimo senator veneto*	
	Lat. 171		Lea 356
Santini, Leonardo	Lea 310	*Sept sages de Rome*	Fr. 14
Santi Veronese, Card.	Lea 395	*Sequences* and *Lectiones*	Ital. 75
Santo Stefano, Ordine de', cavalieri		Sergardi, Lodovico	Ital. 174
	Lea 65, 132	Serloni, Geronimo	Lea 353
Sanudo, Marino	Lea 4	*Sermone sopra la beatitudine dell' Nostro*	
Sanuto, Livio	Ital. 61	*Salvator*	Ital. 163
Saône, Franciscan convent	Lat. 93	*Sermones*	Lat. 55.—Ital. 11
Saponara, Nunnery of S. Croce	Ital. 74	*Sermones anonymi*	Lat. 84
Sappho	Ital. 118	*Sermones de B. Maria*	Lat. 118
Sarasin, Jean François	Fr. 5	*Sermones de tempore*	Lat. 61
Sarpi, Paolo		*Sermones dominicales per circulum anni*	
Ital. 204.—Lea 33, 35, 94, 96			Lat. 96
Sarrazius de Bethencourt	Lea 197	*Sermones quadragesimales*	Lat. 196
Sasso Forte, San Bartolomeo	Lea 122	*Sermones varii*	Lat. 158
Savelli, Troilo	Lea 154	*Sermones varii et exempla*	Lat. 118
Savigliano	Lat. 168	*Sermons*	Rhaeto-Rom. 2
Savini, Scipione	Ital. 174	Serra, Mansi	Lea 371
Savio Romano	Ital. 75	Serra, N.	Lea 371
Savorgnano, Ascanio	Ital. 85	Serrano, Juan	Span. 13
Savoy Fr. 69.—Ital. 23, 110.—Lea 83		Serto, Abbot	Ital. 79
Saxony Fr. 37, 67.—Ger. 40.—Ital. 43		Serzelli, Vincenzio	Lea 77
Scaglia, Desiderio	Lea 184	Sessa, Duke of	Span. 3, 50
Scarron, Paul	Fr. 5	Sette comuni	Lea 365
Scelta di canzoni	Ital. 162	*Sette Salmi Penitenziali*	Ital. 125
Scheyern, Monastery	Lat. 175	Settius, Joannes Garcio	Lea 20
Schickard, Wilhelm	Ital. 204	*Seven Deadly Sins*	Ital. 76
Schmidt, Nicolaus	Ger. 51	*Seven Penitential Psalms*	Eng. 1
Schmieher, Peter	Ger. 14	Severinus, Domnus	Lat. 108
Schönn neu Liedt vonn dem . . . Bischoff		Sevilla	Span. 48
von Collnn	Ger. 9	Sevilla, Universidad	Span. 39
Schöppl	Ger. 38	*Sex documenta homini morituro . . .*	
Schopper, Hartmann	Lat. 188	*necessaria*	Lat. 118
Schrauf	Lat. 116	Seybert, Henry	Port. 1.—Smith 32
Schubert, Kristian Benjamin	Ger. 32	Sforza	Ital. 120
Schulz, Ernst	Lat. 12, 43–4, 52	Sforza, Bona	Lea 384
Schum, Friedrich	Lat. 31	Sforza, Francesco	Ital. 152
Schwarz, Hanns	Ger. 51	Sforza, Francesco Maria	Span. 36
Schweizer, Joseph	Lea 356	Sforza, Ludovico Maria	Ital. 153
Scielta delle pratiche	Smith 10	Sforza, Pallavicino, Card.	Ital. 139
Scientific Miscellany	Lea 19	*Sicilian Religious Poetry*	Ital. 115
Scilly Islands	Eng. 22	Sicily	Span. 27.—Lea 6, 397
Scipio Africanus, Publius Cornelius		Sicily, Castello	Lea 397
	Lat. 7	Siena	Lat. 137.—
Scotland	Eng. 15	Ital. 73, 81.—Lea 119, 398	
Scotta, Francisca	Ital. 77	Siena, St. Mary of the Angels	Lea 70
Sea Horse, H. M. S.	Eng. 22	Sifonte, Conte di	Lea 14
Seaulx	Lea 202	Sigismund, German Emperor	
Sebastian, St.	Ital. 106		Lat. 92.—Lea 362
Sechia, Tisabesano	Ital. 194	Sigismund I, King of Poland	Lea 401
Secrani, Marco	Lea 344	Sigismund II, King of Poland	Lea 384
Secrani, Parrino	Lea 344	Silesia	Fr. 103
Secreta des Doctor Krug	Smith 20	Silva, Donato de	Ital. 188
Sedulius	Lat. 99, 132	Silva, Hercules	Ital. 14
Sega, Filippo	Fr. 102	Silvestri, E.	Ital. 62
Segardi, Filippo	Ital. 174	Simonius, Joannes	Lat. 137

Sirigatti, Giuliano	Lea 353
Six, J. W.	Lat. 118
Sixtus IV, Pope	Lat. 93, 189
Sixtus V, Pope	Ital. 148.—Lea 154, 362
Slavery	Lea 210, 353, 397
Smyrna	Eng. 21
Sneyd, Walter	Lat. 143.—Fr. 83.—Ital. 7, 77, 114.—Lea 5, 360
Solis y Ribadeneira, Antonio de	Span. 28
Soltau, Conradus de	Lat. 10
Somen, Conrad	Ger. 22
Sommario delle vere croniche di Venetia	Lea 360
Sompniales Danielis	Lat. 118
Soncino	Lea 58
Sonetto dize el libro	Ital. 11
Sotheby, J.	Fr. 26
Southey, Robert	Span. 19
Spada, Card.	Lea 75
Spahn, Andreas Ignatius	Lat. 65
Spain	Fr. 3.—Ital. 46, 96, 164, 178.—Lea 172, 353, 360, 397
(see also names of sovereigns)	
Spain, Consejo real	Lea 108, 141
Spain, Inquisition	Lea 108, 112, 117, 139
Spalatin, Georg	Ger. 28–30
Spalato	Ital. 64
Spanish Fragment	Lat. 139
Spanish Universities	Span. 40, 42, 48
Spanocchi, Pandolfo	Ital. 174
Speculum mortis	Lea 152
Spekhosen, Oltze	Ger. 57
Spezzani, Alfonso	Lat. 68
Spinola	Ital. 120
Spinola, Cipriano	Lea 397
Spiro	Lea 397
Splendor solis	Smith 1
Spreti, Michele Giambattista	Ital. 140
Squarci, Giovanbattista	Lea 251
Squarci, Tommaso Maria	Ital. 174
Stadion, J. P. K. J. von	Fr. 55
Stäudlin, Gotthold	Ger. 32
Staimbourg, Villegas de	Lea 37
Statuta regni Poloniae	Lea 384
Stauffenburg	Ger. 18
Steborius, Christophorus	Lat. 27
Stefani, Gaetano	Ital. 170
Stefano, Bartolomeo di	Lea 341
Stefanus de Maneriis	Lat. 54
Stefonio, Bernardino	Lat. 153
Steiner, Maximus	Lat. 65
Stellati, F. B. M.	Lat. 171
Stephan, St., Order of	Lea 65, 132
Stephanonio, Petro	Lea 362
Stetson, John B., Jr.	Span. 3
Stillio, Antonio	Lea 360
Stilz, Michael	Ger. 49
Stirling, William	Ital. 168–72
Stoneby, Richard	Lea 66
Stonor, Thomas	Eng. 8
Storia dell'impero d'occidente	Ital. 137–8
Storia di Santo Sebasstiano	Ital. 106
Strada, Cesare Luigi	Lat. 42
Stram, Henry von	Smith 41
Strode, Ralph	Lat. 16
Stroehlin Collection	Lat. 89
Strong, George T.	Lea 19
Strozzi family	Lea 317
Strozzi, F.	Ital. 39
Strozzi, Filippo di Filippo	Lea 77
Strozzi, Marcello	Lea 251
Strozzi, Piero	Lea 77
Stubbs, William	Eng. 19
Styleman-le Strange, Hamon	Smith 3
Sublingny, Adrien Thomas Perdou de	Fr. 100
Suchier, Hermann	Lat. 50.—Fr. 11.—Ital. 70–1, 106, 111.—Rhaeto-Rom.2.—Lea 47
Suchten, Alexander von	Smith 22
Suetonius Tranquillus, Caius	Lat. 81
Summa de las coronicas de Viscaya	Span. 12
Summa de virtutibus et vitiis	Ger. 3
Summa metrica	Lat. 165
Summula de casibus	Lea 17
Summula de summa Raymundi	Lat. 164
Suneborn, Hinrik von	Ger. 57
Supplementa quedam anatomica	Lat. 133
Susanna	Ital, 106, 117
Suso, Henricus	Lat. 36, 69
Swartzwelder, M.	Lat. 11
Switzerland	Ital. 143.—Lea 83
Sydrach	Fr. 23
Synonima corporum	Lea 19
System of Physicks	Eng. 11
Tacitus, Publius Cornelius	Ger. 54.—Ital. 134, 159
Taillandier, A.	Lea 50
Taintor, Charles M.	Smith 22
Tale of Melibeus	Lat. 107
Tamarit, Agostin	Lea 371
Tambaco, Johannes de	Lat. 36
Taparelli, Domenico	Lat. 168
Taris, Egidius	Lea 371
Tarlati, Galleotto	Lea 28
Tarn	Lat. 178
Tarsia, Giovan' Maria	Ital. 92
Tarsis, Juan de	Span. 30
Tartaleoni family	Lat. 94
Tassas de la corte de Roma	Lea 38
Tasso, Torquato	Ital. 15
Tassoni, Alessandro	Ital. 155–6
Taurelli family	Lea 181, 402
Tautha, Haubitz von	Ger. 29
Tebalducci Malespini, Lorenzo Giacomino de	Ital. 182
Tebaldus Placentinus	Lat. 152
Terentius Afer, Publius	Lat. 57, 72

[275]

Tertullianus, Quintus Septimius Florens	Eng. 28.—Ger. 60
Teruel	Span. 6
Tessier, Alexandre-Henri	Ital. 88
Testamento di Mantova	Lea 362
Teutonic Knights	Ger. 10
Teynton, Edmund	Smith 22
Thanhausen, Johann Bernard	Lat. 31
Thayer, John	Fr. 56
Thebaid Legion	Ital. 48
Theological Miscellany	Lat. 103, 196.—Ital. 71, 75
Theresa, St.	Lea 130
Theupulos, Nicolaos	Lat. 160
Thiebaus de Maliers	Lea 197
Thierry, Jules	Fr. 78
Thirault, François	Fr. 93
Thomas Aquinas, St.	Lat. 76, 116.—Ger. 60.—Ital. 13, 76.—Span. 43
Thomas de Bologna	Smith 15
Thomas de Capua	Lea 3, 16
Thomas Hibernicus	Lat. 92
Thomas of Erfurt	Lat. 118
Thomasset, Jean de Chastellar	Lat. 106
Thorndike, Andrew	Lea 371
Thorndike, G. Herbert	Lea 371
Thugut, Johann von	Fr. 55
Tienne, Mlle. de	Fr. 100
Tiepolo, Biagiamonte	Lea 360
Timmers, J.	Fr. 53
Titolario posto nelle patenti	Lea 362
Todd, Henry J.	Ital. 165
Todi, Jacomo	Ital. 29
Toledo, Inquisition	Lea 379
Toledo, Pietro di	Lea 172
Tolomei, C.	Ital. 37
Tonello	Ital. 7
Tontoli, And.	Lea 172
Torelli family	Lea 181, 402
Torelli, Francesco	Lea 402
Torelli, Lodovica	Lea 402
Torelli, Marcantonio	Lea 402
Torelli, Paolo	Lea 402
Torgau, Landtag	Ger. 58
Torneo di cento dame genovesi	Lea 360
Torquemada, Geronimo Gascon de	Lea 130
Torquemada, Juan de	Lat. 37
Torre, Giovanni Battista della	Ital. 72
Torres, L. de	Lea 366
Tostius, Johannes	Lat. 161
Townley, John	Fr. 49
Toxites, Michael	Smith 22
Tractato breve della perfectione della vita spirituale	Ital. 163
Tractato breve della via della salute	Ital. 163
Tractatus bonus de mortuis	Lat. 61
Tractatus de civitate sancta Jerusalem	Lat. 103
Tractatus de incarnatione	Lea 152
Tractatus de nativitate	Ger. 1
Tractatus de quattuor virtutibus	Lat. 61
Tractatus de restitutione	Lat. 61
Tractatus de sacramentis	Lat. 118
Tractatus perpulcer de generatione	Lea 19
Tractatus utilis de materia	Lea 19
Traité des droits du domaine du roy	Fr. 99
Traités alchémiques	Smith 15
Tramin	Ger. 42
Traneria, Marçal	Lea 371
Transylvania	Ital. 46
Trattato come si coltivino li giardini	Ital. 53
Trattato dell' astrologia	Ital. 206
Trattato delle commende	Lea 389
Trauttmansdorf, Ferdinand von	Fr. 55
Trent, Council	Ital. 26, 54, 141.—Lea 26, 401
Trespiano, Spedale di San Bartolomeo	Lea 292
Treviso	Ital. 121, 205
Triptis	Ger. 24
Triumpho de la morte	Ital. 120
Trivet, Nicholas	Lat. 8, 51
Trivulzio, Damigella di Giovanni	Lea 402
Trivulzio, Renato	Lea 402
Tromba sacra	Lea 361
Trousse, Jean	Lat. 106
Tuccius, Marianus	Ital. 93
Tuderto, Jacobus de	Lat. 122
Tunis	Eng. 21
Turano, Girolamo	Lea 397
Turenne, Vicomte de	Fr. 100
Turin	Ital. 95
Turkey	Ital. 164
Turkish-Persian War	Lea 15
Turkish Wars	Ital. 80
Turks	Lat. 167, 195.—Ital. 43, 46, 84, 132, 139–40, 207.—Span. 27.—Lea 107, 360
Turner, Dawson	Eng. 19
Turner, James	Eng. 19
Turner, Robert	Smith 11
Turner, Robert Samuel	Lea 20
Turrecremata, Joannes de	Lat. 37
Tuscany	Ital. 157.—Lea 198, 385, 399
(see also under names of sovereigns)	
Twenthe	Dutch 4
Two Sicilies, Kingdom	Lea 397
Tycho de Brahe	Lat. 162
Ubaldini, Antonio	Ital. 148
Ubaldini, Giulelmo	Lea 279
Ueber den Bauernkrieg zu Windsheim	Ger. 51
Ughi, Giuliano	Lea 103
Ugholini, Bartolomeo	Lea 280
Ugo of St. Victor	Lat. 122
Ulricus, scribe	Lat. 118
Ultima rimostranza della Republica Fiorentina	Lea 14
Umbertus Decembrius	Lat. 40, note

Universale, quomodo corpora . . . reducantur	Lea 19
Universalis alchymiae compendium	Smith 16
Uppelingh, Hinrik	Ger. 57
Urban V, Pope	Lea 6
Urban VI, Pope	Lat. 189
Urban VIII, Pope	Ital. 33, 178.—Span. 17.—Lea 154, 359
Urbino, Conte de	Smith 9
Urgel, Canons Regular	Span. 26, 39
Urgurgieri, Muzio	Ital. 174
Urria, Juan de	Span. 13
Urria, Maria de	Span. 13
Ursmiewsky, Michat	Lea 139
Ursulines	Lea 195
Ursus, St.	Lea 10
Urturi y Ibáñez, Iacinto de	Lea 156
Utrecht, Treaty	Ital. 189
Utrum peccata dismissa redeantur	Lat. 196
Vagad, Ganberto Fabricio	Span. 5
Val d'Aosta	Lat. 106
Valdenievole	Lea 243–4, 266
Valdenoceda	Span. 23–5
Valée, F.	Lea 152
Valencia, Inquisition	Lea 106
Valencia, Universidad	Lat. 190
Valeriano, Pierio	Ital. 204
Valette-Travesac, Antoine de	Lea 48
Valgulius, Carolus	Lat. 13
Valiero, Zaccaria	Lea 360
Valladolid	Lea 387
Valladolid, Universidad	Span. 39–40, 42, 48
Vallen, Hans von	Lat. 158
Valletta, Giuseppe	Ital. 210.—Lea 167, 169–70, 187
Valli, Leo	Ital. 34
Valli, Matteo	Ital. 34
Valperga	Lea 52
Val Secret, Abbaye de Nôtre Dame	Fr. 82
Valtellina	Ital. 178
Vandarmeulin, Louise Marie Therèse	Fr. 93
Van dem Scholer van Parisz	Ger. 4
Vandenyer, S.	Lat. 21
Vanni, Girolamo di Domenico	Lea 331
Vargas, Ambassador	Lea 384
Varios papeles de poesias	Span. 22
Vasa chemica	Lea 19
Vaticinia	Lat. 174
Vaticinia data Sigismundo	Lea 362
Vaticinia varia	Lea 144
Vaticinium de religione	Lea 362
Vaud	Fr. 30
Vaudeville	Fr. 57
Vautoullon, Jean	Fr. 93
Vázquez, Rodrigo	Lea 151
Vecelli, Francesco	Ital. 205
Vedovadi, Meglio	Lea 340
Vega Carpio, Lope de	Span. 3, 22, 50
Vegius, Mapheus	Lat. 117
Velo Luxiane, Bartholomeus de	Lea 365
Venetian War	Ger. 19
Veneziano, Antonio	Ital. 162
Venice	Lat. 160, 169, 176–7.—Eng. 21.—Ger. 52.—Ital. 14, 19, 36, 44, 46, 60, 64, 95, 99–100, 116, 132, 143, 146–7, 152, 158, 184.—Lea 35, 41, 49, 83, 85, 91, 94, 261, 356, 360, 372, 391–3
Venice, Inquisition	Lea 93
Venice, St. Antonius	Lat. 5
Ventimiglia family	Lea 397
Ventimiglia, Francesco de	Lea 397
Ventos, Joan	Lea 371
Ventura, Giovanni Vincenzo	Ital. 167
Vergerio, Pietro Paolo	Lat. 34
Vergilius Maro, Publius	Lat. 105.—Fr. 4
Verneil, Duc de	Smith 42
Vernoils, Joham de	Fr. 87
Verona, Monastery of the Holy Spirit	Ital. 13
Verospi, Governor of Umbria	Ital. 177
Verrazzano family	Lea 128
Verazzano, Alessandro da	Lea 198
Verrier, Charles	Fr. 93
Versailles, Treaty, 1756	Fr. 89
Versus . . . ac sobrie et caute legendi	Lat. 108
Versus de facetia mensae	Lat. 118
Versus de morte	Lat. 108
Verzameling von Latynsche, Fransche en Nederduytsche Keurdichten	Fr. 100
Vettori, Pietro	Lea 287
Viaggio di Edoardo	Lea 360
Vianne	Fr. 97
Vibo, Michele Antonio	Lea 46
Vicariis, Gioseffo de	Lea 158
Vicario, Constantius and Daniel de	Lea 8
Vichard de Saint-Real, César	Lea 39
Vico	Lea 398
Vidoni, Tomaso	Lea 75
Vienna	Lat. 128.—Ger. 49.—Lea 159, 391, 399
Vienna, Bibl. Imp.	Lat. 69
Vienna, Council	Lat. 95
Vienna, University	Lat. 92
Viettinghoff, R. von	Ger. 32
Vigliano d'Asti	Lea 53
Vilardebó, José	Lea 150
Vilardebó, Sebastián	Lea 131, 150
Vilbois, Pierre Gabriel de	Fr. 93
Villa, Marchese	Lea 360
Villafiorita	Lea 397
Villamediana, Juan de Tarsis, Count	Span. 30

Villani, Giovanni	Lea 90	Voltaire, François M. A. de	Eng. 7.—Fr. 29.—Ital. 140.—Smith 36
Villanova	Lea 56		
Villanova, Arnaldus de	Lea 19.—Smith 4, 9, 15	Volterra	Lea 230, 259, 284
		Von allen Rechten	Ger. 3
Villanueva, Antonio	Span. 45	*Vorbereitung auf die Beichte*	Ger. 4
Villars, Duc de	Fr. 29	Voss, Wilhelm	Ger. 36
Villaviciosa, Bartolomé Francisco de	Lea 156	Voynich, E.	Lat. 60
		Voynich, W. M.	Smith 3
Villefranche, Académie	Fr. 50	Vullenhoe	Dutch 4
Villeneuve, Dumont de	Fr. 52		
Villeroy, Maréchal de	Fr. 94		
Villers, Bernier de	Fr. 55		
Villetard, Château de	Flemish 3	Wahrendorf, Gustav	Smith 20
Villiers, Vicomte de	Fr. 16	Waitzen	Lat. 127
Villon, François	Fr. 5, 21	Waldersee, de	Smith 26
Vimercati-Sozzi, Paolo	Ital. 207.—Lea 18, 21	*War of Polish Succession*	Lea 362
		Wasseron	Smith 41
Vimercato, Giovanni Andrea	Ital. 132	*Wassersnot in Nürnberg*	Ger. 51
Vicentius de Alba	Lat. 168	Wassonius de Pontemontione	Lat. 93
Vinta, Belisario	Lea 369	Weiroth	Lat. 100
Vio family	Lea 397	Welack, Matthäus	Lat. 161
Vio, Tommaso de	Lat. 150	Welckers, H.	Ger. 50
Viollet-Le-Duc, Eugène Emmanuel	Fr. 63	Wells, Gabriel	Fr. 4
		Wenceslaus, King of Bohemia	Lat. 92
Viridarium consolationis	Ital. 111	Wernigerode	Ger. 57
Viridarium regale	Smith 39	Wesel, Johann	Lea 68
Virtù trionfante	Ital. 180	Westhaus, Hubertus	Ger. 50
Viscaya	Span. 12	White, Stephen	Lat. 76
Visconti, Carlo	Ital. 141	White Windows	Smith 30
Visio Philiberti	Lat. 90	Widen, Library	Ger. 6
Visione contemplativa	Ital. 73	Wieland, Christoph	Ger. 32
Visnievsciana, Biblioteca	Lea 139	Wigg, Johannes	Lat. 118
Visula, P., Bp. of	Lat. 174	Wilbraham, Roger	Ital. 165
Vita Amelii	Ital. 71	Wilhelm, Duke of Bavaria	Ger. 35
Vita de Joachim	Ital. 13	Wilhelm, Count Palatine	Ger. 48
Vita de Sancto Honofrio	Ital. 29	Wilhelm, Landgrave of Hesse	Ger. 58
Vita di Filippo di Filippo Strozzi	Lea 77	Willart de Grécourt, J. B. J.	Smith 36
Vita di Ladislao	Ital. 25	William, Cardinal Deacon of St. Eustachius	Lat. 91
Vita di Lorenzino de' Medici	Lea 77	William de Cenes	Smith 4
Vita di Papa Alessandro VI	Lea 82	William, John C.	Lea 373
Vita di Piero Strozzi	Lea 77	Williams, Robert	Eng. 21
Vita di Santa Domitilla	Ital. 3	Wilmersdoerffer, M. D.	Lat. 73
Vita e leggenda della beata Eugenia	Ital. 3	Windsheim	Ger. 51
Vita & morte di Papa Sisto V	Lea 154	Winthrop, Thomas	Smith 22
Vita Jesu Christi	Ital. 18	Wittenberg	Lat. 161
Vita, profezie, miracoli . . . del Ven. Bartolomeo Carosi (also *Vita, morte . . . di Bartolomeo Garosi*)	Ital. 45.—Lea 173	Wolfframsdorf, Johann Friedrich von	Fr. 37, 67
		Woodhull, M.	Lea 358
Vitae episcoporum aquilensium	Lat. 143	Woodward, William Harrison	Lat. 47
Vitelius, Franciscus	Lat. 123	Wyclif, John	Lat. 92.—Eng. 2, 6
Viterbo	Ital. 8.—Lea 366	Wyle, Nicolas von	Ger. 6
Viterbo, Convento di S. Maria della Quercia	Lea 26	Wynants, G. A. de	Fr. 53
Vittoria Nicoletta, Prioress	Lea 397		
Vives, Antonio	Lea 371	Xaraquemada	Fr. 18
Vlaemynck, François	Flemish 3	Ximenes, Fernando	Lea 80
Vocabularius ex quo	Lat. 142	Ximenes, Pedro	Lea 80
Vögeli, Jörg	Ger. 22		
Vogel, Johann	Lat. 100		
Vollenhove, Joannes (or Bernard)	Fr. 100	Yerma family	Lea 397
		Yvon, Thomas	Fr. 93

Zaccharia, Michele	Lea 46	Zeni, Marco	Lea 41
Zacchia, Ambassador	Lea 85	Zeno, Alessandro	Lea 60
Zampesca, Brunoro	Lea 83	Zeno, Carolo	Lat. 7
Zanardo, Antonio	Ital. 153	Znoyma, Stanislaus de	Lat. 92
Zandonella, G. Battista	Ital. 203	Zomernaet, Johannes	Lat. 121
Zanobini, Niccolò	Lea 65	Zorn, Johann	Lat. 29–30
Zapata de Mendoza, Antonio	Lea 141	Zorzi, Marco	Lat. 177
Zaragoza	Span. 48	Zürich	Ger. 52
Zeeland	Dutch 4	Zwingli, Ulrich	Ger. 22, 51

1/2/68